THE CONCISE ENCYCLOPAEDIA
AND
2000 PRICE GUIDE TO GOSS CHINA

To

Jacqui & Trevor

Especially for you

Lynda &

Nicholas

A massive Goss & Peake Bust of Charles Dickens 650mm high (a 160mm Bust of W H Goss and a 100mm Bust of Queen Victoria are shown for comparison).

THE CONCISE ENCYCLOPAEDIA

AND

2000 PRICE GUIDE TO GOSS CHINA

Nicholas Pine

Published by Milestone Publications
Goss & Crested China Ltd.
62 Murray Road Horndean
Waterlooville Hampshire P08 9JL.

1992 Edition edited by the late Lt. Cdr. N.H. Pratten RD FCIS RNR (Ret'd.).
Photography by Michael Edwards Studio Havant and Images Waterlooville.

Typeset by Hilite Design & Reprographics Ltd. Portswood Southampton Hampshire.

Printed and bound in Great Britain by MPG Books Ltd. Bodmin Cornwall.

First printed 1978
Revised 1981, 1984, 1986, 1989, 1992, 1999.

British Library Cataloguing in Publication Data
The concise encyclopaedia and price guide to goss china 2000
A catalogue record for this book is available from the British Library.

ISBN 1-85265-128-8

Contents

Acknowledgements

I wish to thank the following who have been kind enough to notify me of new pieces, or provided information concerning alterations and amendments, inscriptions and descriptions, dimensions and variations, in order that this encyclopaedia might be updated: Mrs M Albrighton, V Alliez, D Bates, G Bishop, C Blakeborough, E Bond, F R J Blasket, P Bolton, M J Boyle, Mrs Cawdron, W F Cover, A Dalton, J Darrah, J Davies, P R Dobson, A Donnelly, S Godly, M Growns, F Green, N Griffin, P Guy, Mr & Mrs J Hall, L Harris, P Hawker, L Hemsley, R Holmes, B Johnson, Mrs J Lewes, Mrs Z Mills, T Millward, A Munday, E Miskelly, Mrs C Owen, F Owen, A Peters, Mrs V Ralph, Mr & Mrs P Riley, P T Roberts, J A Seed, R Smith, W Smith, Mrs J G Spaulding, M Stedman, Mrs P M Swift, Mr J Swift, P Tasker, J R Trie, B Thacker, B D Underwood, T Usher, D Waine, M Welland, T F Wellings, M J Willis–Fear and Mrs R Wind .

The late Norman Pratten, edited previous editions of this work in a meticulous manner. His energy, diligence, expert advice, attention to detail and depth of knowledge in the field of Goss porcelain has been of incalculable value and Goss collectors everywhere owe him a debt of gratitude.

Unfortunately, Norman died six weeks after the previous edition of this work was published in 1991 but has indeed left a lasting legacy.

I also wish to particularly thank David Wiscombe who has followed on where Norman left off and has submitted hundreds of factual corrections and much information in order that this edition be updated. His painstaking research and checking of facts has improved this book enormously and I am most grateful to him.

I also wish to thank members of the Goss family for their assistance with previous editions ; in particular, Major W R Goss and also Clara Goss, Louise Goss and the late Valentine Taggart.

John Galpin was instrumental in compiling the first *Price Guide to Goss China*, and his meticulous measuring and recording has been invaluable. I thank him for his willing assistance to Goss Collectors for over 30 years.

In addition, I wish to thank The *Leicester Mercury* for kindly allowing me to use their photographs of the Goss factory and surrounds.

Special thanks are due to Alan Glover for his contribution to the work, particularly for his knowledge and guidance on the Winchester theme, and for contributing and updating his history of Goss in Winchester which was prepared especially for this book.

Dr Pat Herley has researched Godfrey Goss and American wares resulting in a completely revised section in this volume. He has also researched in his usual scholarly manner the Bullock and two sheep group and two bulls fighting oval plaque for which I am most greatful.

Without the knowledge and support of my wife, Lynda, this book would be incomplete. I thank her together with the staff of Goss & Crested China Ltd who constantly record new models and suggest improvements, in particular, in house editor Patricia Welbourne.

John Magee will always merit a credit in any book about Goss China. He set Goss China on its present popular course and even now in his retirement from the world of Goss, his legacy remains undiminished.

Introduction

This second edition of *The Concise Encyclopaedia and Price Guide to Goss China*, a seventh edition successor to the original 1978 First Edition of *The Price Guide to Goss China*, includes details of new pieces and variations which have been discovered since publication of the 1992 guide. Numerous detail corrections and improvements have been made, no less than 1000 in number.

The author has divided the wares produced by the Goss Factory into three periods as follows:

> The First Period 1858-1887
> The Second Period 1881-1934
> The Third Period 1929-1939

The First Period covers ware manufactured by William Henry Goss whilst he owned and ran the factory. The Second Period spans the stewardship of his sons Adolphus, Victor and William Huntley Goss. The Third Period embraces wares made by other factories, but which carry the Goss mark.

The guide has been structured to divide the products of The House of Goss into the three periods. The First Period covers ware produced from the start of the firm in 1858 to 1887 and includes the early Victorian unglazed figurines, together with a series of famous portrait busts and terracotta wares.

The earliest crested models were made towards the end of the First Period, and the reader's attention is drawn to the introductory comments in each chapter in order to be able to differentiate between the wares of one period from another. In particular, the First Period ornamental ware chapter introduction establishes the distinguishing features of the early crested wares which will enable such pieces to be accurately identified.

The Second Period from 1881-1934 encompasses the introduction of heraldic china, the bulk of which was mass produced and comprises historic models and special shapes, ornamental and domestic wares. The pieces that were also produced during the First Period have the symbol [1] after their respective entries, but as the models and shapes were also made for many years during the Second Period, and it would be confusing to have chapters on both historic models and special shapes in two periods, they are all catalogued in one chapter in the Second Period. Also included are dolls, miniatures, cottages, crosses, fonts and animals, all under separate headings due to their importance.

The first of the named models appeared around 1881 and were of an uneven, heavy, creamy consistency with mould lines clearly visible down both sides. The gilding had to be fired at exactly the right temperature in order for it to be permanent. However, the factory was unable to perfect this until

The warehouses and production areas of the Sturgess Street factory complex.

The Goss ovens pictured in 1984. Since this photograph was taken, all the original outbuildings have been cleared, a large warehouse now abuts the rear of the ovens and the ovens have been listed and restored by the current owners of the site, Portmeirion Potteries plc.

approximately 1885-1890, hence the poor or complete lack of gilding to be found on the majority of First Period pieces, but which nevertheless does not affect values.

Another characteristic of these early wares is the somewhat diluted, patchy or pastel-like appearance of the colours used for the coats of arms.

The titles of these models were also printed in large capitals on the base and the inscriptions were shorter. Early domestic shapes were also slightly indented on the base and glazed underneath.

From about 1887 onwards, production techniques improved dramatically. The porcelain mix became thinner, more delicate and more perfectly formed. The gilding was better, brighter and permanent. Coats of arms were painted with richer colours and more detailed. The type-size used for the transfer of descriptions to be affixed to the base was smaller and the descriptions lengthier. Various sizes of shield for the arms were introduced in order to suit the proportions of the shape or model. The first models on the production line were of the larger size, but it soon became evident that the general public were more appreciative of the smaller shapes: perhaps because they were prettier, or easier to carry home, and, as collectors today find, more can be fitted into a china cabinet.

Separate chapters are included on domestic, utility and ornamental wares, so as to assist the reader to locate pieces more easily. The tiny domestic items not made for daily use have been classified as ornamental and will be found given as Fairy Shapes, as this is how they were originally known. Each piece is catalogued according to the 8th, 9th and War editions of *The Goss Record*, and page references are given. These books were published originally between 1913 and 1921. They have been reprinted by Milestone and give the flavour of Goss collecting at the time, as well as having a full description of the history and origin of most of the originals from which the Goss models were made.

Although the last member of the Goss family to own the pottery sold out in 1929, heraldic souvenir china continued to be made in the same way until 1934. Therefore, the date given for the end of the Second Period is 1934 when the firm went into receivership.

The Third Period, from 1929-1939 covers the heavier and more colourful ranges of pottery introduced to revitalise flagging sales. Although the coats of arms still continued to appear on a range of vases, utility shapes, comical animals and buildings, they are very different from those of the previous period and values are generally lower. Not all of these have the mark W.H. Goss England, but the heavier, duller quality and more garish colours used in the decoration are easily distinguished. Also in this section are the brightly coloured Toby Jugs, Flower Girls, the beige pottery Royal Buff tea sets, and the Cottage Pottery domestic ware attractively shaped as thatched cottages. This beige pottery is comparatively fine with a quite noticeable resonance.

Information on *The Goss Record*, Postcards, the League of Goss Collectors, Cabinets and Leaflets are contained in the earlier chapters, thereby providing the reader with as much information as possible.

The inside of one of the bottle ovens.

Ashfield Cottage, formerly the home of William Henry Goss, which stands above the main factory building. Banks of forget–me–nots were grown against the front wall. This was W H's favourite flower and turquoise his favourite colour.

The final warehouse, completed in 1906. Note the carved stone Goshawk in the gable wall.

The interior of the warehouse. The girls are sorting the wares and applying transfers, on the right is the firms reference collection. Note the tray of Portman Lodges perched precariously on the straw baskets.

The Goss pottery was ahead of its time and a market leader. The difficult times shared by the pottery industry in England in the last century led the other three hundred or so local potbanks to copy Goss's successful heraldic lines before the turn of the century, and they capitalized on the serious flavour of Goss models by producing generally more light-hearted and amusing shapes. All known crested china made by these other firms is contained, along with their values, in *The Price Guide to Crested China* by Nicholas Pine.

It should be noted that the values indicated in this guide are for shapes only and do not take into account the value of any arms or decorations. Exceptions to this are the League models and the historic models bearing matching arms. Prices are given for both matching and non-matching where both exist, and the correct matching arms are listed. Elsewhere, the additional premium is given for matching arms. For all other additional crest and decoration values, see the companion volume to this guide: *The Price Guide to Arms and Decorations on Goss China* by the same author, which lists and values some 10,000 different decorations to be found on Goss porcelain.

Therefore, to find the value of any given piece, first look it up in the Price Guide, then add any plusage for the motif or decoration as given in the companion volume.

This edition contains additional illustrations, especially of First Period wares, all of which are now over 100 years old. As for previous editions, the improvement and updating of the listings will be ongoing, and the author will be very pleased to hear about any item of Goss which has not yet been catalogued .

Prices quoted in this guide are for pieces in perfect condition. Worn gilding, faded coats of arms, chips, cracks and bad firing flaws will all affect values substantially. A small crack could easily halve the value, whilst a cottage worth £100 would probably only be worth £25 with a chimney missing.

Although it is always possible to get a damaged piece restored, it is easy to detect restoration. Where the value of a restored item would be greater than that of the same piece in a damaged state, then restoration would be worthwhile. However, inexpensive, sub-standard pieces have always been popular, thus making it possible for those with limited resources to obtain the rarest specimens. Indeed, damaged Goss has risen in value proportionately more than perfect Goss during the past 20 years.

A faded coat of arms devalues a piece considerably. Fading is caused by prolonged exposure to sunlight and is irreversible. The colours most likely to be affected in this way are blue and black. Fading should not be confused with oxidization, which often occurs in the case of pieces stored in newspaper for many years. Oxygen in the air reacts with the surface of the coat of arms and causes a brown metallic film to spread over the enamel, mostly on yellows and reds. A little moistened detergent gently applied will remove this oxidized film and reveal the arms as perfect. Do not forget to thoroughly rinse off the detergent. It is important to note that oxidization will not render a piece substandard, whereas fading would.

Over the last few years, the majority of prices have increased at approximately the rate of inflation. Models with matching arms however, have increased by between 50 - 100% whilst First Period busts have shown little improvement due to lack of demand.

When the first edition of the precursor of this guide was published in 1978, the name Goss was still relatively unknown in the antique world. Now nearly all collecting authorities are aware of Goss china and now appreciate its quality. It is now accepted as being as important as the products of many of the more well known manufacturers.

Prices herein are drawn from over twenty five years of experience in buying and selling Goss china, and for the majority of that period making an orderly market in this ware and researching the subject. Auctions have never been a good source of price information, as such outlets often tend to be used as clearing houses for sub-standard and inferior wares. No auction house as yet really understands or cares about Goss china and this often results in as many bargains as rogue pieces being knocked down. Auction houses are, in the author's experience, potential minefields for the unwary, and there really can be no substitute for knowledge. In the 1970s and 1980s the three leading London auction houses would have regular sales of Goss china but these have ceased in the 1990s probably due to a shortage of supply.

All pieces that should have lids are priced inclusive of having them. In addition, the individual price of a lid is also given in the entry for those pieces which should have them.

Full inscriptions are given in italic type for each piece. There is no inscription if none is stated.

All dimensions stated are of the height with the exception of cottages and coloured buildings which are of the length of the piece.

Value Added Tax has always been a problem, in that it is included as part of the normal retail selling price by Goss & Crested China Ltd, the leading dealers, but not apparently by many others. Indeed, it has often been found that minor unregistered dealers have been charging the same prices as this company and in so doing have in effect been overcharging by some $17^{1}/2\%$.

In order, therefore, that prices in this guide should be directly comparable with those quoted elsewhere, VAT has not been included in the value of items under 100 years old which attract this tax.

The leading forum for buying and selling is *Goss & Crested China*, a 32 page illustrated monthly catalogue published by Goss & Crested China Ltd.

Each edition contains examples of pieces from every period of the factory and is available by annual subscription. See the final pages in this book for further details.

There are two clubs for Collectors of Goss china. The Goss and Crested China Club publishes a monthly catalogue, holds regular open days, values pieces, answers collectors queries and provides many other services. See the final pages in this book for further details. The Goss Collectors' Club publishes a monthly magazine, holds regular regional meetings and twice yearly Goss fairs. The third club, The Crested Circle is currently defunct.

William Henry Goss. This photograph appeared in his own album.

Victor Goss. A captain in the Territorial Army, who managed the factory from the time of William Henry's death in 1906 until his own in 1913 from a riding accident.

1. A History of the Goss Factory

The production of porcelain at the firm of W H Goss of Stoke-on-Trent spanned four reigns and some 70 years from 1858 to 1929. The family-run firm was headed by William Henry Goss, who was born in 1833, and who had learned his trade and gained a sound grounding in chemistry under the personal guidance of Alderman Copeland of the Copeland Works, also at Stoke. It was a small business in the early days when the founder's children were all young, and the total workforce numbered less than twenty. The Falcon Works was one of 120 potteries struggling to survive in the smoke, dirt and grime of the area known as The Potteries in Staffordshire. The pottery towns include Burslem, Hanley, Lane End, Shelton, Fenton, Tunstall, Longport (Longton) as well as Stoke. These towns had sprung up along the same turnpike road in an area where coal, water power, canals, lime-stone and raw clay were all available or easily accessible.

In a line of business where masters notoriously ill-treated their work force and used child labour (children down the mines at this time fared better), William Henry Goss, along with other enlightened potters, including Minton, Copeland and Wedgwood, campaigned for better working conditions and treated his own staff generously.

When Goss was an impressionable young man of thirteen (he married at nineteen!) the first parian was produced at the Copeland Works by John Mountford in 1846. This was quickly followed by a similar material at Minton, and very soon all the major factories were using this medium to produce elegant classically styled figures, portrait busts of politicians, notable dignitaries of the day, royalty, poets, authors and musicians. Eventually Goss became chief artist and designer at Copeland, and continued to produce similar lines when he became his own boss. These were difficult and costly to produce, and the larger part of his substantial income was derived from the sale of coloured enamels, made up to his own special recipes, to other potteries for decorating china.

Goss also produced a small range of terracotta ware, using the local marl or clay. In 1867 he had a brief partnership with a Mr. Peake, and a few pieces exist marked *Goss and Peake,* mainly terracotta, but after a few large classical figurines were produced in parian ware Peake had financial difficulties as a result of his own activities, and Goss dissolved the partnership after one year.

Goss's other specialities included jewelled scent bottles and vases, which were produced from pierced and fretted parian, with inset cut-glass jewels in the Sevres style, but more successful than that firm in the setting and firing of the stones. This method was patented in 1872, but jewelled ware ceased to be made after 1885. The noted perfumier Eugene Rimmel, was one of the factory's customers, having perfumeries in Rome, Paris and London.

Other lines during this First Period of Goss china production included

Adolphus Goss when he was the firm's commercial traveller.

intricate flower baskets for table decorations, brooches, spill holders (one in the shape of Dr. Kenealy, the then Member of Parliament for Stoke, whom Goss loathed) and a bullock and two sheep group - a special order from America.

The Second Period of Goss production is marked by the entry of his eldest son, Adolphus, into the management and the introduction of heraldic ware. This was to completely supersede the previous ware due to its popularity and ability to be mass produced (though not in the way things are today!) More importantly, Goss became a household name, and collecting Goss china a national hobby.

It was Adolphus who realised there was a growing market in providing for the day tripper, because of the introduction of bank holidays for workers by Queen Victoria in 1871, the expanding network of railways across Britain, and the increasing popularity of the seaside, approved of by the Queen herself.

It was his idea that visitors to seaside resorts and other places might like to take home a miniature china ornament as a souvenir. To give it local interest, he proposed that it should bear the town's coat of arms. The shape would be the reproduction of some vase, jar or urn of antiquarian interest, such as those found in the local museum. He and his father shared a love of heraldry and archaeology, and Adolphus hoped to use the porcelain models to create an interest amongst the middle and working classes in the subjects, whilst at the same time enticing the public to buy Goss china as an artistic memento of holiday visits.

He enthusiastically explained his idea to his father, expecting him to be delighted, but instead was immediately turned down and told that the scheme was not a viable proposition. Adolphus was naturally very disappointed, but being the strong minded person he was - his motto being to make up one's mind, and let no one alter it, he made up a few prototype glazed parian models, applied coats of arms in the form of transfers hand painted with enamels, and managed to get William to agree. Crested China, as it is now popularly known, started from there. It was not long before this heraldic ware entirely replaced the factory's previous output of figures and busts. This led to a five year building plan to treble the floor space in order to cope with the incredible demand .

Throughout this period of production, only one selected agent was appointed in each town. These agencies were only allowed to sell their own town's coat of arms or transfer printed views. After 1883 they could order any shape instead of being restricted to their own local shapes. For instance, the Gloucester agent could only sell Gloucester Jugs up until that date, and thereafter he would stock a wide variety of models, but they all bore the Gloucester crest. In those days, to obtain a Land's End crest entailed a journey there to purchase it; there was no other way!

It fell to Adolphus, with his business drive and enthusiasm, to be the firm's travelling salesman, spending more and more time away from home visiting suitable places to obtain permission to use the local arms, sketching new

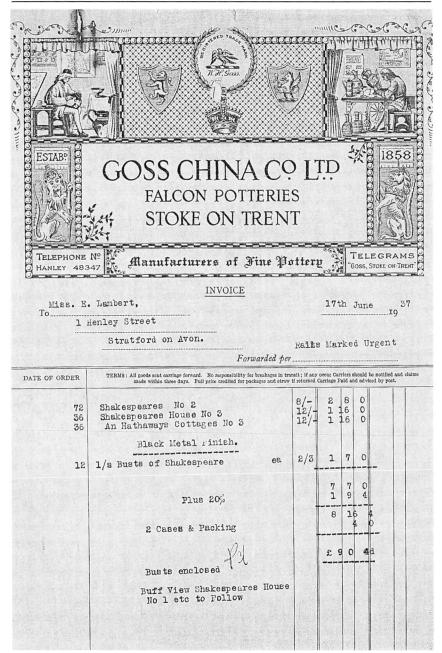

Invoice for Goss heraldic Porcelain supplied to the Stratford–upon–Avon agent in 1937. Note the very ornate letterhead used by Harold Taylor Robinson who now owned the firm.

models for reproduction, securing and taking orders. He was so thorough and successful that he ceased to have anything more to do with the daily running of the firm. By 1900 he had organised 481 agencies inland. He considered he was the mainstay of the business and called himself Goss Boss, which irritated his father intensely. Letters that passed between father and son reveal a strained relationship and, as the author's research has shown, life in the Goss household was not easy with such a stern Victorian father as William.

In 1893 Adolphus introduced a new range of coloured miniature cottages. The first three were Ann Hathaway's, Shakespeare's Birthplace, and Burns' Cottage, Ayrshire. This new line proved immensely popular, and it was gradually extended to 42 buildings in various sizes. In the latter half of the firm's life, some cottages were glazed which tended to intensify the colouring. This was a good line for improving sales at a time that was particularly poor for British exports, and when the china trade was suffering a depression.

It is hardly surprising, therefore, that most of the other pot banks turned to producing crested china, though not one ever equalled the Goss quality in glaze, parian body, gilding or enamel colour. These were all the secret recipes of William Henry Goss, though they were leaked to the Irish firm Belleek in 1863 when eleven Goss workers were persuaded to leave in order to save the factory at Belleek in Co Fermanagh. Belleek china, using Goss recipes, was produced from 1863 onwards, and even today's pieces are similar to Goss. Far sighted firms such as Arcadian, Carlton, Shelley and Willow Art, found a viable trade in modelling animals, especially in amusing and comical poses; also buildings, the originals of which were to be found throughout Britain, and household objects, military and other items. In this way they catered for the lower end of the market. True Goss enthusiasts, however, would not accept these imitations.

JJ Jarvis, a keen collector, began producing a series of booklets entitled *The Goss Record*, the purpose of which was to provide a catalogue of agents' names, addresses and opening hours. Agencies ranged from restaurants, bazaars, hotels, chemists, and station bookstalls to local libraries. The first edition was in 1900, and a supplement in 1902 includes 601 British agents, and the first foreign agent in Bermuda. By 1921, in the ninth edition, there were 1,378 British agencies, and 186 overseas in 24 countries.

The range of arms and models was extensive, all made with care and hand-painted to ensure perfection, with an exactness that could only be admired. The modern souvenir of today formed from Plaster of Paris is a sad reminder of how standards have fallen.

The death of the head of the firm in 1906, and Adolphus's exclusion from a share of the firm in his father's will, did not affect the boom years of 1900-1914. The third son, Victor, who took over the firm (second son Godfrey had also fallen from favour) was killed in a riding accident in 1913. Victor had been a good businessman, but not so Huntley, who was the last son and left in sole charge of the firm. In an attempt to survive the Great War, a range of warship crests and regimental badges was introduced, as were a couple of dozen copyright models. However, this was not enough to save the pottery from the decline in trade after the war, and Huntley Goss sold the firm, and the rights to the trademark, in 1929 to Cauldon Potteries, having paid every bill and all wages due.

William Henry Goss in the summer-house at Ashfield Cottage. This photograph was taken by his son Adolphus, a keen photographer, around 1880 when William was in his forties.

The new owners continued producing heraldic ware for another four years, but began to specialise in good quality earthenware and pottery similar to that of their other factories which included Arcadian. All of this new ware was marked *Goss, Goss England,* or *Made in England* . A new company formed in 1931 by Harold Taylor Robinson, known as W H Goss Ltd, with himself as director, began trading, using the Goss mark on shapes made from moulds from other factories. He was declared bankrupt in 1932, having been personally responsible for the takeover of 32 companies, including firms which supplied his potteries with fuel and clay in order to produce more cheaply. He had had to weather the Great War, the 1921 Coal strike, and the loss of foreign trade with unsettled international markets; with Britain going off the gold standard in 1924, and the worldwide depression of the 30's. He said: ' When I saw the depression was developing to the extent it was, I left my country house and came to live practically next door to the works and I have been working 50 weeks out of 52 to try to circumvent the terrible effects of the depression. When you get down to the basic facts you realise that as the largest potter in Staffordshire, I have been the largest victim.'

The range produced during this Third Period of the factory was very colourful and distinctive. William Henry Goss would certainly not have approved, but it suited the changing tastes and moods of the roaring 20's. A popular line was the beige pottery tea sets called Cottage Pottery, decorated with pictures of cottages with hollyhocks and full beds of flowers.

Commemorative mugs and beakers were issued for the Silver Jubilee of King George V and Queen Mary in 1935, and for the Coronations of Edward VIII, and King George VI and Queen Elizabeth in 1937. The last commemoratives were for the 1938 Scottish Empire Exhibition at Glasgow, and were decorated with green trim instead of the usual gilding.

Production ended mid 1940 and all lines stopped, including the coloured Flower Girls in the style of the modern Doulton ladies. The Falcon works were used by a number of different companies after 1940, including a manufacturer of parachutes during the Second World War, and by a clothing manufacturer. One pair of Goss ovens still stand, those used for glost firing, which have been restored by the current owners of the whole site, Portmeirion Potteries, plc.

A series of pictorial wall boards in the Goss & Crested China museum at Horndean also explains the history of the factory. Permanent exhibits in the museum include William Henry Goss' original recipe books, many original pictorial views sketched and coloured by Adolphus Goss and other personal items belonging to the Goss family. These include William Henry's photograph album which contains the original photographs from which the range of portrait busts was modelled.

In 1987, the current owner of the trademarks, Royal Doulton Tableware plc, introduced a range of two flat dishes and two plates in modern porcelain with a Goss backstamp which could be specially ordered in several quantities by clubs and societies to special order to commemorate particular events. This ware I have termed Fourth Period and it is not listed in this encyclopaedia.

For the complete history of the Goss family, the factory and their china see WILLIAM HENRY GOSS The story of the Staffordshire family of Potters who invented Heraldic Porcelain, by Lynda and Nicholas Pine (Milestone Publications). See the final pages in this book for further details

The Goss Agency at Poole in the 1920s. Note the two cabinets of Goss China either side of the closed door.

View of Stoke on Trent in Victorian times.

Mr. W. H. Goss' Exhibit in the King's Hall, Stoke on Trent, 22nd April 1913, on the occasion of Their Majesties' visit to the Potteries

Huntley and daughter Margaret Goss, 1920.

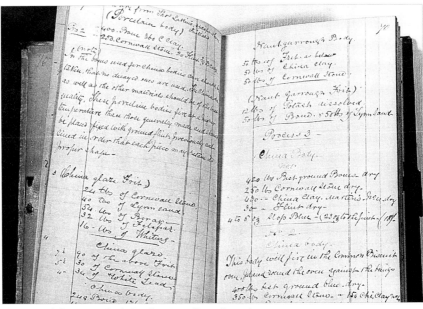

An original Goss recipe book detailing ingredients for parian.

The Goss china agency at Wells, Somerset in 1958. Note the agents sign.

Addisons' Goss agency at Woking in the 1920s.

Agents ordering card from 1931–1934

2 Factory Marks on W H Goss Porcelain

The wares of this factory are easy to recognise because virtually every piece was marked, usually on the base. W H Goss himself said that the black printed Goshawk with wings outstretched and the firm's name in capitals underneath, was in continuous use from 1862 onwards. This distinctive factory mark gave rise to the name of the Falcon Works, by which the pottery was known locally.

The earliest Goshawk was coloured red, gold, blue or puce, and appears without the firm's name printed beneath it. These marks appear on the earliest First Period pieces from 1858 to approximately 1862, and such pieces are rare. The earliest products from the beginning of the firm in 1858 were impressed during manufacture whilst the clay was still damp. They were impressed **W H Goss** with serif type-face, that is, with cross-lines to the end of a stroke on a letter. This mark was used up until 1887 when the **W H GOSS** mark was used sans serif, i.e. plain lettering. This seems to have been applied to some shapes and not others right up until 1916 at least, usually with the Goshawk as well.

There are many examples of poorly placed impressed factory marks. Often just W H G is visible, or even perhaps the last two letters of GOSS. When inspecting an unmarked piece, it is advisable to carefully check the base and sides, and in the case of busts, the shoulders and back, for even a hint of the magic mark. Positive Goss identification will certainly add to the value of anything that at first sight appears unmarked.

Many of the First Period busts and figures were incised or printed in manuscript with details such as the following example, with minor variations occurring in the wording:

> Published as the Act directs (See 54.Geo.III.C 56.)
> W. H. Goss.
> Stoke-on-Trent.
> 1 Dec 1873.
> Copyright

This identification became standard when used on the majority of the Parian busts, figures and groups produced during toe mid-1870's through to 1911. It was either stamped into the still-wet porcelain or transfer printed on to the finished piece in black, for example:

> Copyright as Act directs
> W. H. GOSS.
> Stoke-on-Trent.
> I November 1881.

Gold, red, blue or puce mark without words. Approx. 1858

Incised inscription on large bust in W H Goss's own hand

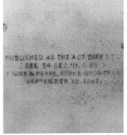

Black detailed printed mark on Figurine

Black painted mark, 1867

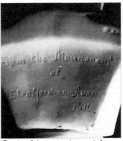

Incised inscription with impressed W H Goss

Black painted mark on terracotta

Serif impressed mark 1858–1887 approximately

Impressed serif copyright mark on bust, 1876

Sans-serif impressed mark 1887–1916 approximately

Incised mark on Dr Kenealy spill holder in W H Goss's own hand

Impressed serif copyright mark on a bust. 1881

Incised inscription on a bust in W H Goss's own hand

or, more fully:

Copyright
Pub. as Act Directs
(See 54. Geo III. C 56)
W. H. GOSS.
Stoke-on-Trent.
22 Jany 1893.

Identification details varied, and this style of marking, usually on the reverse, was in use from the early 1870s until 1911. The dates used in this way are the publication dates of the respective shapes, and not necessarily the date of manufacture. Often only one of a pair of figures, vases or ewers was marked.

Terracotta wares were marked with a black printed **W H GOSS or GOSS & PEAKE,** during a brief period of financial partnership with a Mr. Peake. See TERRACOTTA, Chapter 9D for full details.

Some First Period figures also carry a GOSS & PEAKE printed mark, usually the four or six line transfer printed mark.

Some Second and Third Period pieces made for the French and Belgian markets also carry the words EXPORTE ANGLETERRE or IMPORTE ANGLETERRE. For worldwide use MADE IN ENGLAND was used, particularly on pieces destined for the Australian market.

The common black Goshawk was used up until 1934 on heraldic ware, and after 1935 the mark was distinctively blacker and thicker, and often applied over the glazed bases of the late colourful pottery, usually accompanied by the word ENGLAND under the firm's name. The printed titles on the base of beige pottery include Cottage Pottery, Royal Buff, and Hand Painted. These were Third Period and date between 1930 and 1939. Margaret (Peggy) Goss is said by her family to have introduced the Little Brown Jug as a new line. As her father, Huntley, sold the works in 1929, quite possibly some of the beige ware made afterwards could have been planned by Peggy and Huntley Goss.

Another late line was delicately coloured lustre which was applied to named models as well as to domestic ivory porcelain. No arms were applied to these pieces, and handles were thickly coated with gold as well as having gilded rims. It is generally believed these date from 1925 and were rubber stamped with an enlarged Goshawk some 16mm square.

The tiny coloured brush strokes on the bases of most armorial Goss are the factory signatures of the paintresses. W H Goss was particularly concerned to keep up his high standards, and in order to be able to detect any shoddy workmanship or incorrect colouring of the arms, each paintress had her own mark, which she painted on the base of each of her pieces, in whatever colour she happened to be using at the time. Offenders were given three warnings before being sacked, so in all probability this clever system kept them all on their toes! One only has to compare the products with those of other manufacturers to appreciate their skill. Occasionally a gilder's mark in gold can also be seen.

A blue Goshawk was used on an experimental range of models decorated with underglaze blue designs which are also marked SECONDS or REJECTS.

Incised mark on Dr Kenealy Match and Spill Holder

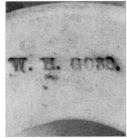

Serif impressed mark 1858-1887 approximately

Incised mark on The Boot Black. 1873

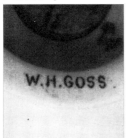

Written mark on Pepper Pot 1895-1925

The normal Goshawk 1862-1927

Black printed mark on a bust

Black printed mark on a bust

Black printed commemorative mark on bust of Queen Victoria

Serif impressed mark 1887-1918 approximately stamped mark with registration date.

Scarborough Flags Plate special mark

Third Period Black Printed Mark

Goshawk and date on Churchill Toby Jug

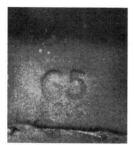

Impressed mark G5 on a
Goss doll

Model name, registration
number and agents name

League model inscription.
Note the artists mark

Goss England mark on a Flower
girl. Note also the Artists mark

Very late Goshawk mark.
Post 1930

Post 1930 late mark.

Large rubber stamp
Goshawk 1925 and after

Royal Cauldon mark over-printed
by a Goshawk. Post 1925

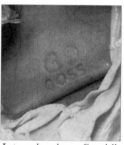

Impressed mark on a Goss doll
1916-1918 approximately

W H Goss England Cottage
Pottery mark

W H Goss England Royal
Buff mark

W H Goss England Hand
Painted late mark

Many pieces are marked COPYRIGHT, and others have registration numbers on the base. For a detailed explanation of these see REGISTRATION NUMBERS and COPYRIGHT MARKS Chapter.

In recent years, the term backstamp has replaced the words factory mark, but here the author has used the original terminology.

Some Goss pieces have been found marked **EMBLEMATIC T ENGLAND**. One example seen is a beaker with the Harvard University Seal version decoration [1], and another, a wall-pocket or posy-holder 173mm, with the United States decoration E PLURIBUS UNUM.

Mark used on pieces for the U.S. Market

Lower portion of unusual Goshawk mark on an Oviform Salt Castor

Empire Exhibition Scotland 1938. Red mark

Black printed mark on a bust of Lady Godiva

Black printed mark on a bust

Black printed marks on busts of Edward and Alexandra

League Model inscription

Third Period printed mark

Mark on Cottage Pottery Shakespearian Cottage Plate

3 Notes for the Collector

MINOR VARIATIONS IN SIZE

Where the dimensions of items are given, these have been obtained from actual specimens and refer to the height unless otherwise stated. Where an approximate measurement is quoted, no immediate specimen has been to hand, and the best available information source has been used.

Where no dimension is given, it has not been possible to gain access to information other than to confirm the existence of that model.

With regard to slight fluctuations in size in the same model, it must be borne in mind that variations in firing temperature can give rise to these and, in any case, shrinkage in firing can be as high as ten per cent. In early Goss items this figure is said to be higher, and certainly First Period wares have a tendency to firing cracks and flaws, but which the factory overcame around 1890. Examples of items particularly prone to having many minor differences in size are Loving Cups, Wall Pockets and Busts. These pieces, whilst lacking the excellence of Second Period wares, are rarer and equally desirable.

FORGERIES

Very few forgeries of Goss china have appeared. Those that have, usually take the form of a forged Goshawk on a piece that clearly did not originate from the Goss factory. These Goshawks are either crudely rubber stamped or drawn in Indian Ink. The giveaway must always be the quality of the piece the mark appears on. If it is not the fine parian body that is consistent with Goss, then look very closely at the mark. Compare a possible forgery with a correct normal mark, and also look at the quality of the porcelain.

In the end, however, recognition of forgeries rests with the experience and the knowledge of the collector, and there can be no substitute for handling Goss as often as possible in order to familiarise oneself with the ware.

Occasionally forged cottages appear. All Goss cottages produced are listed in the apppropriate chapter in this book. Any other cottage which is purported to be Goss is most definitely not so, if it does not feature in the exhaustive list given. Shakespeare's Cottage is a particular exception, so many sizes having been produced by Goss and other crested manufacturers. A forged example has been found of the half-size solid base model, as well as the 110mm full length size. The latter cottage is well made and is only prevented from being condemned as a true forgery by carrying the inscription *Reproduction of Model of Shakespeare's House*. It carries the correct registration number and the usual Goshawk, so the words *Reproduction of.....* should be looked for in this particular case.

In 1990 a bronze/gold metallic bust of Queen Victoria came to light. The example seen had had the usual crown for the version in question filed down to a rim. The mark was the usual four line *Copyright as the Act directs, W. H. Gos.s, Stoke-on-Trent,* and the year. This piece, whilst looking correct, is now believed to be a modern forgery.

*Three Goss forgeries. They are easily identifiable as not being Goss.
The quality, shape and feel of these pieces is completely wrong.*

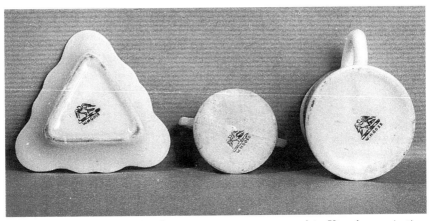

*The triangular dish is German, the other two pieces are pottery - not porcelain. Upon close examination,
the marks are easily identifiable as forgeries.*

In the 1970s, the author saw a bust of John Bull, 165mm high that was definitely a forgery. Every forgery that has come into the possession of Goss & Crested China Ltd. has been retained and this small collection numbering no more than 20 pieces in 25 years is permanently on show at the Goss & Crested China Museum as an aid to collectors.

THE BLACKPOOL COAT OF ARMS

Presumably at the request of the then Blackpool Agent, the Blackpool coat of arms was placed on a number of items which would not normally carry a coat of arms, the Abbot's Kitchen Glastonbury, Manx Cottage, Lincoln Imp, St. Columb Major Cross, Lucerne Lion, Goss Oven, and Cornish Stile, being but a few of over 50 examples found.

Another practice of Mr. Naylor, the Blackpool Agent after 1913, was the sale of named models from which the descriptive matter had been omitted. This, together with an over generous use of gilding (e.g. on the ears of the Lincoln Imp) has tended to give some collectors the impression that Blackpool wares are second-rate and should be generally avoided. Almost all, however, that were sold through the Blackpool Agency, which changed hands at least four times between the years 1901 and 1921, were perfectly normal and correct.

With regard to value, items which should not be carrying arms, but are found to have the Blackpool coat of arms, tend to detract, thus reducing the value of the item by, say, one third and two-thirds.

However, many items which would otherwise have been factory rejects (by virtue of firing flaws, distortion, etc.,) have been sold through the Blackpool agency and, therefore, carry the Blackpool arms. Such pieces would be worth around one-third of the normal perfect model, and every Blackpool crest item should accordingly be closely inspected in order to determine whether or not it was a factory second.

REGISTRATION NUMBERS

No piece of Goss is worth any more or less whether or not it carries a registration number. There is no reason why some pieces carry their number and some not. The production of Goss china was never an exact science, and the only reason for putting the registration number on a piece was to prevent other firms from using the design.

Two different aspects were registered. First, the shape or model, and secondly the decoration. Some pieces have one number which could refer to either, and some carry two numbers, indicating that both the model and decoration were designed and registered by the Goss factory.

Registration numbers were used from 1884 up until their discontinuance in 1914. The following tables give the dates of first registration of numbers between I and 630174. It should be noted that the dates given here indicate only the first registration of a design and not the exact year of manufacture. From the time patents began in 1883, registered designs could only run for four years, but were renewable, with a maximum life of 15 years.

Registration numbers were not used by the factory after July 1914, but it should also be remembered that a number indicates only when the registration took place, not when the piece was made, which might well be years afterwards.

In many cases a piece was registered some years after its first year of manufacture, in others the earlier large size wasn't registered but the later smaller size was.

Rd. No.   1 registered in Jan.1884
Rd. No.   19754 registered in Jan.1885
Rd. No.   40480 registered in Jan.1886
Rd. No.   64520 registered in Jan.1887
Rd. No.   90483 registered in Jan.1888
Rd. No. 116648 registered in Jan.1889
Rd. No. 141273 registered in Jan.1890
Rd. No. 163767 registered in Jan.1891
Rd. No. 185713 registered in Jan.1892
Rd. No. 205240 registered in Jan.1893
Rd. No. 224720 registered in Jan.1894
Rd. No. 246975 registered in Jan.1895
Rd. No. 268392 registered in Jan.1896
Rd. No. 291241 registered in Jan.1897
Rd. No. 311658 registered in Jan.1898
Rd. No. 331707 registered in Jan.1899
Rd. No. 351202 registered in Jan.1900
Rd. No. 368154 registered in Jan.1901

First Registration No. for 1902 385088
First Registration No. for 1903 402913
First Registration No. for 1904 424017
First Registration No. for 1905 447548
First Registration No. for 1906 471486
First Registration No. for 1907 493487
First Registration No. for 1908 518415
First Registration No. for 1909 534963
First Registration No. for 1910 554801
First Registration No. for 1911 575787
First Registration No. for 1912 594175
First Registration No. for 1913 612382
First Registration No. for 1914 630174

COPYRIGHT MARKS

After the Great War the firm brought out a new range of models including numbered Egyptian and many other foreign shapes. Most of these had the word COPYRIGHT printed underneath in an attempt to stop other factories copying them. This does not add to, or detract from the value of the piece, but it does indicate that it was produced in the latter stages of the Second Period, or early part of the Third Period.

When the factory could not obtain a local authority's permission to use their coat of arms, or where local family arms were not available, it became necessary to design them. These home-made arms were like Seal crests, within a consistent circular pattern, using some local symbol usually lifted from the town's arms, for the centre, such as a fish for Newquay to denote a fishing port. The registration number for these seals was 77966 and this was printed on the base of every piece bearing such arms, some 20 in all. For further information, see *The Price Guide to Arms and Decorations on Goss China*, Section A, Geographical Place Names.

NON-PRODUCTION WARE

Fragments of pieces that did not go into production have been found in the factory spoil heap. Models seen have been listed below, and should perfect examples come to light, the author will be pleased to receive details. Some items are, of course, known with different colouring and glazing and will be found elsewhere in this Guide.

White Glazed:
Stratford Toby jug and basin
Churchill Toby jug
Bust of Lady Godiva
Monmouth Mask, The Knight
Crucifix Pendants, varying floral designs
Cigarette Holders numerous, with occasional examples in coloured lustres
Single Ear on flat base with pierced hole for hanging. Not made as part of a head. 70mm
Pixie on a toadstool

White Unglazed:
Shakespeare, standing, leaning on a lectern
Very large size. Estimated height 330mm

Coloured:
Massachusetts Hall
Sandbach Crosses, brown
As listed in *The 1978 Price Guide to Goss China* but not seen in one piece
St. Tudno's Church Font. Pale yellow
Brooches, black
Preserve Pot and lid. Multicoloured, Geometric Art Deco decoration.
Dolls Heads impressed Dorothy 10 or 12.

4 The Goss Records

Around 1900, it became obvious to the many collectors all over Great Britain that some sort of catalogue of agents' names and addresses was necessary to enable enthusiasts to plan their excursions. It could prove daunting to make a long, difficult trip to a far away town in search of a Goss agency which may or may not exist. Also the agent for any area could be a shopkeeper, hotel owner, pharmacist, librarian, or the owner of the local fancy stores or bazaar who often kept irregular hours.

J J Jarvis, an enterprising collector, approached William Henry Goss and put forward his idea of producing such a listing of agencies. William told him that he had been asked many times before, but he was a busy man, and thought it would be too time-consuming to continually keep updating such a publication with additions and changes of addresses. The thought of constant revision had deterred him. Eventually, mainly through Huntley Goss's help, Mr. Jarvis won William's confidence and gained the vital permission required to publish the first edition of *The Goss Record* towards the end of 1900, for a shilling a copy. Mr. Jarvis, who lived at Riverside, Enfield, Middlesex, did not have any financial interest in the Record's production, and the proceeds were donated entirely to a fund promoted by the Misses Evans of 58 Holly Road, Handsworth, Birmingham, for giving a Christmas tea and entertainment to some of the poor slum children in their area.

The first Record produced in 1900 was a hand-duplicated sheet not even stapled or bound. It listed the authorised agent in each town for which the factory produced arms, the address, the models and coats of arms stocked, together with details of opening hours. Jarvis was limited in the number of copies he could provide by duplication, and the few that he did produce sold out immediately. He was by now receiving letters from all over the country requesting still further copies, and he became determined to write a further edition with all the latest information about new models being made, to bind it properly, and to make this into a book. By having the Record printed and bound professionally, he could have a large quantity produced. Huntley Goss checked the rough draft and made any corrections and additions. In the interests of accuracy, Mr. Jarvis wrote to every known agent and asked them to reply confirming the particulars he had of them. Most complied with this request, but some were too lazy or too busy to reply, and so providing he thought their addresses were still correct, Jarvis kept them in his listing with their entries in italics. He was quite happy to send collectors details of any later changes on a free list that he was continually adding to, upon receipt of the stamps for the postage.

Certain statements had to be made in *The Goss Record* in order to satisfy the Goss factory arrangement. One was: 'I am not personally acquainted with Mr. Goss, or in any way financially interested in his business, but I take this opportunity of thanking him most sincerely for the trouble he has taken, and

The Goss Record War Edition 1916-1918.
Note The International league of
Goss Collectors Motif

The Goss Record 3rd Edition 1903

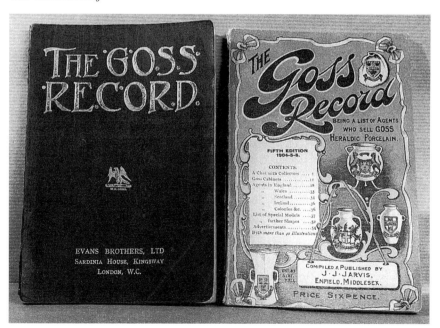

The Goss Record 8th Edition

The Goss Record 5th Edition 1904 - 05 - 06

the assistance he has given me in compiling this book. J J Jarvis.' Another statement was: 'Mr. Goss will not supply any of his porcelain except through individual agents; arms of one town where an agency exists cannot be obtained off an agent in another town. ' Also contained in *The Goss Record* was the warning: 'Collectors are warned against many inferior imitations of Goss porcelain, mostly of foreign manufacture, that are being sold.'

The agents themselves were very pleased with Jarvis as their trade increased. In April 1902, he published an 8-page supplement giving the latest corrections and amendments. In August of that year he produced the second of *The Goss Record*. By the time of the third edition, it was not just a list of agencies, but it also contained snippets and hints to collectors and details of the latest shapes being made, together with their historical background. With this edition there were also asterisks against certain agencies in the list signifying which particular shopkeepers would be prepared to open after hours to sell Goss to those collectors unfortunate enough to arrive after the close of business for that day. It also contained photographs of the latest Goss models, which were numbered. For example, the Salisbury Gill was No. 127. This was to facilitate the ordering of pieces from agents by post. Agents also advertised their own wares in *The Goss Record,* and other adverts included were for such ingenious inventions as the Doylesava, a circular glass pane for protecting lace doilies from cake stains, and the Dursley Pederson cycle, which looked remarkably uncomfortable and was supposed to be the featherweight of featherweights in cycling. The 4th edition was a supplement to the 3rd.

The 5th edition in 1905 had a shiny grey cover decorated with artistic sketches of various matching Goss models, which, incidentally, Jarvis collected. He related a tale in which he admitted he was responsible for Mr. Goss's office being bombarded with requests for an agency list in 1900 from all over Great Britain. This had led to Mr. Goss sending the requests to Jarvis' home in Enfield, together with permission for him to produce the first edition of *The Goss Record*.

By now his printing bills were in pounds, not shillings, and his postage bill was £50 a year alone - a terrific sum in those days when one considers that small Goss models were retailing for 9d each! *The Goss Record* could be obtained directly through him or through most Goss agencies. This fifth edition was 68 pages long and very much larger, thus reflecting the growing popularity of the porcelain and the increased output of the factory. Also announced was The League of Goss Collectors. Jarvis formed this in 1904 and was advertising for members in the 5th edition. All readers were eligible for membership.

A few years earlier he had formed a small exclusive club for his own friends, but now decided to make it national, as its usefulness might be extended if it had a wide following. Leaflets were enclosed advertising the aims of the League, and a form for joining. Cabinets were also advertised from this edition onwards.

The 6th edition of *The Goss Record* appeared in 1906. The copies produced before W. H. Goss's death on January 4th 1906 were encased in a red binding: those produced after his death had a purple binding and contained an obituary, extending the book to 96 pages. This was a very interesting booklet, full of information.

Three years elapsed before the 7th edition appeared in October 1909. Jarvis announced that a total of 70,000 of the various editions had been sold to date, and that the 8th would be printed in 1912. In fact, there was a short supplement to the 7th in 1911, and the 8th did not appear until 1913, not long before the outbreak of war. Jarvis had by that time handed over publication to Evans Bros, the London publishers, who produced a 104 page book. It may be said that Goss collecting reached its peak that year and this edition was the best of them all.

The War edition was a supplement to the 8th and was produced in 1916 as a concise booklet due to the shortage of paper, and sold for only 3d. Earlier editions cost 6d, and the 9th and last edition in 1921 was one shilling. The War Edition announced the International League of Goss Collectors, and the Regimental badges, Naval crests, and war shapes available.

The 9th edition was 80 pages in length and in it Jarvis regretted that the Goss cabinets were no longer available due to difficulties in the furniture trade and the heavy demand for essential articles. Nine years after the last of *The Goss Record*, the Goss family sold the pottery. The editor became Sir Joseph John Jarvis, who kept his Goss collection until his death at Godalming in 1950.

A List of Every Edition with Present Value:-

		Value
The Goss Record		£ p
1900	1st edition. Duplicated leaflet with 4 subsequent pamphlets.	75.00
1901	1st edition. Printed booklet	75.00
1902-3	2nd edition The Goss Record (supplement to 1st) August 1902	60.00
1903	3rd edition	60.00
1903	4th edition First edition 1903-4 (supplement assumed to be 4th edition)	60.00
1904-6	5th edition The Goss Record (1904-5-6)	40.00
1906- 7	6th edition Red binding (no obituary)	40.00
	Purple binding containing an obituary of W. H. Goss	45.00
1909-11	7th edition -1910-11	45.00
1911	Supplement to 7th edition	45.00
1913- 14	8th edition Published by Evans Brothers.	25.00
1916- 18	War Edition (supplement to 8th) . Published by Evans Bros .	35.00
1921	9th edition. Published by Evans Bros.	25.00

5 Postcards

Goss postcards were published with the permission of W. H. Goss by S. A. Oates & Co. of Halifax who printed on them: None genuine without the name "Goss"

These cards were published in the latter half of the Edwardian era, postmarks ranging from 1905 to 1912.

They carry the word *Goss* in gold on a dark blue circular motif at the top lefthand corner, and the description of the particular model at the bottom, similarly in gold and on a blue background. The cards are basically photographs of selected models without coats of arms. It was then up to the local agent or stationer to order cards with their own particular town's coat of arms on them. These arms were then over-printed, a process which gives certain combinations of arms and models a peculiar flat/round appearance.

Originally, six cards were produced and sold, if required, in sets, in special envelopes. Later, two further cards were added to the range, and it is these two which are the rarities. The cards are numbered in gold in the top righthand corner, and are as follows:

Card No.	Model	Value
		£ p
1	**Abbot's Cup, Fountains Abbey**	8.50
2	**Aberdeen Bronze Pot**	8.50
3	**Ancient Welsh Bronze Crochon**	8.50
4	**Roman Ewer from York**	8.50
5	**Loving Cup**	8.50
6	**Roman Vase from Chester**	8.50
7	**Bronze Ewer from Bath**	20.00
8	**Irish Mather**	20.00

Prices quoted are for cards in good condition.

Goss Postcard Album, with a postcard on the front cover, and title *Album for Goss Post Cards;* green cloth cover, with 48 pages holding two cards per page, Height 205mm   Length 270mm   80.00

Envelope in which 6 cards were sold   10.00

No. 1 Fountains Abbey Cup

No. 2 Aberdeen Bronze Pot

No. 3 Ancient Welsh Crochon

No. 4 York Roman Ewer

No. 5 Loving Cup

No. 6 Chester Roman Vase

No. 7 Bath Bronze Ewer

No. 8 Irish Mather

£   p

Postcard advertising the Bournemouth Pilgrim Bottle,
illustrated in stone colour on a green background, with an
heraldic type cross in each corner and carrying the following
descriptive material in a panel below the picture:

Ancient Pilgrim Bottle
One of the most perfect specimens of Early Christian Art ever
discovered in England. It is marked with the Sign of the Cross, and was
made about the year 600 A .D. Found at Southbourne, Bournemouth in
1907.
The Original may be seen and Goss Models obtained at
Bright 's Stores, Ltd ., Bournemouth   25.00

Postcard in sepia: *"Welsh Girls at Snowdon"* in national
costume carrying baskets full of Goss china, including Welsh
Lady coloured cream jugs clearly in view, and with a *"Goss*
Porcelain" plaque attached to each basket.   25.00

Envelope in which the first six Goss Postcards were sold.

6 Goss Cabinets

These were introduced by J. J. Jarvis, Editor of *The Goss Record* and were available from 1905 until 1919.

They were manufactured in six basic types by the firm which made bookcases for the Encyclopaedia Britannica Company. The following details are taken from the Seventh Edition of *The Goss Record;*

> These cabinets have been specially designed to hold Collections of Heraldic Porcelain, although equally suitable for other varieties of China, Bric-a-brac, etc. Made by one of the leading wholesale Cabinet Makers in the country to the personal instructions of the compiler of the Goss Record, no expense has been spared to produce the most suitable Cabinets to display to advantage the varied shapes of Goss Porcelain obtainable, and the Arms emblazoned thereon.
>
> Every cabinet is substantially made and well finished. The shelves are lined with green cloth and the doors fitted with lock and key. They may be had either in Chippendale or Fumed Oak as stated, whilst some are made in both, and each style is priced at the lowest possible figure consistent with the finest workmanship.
>
> A fully illustrated list of Cabinets will be sent on application to the Goss Record Office.
>
> The Cabinets will be sent from the makers direct on receipt of remittance, the carriage being paid by purchasers on delivery; 5s. will be charged for cases and packing unless these are returned carriage paid within 7 days.
>
> The amount paid will be returned in full for any Cabinet not approved of and returned carriage paid upon receipt.
>
> Cabinets may be obtained on the "Times" system of monthly installments, particulars of which may be had on application.
>
> All Cabinets bear the "Goss Arms" on a specially designed porcelain shield, without which none are genuine.

	There are seven types of Cabinets as under	*Current Value £ p*
Design A.	A small revolving cabinet in Chippendale to stand on a pedestal or table.18-ins. square. Holding capacity, 50 average sized pieces inside and 25 outside. Step-shaped shelves from the bottom. Glass side and top. **Price £2 2 0**	1200.00
Design B.	Wall cabinet 3-ft. 3-ins. wide by 3-ft. 8-ins. high. Holding capacity, 85 pieces. Made in Fumed Oak. A very artistic and pleasing case. **Price £2 18 6**	1000.00
Design BB.	The same as B. but with an additional shelf. This will hold 100 pieces **Price £3 3 0**	1050.00
Design C.	A revolving case in Chippendale, somewhat similar to A, but 3-ft. 4-ins. high and I -ft. 5-ins wide. This will hold 120 pieces, and where space is a consideration, is an excellent Cabinet. **Price £3 7 6**	1200.00
Design D.	4-ft. 6-ins. long by 3-ft. high. Made both in Chippendale and Fumed Oak. The centre door is hinged at the bottom enabling the entire contents to be displayed at once. By a unique mechanical contrivance this door is quite firm when opened. Holding capacity, 125 pieces **Price £4 4 0**	1000.00
Design E.	A handsome Cabinet on legs to stand on the ground, and sliding doors 3-ft. wide and 5-ft. high, will hold 160 pieces . Made in Chippendale or Fumed Oak. **Price £5 5 0**	1200.00
Design F.	5-ft. 2-ins. high by Oft. wide. Also made in both woods. A very fine Cabinet to hold nearly 200 pieces. The centre is recessed and enclosed by two doors below and one folding door above (as Cabinet D.) whilst the sides are glazed as well as the front. **Price £7 7 0**	1400.00
Unrecorded Design	Free standing two-tier Cabinet with plate glass elongated mirror between top and bottom sections, with the porcelain shield bearing the Goss Coat of Arms affixed inside the top case at the back of the top shelf. 5-ft. 3-ins. high by 3ft. 6-ins. wide **Original Price Unknown**	1200.00

See *The Goss Record* 8th Edition: Page 109 for illustration of Cabinet D in fumed oak.

The porcelain shield alone is worth £95.00 and this is included in the values given
above. See page 60 for an illustration.

Cabinets A and C were of the revolving variety, A suitable for a table top and C with a weighted base to avoid overturning, Cabinets B and D were for attaching to the wall, whilst E and F were free standing.

Revolving cabinet Design A.
no example of which is currently
known to exist

Arts and Crafts style wall mounted cabinet Design B

Revolving cabinet Design C.

Free standing cabinet E.

Wall-mounted cabinet with drop-down centre door, Design D

An original Goss Cabinet, Type F, finished in Chippendale and packed with Goss china.
Note the porcelain shield affixed to the rear of the centre top section

This unique cabinet was discovered in the 1980s. It was neither advertised nor recorded in The Goss Record. *Comparison with other cabinets reveals that it is definitely a Goss cabinet.*

Photograph Norman Pratten

7 The League and International League of Goss Collectors

The League of Goss Collectors was formed in 1904. The initial subscription was 2/6d which entitled the member to a certificate of membership, a copy of *The Goss Record* as and when published, and a special piece of porcelain bearing the Goss Arms surrounded by the wording: *The League of Goss Collectors.* Each model, except the first-issued, bore beneath it an inscription to the effect that it was issued to members and could not be bought. The inscriptions vary from model to model, for example some stating purchased instead of bought. The actual inscriptions will be found recorded under the individual pieces in SECTION 10E HISTORIC MODELS AND SPECIAL SHAPES.

Towards the end of the 1914- 18 War, the League widened its scope to become the International League of Goss Collectors, and a new model was issued for each year until 1932. These models, together with re-issues of all but the first model, were inscribed *International League of Goss Collectors.* They bore the new arms, incorporating the Goss arms and motto *Se Inserit Astris;* a second shield for England, of the design borne by all the later Plantagenet kings, and a third shield of a design presumed to be indicative of the international aspect of the League.

The arms are surrounded by green laurel wreathing tied with five crossed ribbons, and in tiny insets there appears the letters (FR) and the figures (16).

These are the League Models issued:

On joining the League	The Portland Vase.
For members of two years' standing	Ancient Costril or Pilgrims' Bottle.
For members of four years' standing	Staffordshire Tyg.
For members of six years' standing	King's Newton Anglo-Saxon Cinerary Urn.

1918	Cirencester Roman Ewer.	1925	Cyprus Mycenaean Vase.
1919	Contact Mine.	1926	Staffordshire Drinking Cup.
1920	Gnossus Vase.	1927	Colchester Roman Lamp.
1921	Greek Amphora Vase.	1928	Fimber Cinerary Urn.
1922	Italian Krater.	1929	Irish Cruisken.
1923	Egyptian Lotus Vase.	1930	Northwich Sepulchral Urn.
1924	Wilderspool Roman Tetinae or Feeding Bottle.	1931	Chester Roman Altar.
		1932	Cheshire Roman Urn.

All of the above will be found listed, illustrated and priced in
SECOND PERIOD 10E HISTORIC MODELS AND SPECIAL SHAPES

A Selection of League and International League of Goss Collectors models
Top Row left to right:
Greek Amphora Vase, Fimber Cinerary Urn, Wilderspool Roman Tetinae, Cheshire Roman Urn, Northwich Sepulchral Urn, Staffordshire Drinking Cup, Italian Krater, Cyprus Mycenaean Vase
Bottom Row left to right:
Eygptian Lotus Vase, Ancient Costril or Pilgrims' Bottle, King's Newton Anglo-Saxon Cinerary Urn, Staffordshire Tyg, The Portland Vase, Colchester Roman Lamp.

STORIES IN PORCELAIN

**ARMS OF THE INTERNATIONAL
LEAGUE OF GOSS COLLECTORS**

Front cover

collecting, heraldry, etc. "The Goss Record" may be ordered through the shops which sell the Porcelain.

There is also an International League of Goss Collectors which all purchasers of Goss Porcelain are invited to join. The annual subscription, commencing 1921, to the League is 5/-, and a special Collectors' model is made every year for members. The models of the League cannot be purchased in any shop; they bear the arms of the League and are only issued to members.

If you would like to know more about the League, post the form below or a postcard to-day.

Rear cover

YOU have just been looking at Goss Heraldic Porcelain. Has it ever occurred to you that each of these little models is a story in porcelain? Most of the models are replicas of ancient pieces of British pottery, old Roman vases, fighting and domestic implements. There are, too, models of Tudor relics, such as old British cannon, and Spanish implements of war—all with a wonderful story behind them. The majority of the originals are in private museums which are inaccessible to the general visitor, and these dainty little models are doubly valuable on that account.

On each such model is emblazoned in rich colouring the armorial bearings of some town, city, historic building or person—centuries old in origin and each having its own significance in British history. So, from the models themselves and by a study of the heraldry which they bear, the collector may gain a new insight into the story of Britain.

Some models are of literary interest, showing the birthplaces of famous writers. Others are souvenirs of the Great War. During the War,

too, the arms of all the British regiments and most famous battleships were added to the Goss Heraldry. Each model, in fact, holds a story in porcelain, and to the collector who studies its origins that story will be unfolded.

A beautiful collection of these little creamy models, with their bright heraldic devices, is a charming acquisition to any home. To secure the models provides definite objects for rides and walks from wherever you may be staying, and if you are continually travelling about the country they form delightful souvenirs of your journeys and inexpensive gifts for your friends or relatives.

There are many imitations of Goss Heraldic Porcelain and there is only one shop in any town or village at which the genuine Goss can be bought. There is, therefore, an official list published of shops from which the real Goss Porcelain can be obtained. This publication is entitled "The Goss Record," and contains, also, illustrations of models of special interest, information about many of the original antiquities from which the models were copied, notes on

A four page advertising leaflet for The International League of Goss Collectors containing membership details and an enquiry form published in 1921

8 Advertising Ware and Leaflets

William Henry Goss disliked all forms of advertising, and considered that if a product was good enough it would sell itself. Therefore, the monthly *Pottery Gazette*, the trade magazine for pottery and glass manufacturers, did not carry advertisements for Goss until February 1906 - a month after his death!

It is not surprising that other potteries competed with the firm of Goss. W H Goss had left the field so wide open. Toward the end of his life he did accept that china dealers, solely engaged in legitimate trade, advertised in order to bring their wares prominently to the notice of their potential customers. Goss agents bought space in *The Goss Record* and probably elsewhere as well.

The advertising material below dates from 1905 with the exception of the shield-shaped Goss agents enamel sign which was earlier.

ADVERTISING WARE

		£	p
An unusual Oval Plaque distributed to Goss Agents after 1931 stating AGENT FOR W.H. GOSS ART-POTTERY in red between two Goshawks [3]	Length 220mm	600.00	
The same decoration, in red and blue, also appears on a melon plate decorated in yellow lustre with lettering in blue and red.	Dia. 246mm	500.00	
The Shield from a Goss Cabinet. [2] (see illustration on page 58)	70mm	95.00	
The shield shape carrying the Goss family arms. Can also be found with town arms; BURFORD has been seen.		40.00	
A Goss Agent's Change Tray [2] One was given to each Agent and bore the arms of his particular town. Inscribed around rim: *GOSS ORIGINAL HERALDIC PORCELAIN. CONNOISEURS COLLECT IT*.	Dia. 140mm	375.00	
Examples without arms may also be found		325.00	
Plaque, cottage shaped pottery, with Goshawk in relief at the top and some decoration inscribed : a) *GENUINE GOSS COTTAGE POTTERY* [3] b) *GOSS TOBY JUGS* [3]	100mm	325.00	
Plaque, Cottage Pottery shaped, to form Ann Hathaway's Cottage, coloured [3] inscribed : *GOSS COTTAGE POTTERY*		250.00	

HER MAJESTY'S FIRST LITTLE SHOES.

THE exquisite taste displayed by Mr. William Henry Goss, of Stoke-on-Trent, in his parian and porcelain wares, whether classic and ornamental, or adapted for ordinary domestic use, both in design and material, has been endorsed by prize medals at various of the world's great exhibitions. In one report we read:—"Few displays of porcelain are to be seen in the exhibition which excel those made by Mr. Goss. In the parian statuettes, vases, tazzi, &c., and other ceramic materials under notice, the perfection of art manufacture seems certainly to have been reached."

Mr. Goss is a Fellow of the Royal Geological and of several other learned societies, a chemical expert, an accomplished antiquarian, and the author of a number of valuable biographical, scientific, and literary works.

There is always something touching in looking at the shoe of a little child; for who can forecast the rough and often thorny paths the little pilgrim may have to tread !

Mr. Goss, accidently, in the following manner, got to hear of the Queen's first shoe, which he has now copied and reproduced in porcelain—imitating form, material and colour. The story we give, although it is a story, is quite true.

Her Majesty's father, the Duke of Kent, went to live at Sidmouth, in 1819, to get the benefit of the Devonshire climate. While there, a certain local shoemaker received the order for the first pair of shoes for the infant Princess Victoria. But instead of making two only he made three, while he was about it, facsimiles, and kept one as a memorial and curiosity. It has been preserved to this day, and is now in the possession of his daughter, who is the wife of Mr. Goss's porcelain agent at Sidmouth.

Hearing of this, Mr. Goss borrowed the shoe, and made an exact copy in porcelain. The dainty little shoe is four inches in length, has a brown leather sole, white satin upper, is laced and tied in front with a bow of light blue silk ribbon, and bound with the same round the edge, and down the back of the heel.

In 1820 the shoemaker received the Royal Warrant; and that, also, is preserved with the interesting little shoe.

This little porcelain model, so suggestive, will arouse the loyal thrill of love and blessing in thousands of British hearts, simple little Cinderella sort of thing as it is; while to Her Gracious Majesty herself, it must touch a minor chord that vibrates back to the far reach of memory.

A. J. S.

Queen Victoria's first shoe leaflet

"THE KEY-STONE OF THE KINGDOM.

" WE do not know whether Mr. Goss, to whose exquisite and masterly works of Art we have more than once called attention in our pages, intended in the preparation of the well modelled portrait before us, to pay Lord Beaconsfield the high compliment contained in the words we have placed at the head of these few lines, or not—but this we do know, that the form he has chosen carries out the idea in the most emphatic and striking manner, and conveys to the mind an impression that the compliment was as fully intended as it was deserved. The design is, literally, a key-stone—the centre stone of an arch—and from this, standing out in *alto-relievo*; is a marvellously powerfully modelled, speaking, and well-thought-out life-size head of the present Prime Minister, Lord Beaconsfield, in all the freshness and vigour of that mental capacity that so eminently distinguishes him. Mr. Goss has won a high and deserved reputation for the excellence and truthfulness of his portrait busts, and this one is perhaps one of the happiest and best that even *he* has produced. The head is not only a faithful portrait of the *features* of the man, but is almost an inspired production, that presents a perfect reflex of the mind that animates those features. The modelling is faultless. We ought to add that, as a companion to this one, Mr. Goss has produced in a similar manner a very striking head of Lord Derby, which deserves equal praise with that of Lord Beaconsfield."

Leaflet sold with the Keystones of the Kingdom

				£ p
Plaque inscribed: *Goss Toby Jugs* in black manuscript and *GENUINE GOSS* with coloured scrolls. [3] — Height 100mm — 450.00

Goss Agent's enamel shop-front sign. Shield-shaped Height 300mm — 350.00

Royal Buff Ashtray inscribed: *With Compliments. For all kinds of Sanitary Ware and grates. W.E. Morris & Son Ltd., Stoke-on-Trent Phone 4539.* Length 130mm Width 110mm — 150.00

Taper Cream Jug 95mm carrying a transfer printed pictorial of a milkmaid milking a cow, surrounded by a ribbon containing the wording: *ST. ALDATE'S DAIRY OXFORD F.J. WIGMORE*, the whole being in green. Height 95mm — 200.00

Late Goss agents sign

Goss agents change tray

Goss agents change tray without arms

Royal Buff Advertising Ashtray

The Shield from a Goss cabinet

Third Period Cottage Pottery Advertising Stand

LEAFLETS

These were sold with certain pieces and told the story of the original model, building or decoration.

The most common is the Queen Victoria's shoe leaflet which can occasionally be found, folded, inside the toe of the porcelain model, pre 1901.

The Glastonbury Bronze Bowl was sometimes sold with a small folded card.

Christchurch Norman Tower	20.00
Queen Victoria's First Little Shoes	20.00
George & Mary Coronation 1911	20.00
Keystones of the Kingdom	80.00
The Loving Cup	25.00
Durham Sanctuary Knocker	25.00
The Potters' Oven	45.00
Glastonbury Bronze Bowl Card	30.00

UNIQUE

"Goss" Model

OF

The Norman Tower,

Priory Church, Christchurch,

Built by Ralph Flambard, Bishop of Durham, 1099-1128.

Extracts from Ferrey's "Antiquities of the Priory of Christchurch, Hants":—

"Although many alterations have been made in the original masonry of the north division of the Transept, it must still be regarded as a very curious, and probably unique example of Norman architectural decoration." . . . . . .

"But the most interesting specimen of the Norman work is the Round Tower or Staircase Turret (the undoubted work of Bishop Flambard and his early successors in this deanery), which projects towards the north-east, and which, progressively, exhibits—first, a series of five intersected

semi-circular arches, rising from small columns, and enriched with the fish scale and billet mouldings; secondly, a billetted string-course, surmounted by five small arches springing from double columns; thirdly, a diamond-shaped network or rope-like reticulated division, crowned by a chevron or zig-zag string-course; and fourthly, five small arches similar to the others." . . . . . .

"This Tower is of fresh-water limestone, containing Limnex, which shells have left hollows in the stone where it is weathered. Probably it came from some of the quarries in the north-western part of the Isle of Wight, near Hendon Hill."

THE MODEL may be obtained in either Grey or Brown stone colour, unglazed, or in White porcelain, glazed or unglazed,

FROM

Froud's China Stores,

43, High Street, Christchurch.

Leaflet sold with the Christchurch Norman Tower.

THE POTTERS' OVEN.

A characteristic feature of the Potteries District, are the Potters' Ovens, shaped like immense inverted funnels.

After the potter has formed an article in clay, it has to be subjected to very great heat to change it into pottery. It is placed in a vessel made of a coarser clay, called a saggar, to protect it from fumes and smoke during firing. The saggars are filled and placed one on top of another making a column reaching from the floor to the top of the oven. When the oven is full the entrance is bricked up and the fires are lighted. The heat is raised very gradually, the process taking many hours, till the high temperature necessary is reached; then it is allowed to cool slowly, requiring nearly the same length of time for cooling as for firing.

In consequence of the great heat developed, the oven is usually built away from other parts of the works to reduce the risk of fire. The building at the base gives shelter to the oven workers and provides storage for the saggars.

An interesting MODEL of the POTTERS' OVEN is
made in Goss Porcelain, and may be obtained from

RITCHIE & Co., Station China Stall, STOKE-ON-TRENT, Staffs.

Leaflet sold with the Goss Oven

THE LOVING CUP.

The late Lord Lyons, British Ambassador at Paris, used to relate the following history of the Loving Cup:

KING HENRY of Navarre, (who was also HENRY IV. of France), whilst hunting, became separated from his companions, and, feeling thirsty, called at a wayside inn for a cup of wine. The serving maid on handing it to him as he sat on horseback, neglected to present the handle. Some wine was spilt over, and his Majesty's white gauntlets were soiled. While riding home, he bethought him that a two-handled cup would prevent a recurrence of this, so his Majesty had a two-handled cup made at the Royal Potteries and sent it to the inn. On his next visit, he called again for wine, when, to his astonishment, the maid, (having received instructions from her mistress to be very careful of the King's cup), presented it to him, holding it herself by each of its handles. At once the happy idea struck the King of a cup with three handles, which was promptly acted upon, as his Majesty quaintly remarked, "Surely out of three handles I shall be able to get one." Hence the Loving Cup.

[P.T.O.]

The Loving Cup Leaflet

9 The First Period 1858-1887

Period Symbols

Where a shape was known to have been made during more than one period, the number in brackets after its entry denotes the other period(s) during which it was manufactured.

The First period	**[1]**	**1858-1887**
The Second period	**[2]**	**1881-1934**
The Third period	**[3]**	**1929-1939**

First Period Busts and Figures:

Left to right top row:	*Queen Victoria, mob cap; Northcote; Milton; Longfellow*
Third row:	*Bather, nude, seated on stump; Byron; Montefiore, Sister Dora*
Second row:	*Bunyan; Hartington; Shakespeare standing leaning on lectern*
Bottom row:	*Classical figurine, Meditation; General Gordon; Lady Godiva on horseback; Bather holding apple*

Ophelia. A pair with the bride of Abydos. This study stands 535mm high and was made during the period of the Goss & Peake partnership in 1867 and is so marked.

A rare bust of Llewellyn Jewitt, 380mm

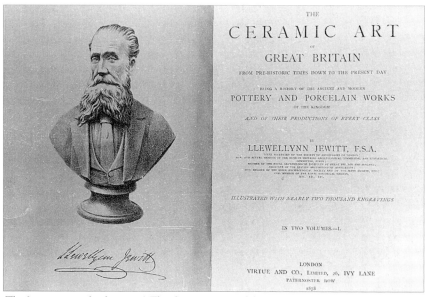

The frontispiece and title page of The Ceramic Art of Great Britain *by Llewellynn Jewitt. The bust of Jewitt is 380mm high and was produced by Goss for Jewitt's son.*

An unique model of Noah's Ark. The interior of the hull is decorated in Goss turquoise blue.

Leda and the Swan and Lady holding a Kid, the Wood Nymph, coloured with brushed gilding, blue dots and jewelling. 430mm and 435mm high respectively.

AN INTRODUCTION TO PARIAN WARE

During his training and career as designer and artist with Copeland's of London and Stoke-on-Trent, William Henry Goss worked with the relatively new medium of parian. Whilst still in London, he made contact with the inventor of parian, John Mountford, and later wrote the history of that discovery. In his *Encyclopaedia of Ceramics,* W P Jervis revealed that 'It's origin has been disputed, both Minton and Copeland claiming to have invented it. Mr W H Goss, who, when all the experiments were being conducted, was a young boy, knew all the parties concerned and afterwards wrote the particulars of the discovery for a book published at The Hague in 1864, entitled *Verslag der Wereldtentoonstelling Te London in 1862,* which was an important work on the London Exhibition produced by order of the Government of Holland. Mr Goss states that it was during the year 1845 that experiments were made at the manufactury of Alderman Copeland to obtain a ceramic material that should resemble marble'.

S C Hall, Editor of the *Art Journal* (and guide and mentor of William Goss), suggested that reductions from stone sculptures of the modern masters be made in a material that could imitate the stone visually. These miniatures could be offered as prizes by the Art Union of London. Following this idea, a reduced model of Gibson's Narcissus was despatched to Copeland's works for the potters to work from, until there was success with John Mountford's invention. These experiments were conducted by several experienced artistic potters at Copeland, but the first parian was produced from Mountford's recipe, in the form of Narcissus, on Christmas Day, 1845.

This new medium was immediately known as porcelain statuary. Mountford's figure was sent to Mr Gibson himself for inspection, and he declared it to be the best material next to marble for the reproduction of sculpture. The new porcelain statuary was an instant success in the industry and it firmly established itself in the ceramic world. It was at about this time that Messrs. H. Minton & Co began similar experiments for imitation marble, and it was not long before they discovered their own version which they termed parian. It was noted that their parian was slightly tinted and approximated freshly chiselled marble as quarried on the Aegean island of Paros. Copeland's efforts were that of marble toned down with age. Each manufacturer obtained his own quality and hue using his own adaptations of the inventions, and William Goss, who conducted his own experiments in the outbuildings in the garden of Ashfield Cottage adjoining his factory, perfected his own recipes in the late 1850's.

Inside a book which once belonged to Llewellynn Jewitt was found a portion of a letter from his best friend Mr Goss, obviously saved for its contents, in which Goss stated his beliefs concerning parian. 'We believe the day will arrive when these cream-colour wares shall again be chosen in preference to the bluish tint. For we certainly think that if the materials were thoroughly magnetted, well lawned, and finely ground so as to leave a clean, pure tint, the prevalence of the cream or ivory colour of the Dorsetshire ball clay would form a much more pleasing ground for decoration in colours and gold than that of the stained ware'.

The term parian, for this new porcelain composition, was derived from Paros, an island in the Aegean Sea. The marble of Paros was known as parian marble. Only the wealthy could afford marble busts and statues. Now the middle classes would be able to obtain the porcelain equivalent.

W P Jervis concluded that parian was a non-plastic body composed of 3 parts china stone to 2 parts felspar. William Goss's ingredients, according to his notebook, were Norwegian and Swedish felspar, white glass (obtained from grinding up old bottles made of clear glass only), flints and kaolin or china clay. Goss obtained the latter from Messrs Varcoes Sales Co Ltd. High Cross Street, St Austell, Cornwall. Incidentally, the type of felspar used came from certain beds in Norway and Sweden, which were almost worked out by the end of the Goss factory's life in 1929, and there was no known similar alternative. It is the felspar which influences the colour, texture and feel of the final result, making each factory's products so different from their rivals. The felspar Goss favoured, resulted in the ivory translucency which was so distinctly his own.

Most pottery was thrown on a wheel and shaped by hand, but parian was mixed and ground into a liquid state and poured into moulds and left only until a sufficient coating had been absorbed into the walls of the moulds, then the excess poured out to be used again. In this way, simple hollow shapes were made in two halves, although for making the more complex figures, up to twenty moulds were used. Most of these were for the detailed floral headbands, or intricate fingers, etc.

Classical figurines, seated on large bases
Left: *Looking to dexter, with two money sacks (not visible) book and scroll. Right arm damaged.* Right: *In pensive mood with right hand under chin.*

A Busts

The most important parian productions by Goss were portrait busts. Llewellynn Jewitt, in his *Ceramic Art of Great Britain,* described these portrait busts as ranking far above the average, and perfect reproductions of the living originals. 'It is not often that this can be said of portrait-busts, but it has been a particular study of Mr Goss, and in it he has succeeded admirably.' He later described Goss in *The Reliquary* as 'the leading portrait bust producer of the age'. Vastly underrated by the majority of collectors who prefer the glazed heraldic ware so much easier to recognise, the busts nearly all date from the last century and mainly bear impressed titles.

The first parian bust to have been made was Mr Punch in 1861. William Goss was on friendly terms with two successive editors of *Punch* and made this study for the then editor Mark Lemmon to commemorate the magazines' 20th anniversary .

Other early portrait busts for retail sale were those of Lord Palmerston whose second term of office was 1859 to 1865. The earliest models were marked *Copyright* and also signed by W H Goss in his own hand, on the shoulder. The majority of parian busts were made during a 30 year period after 1861, with subjects such as eminent musicians, members of the clergy, political and literary figures, royalty, and personal friends. A bust was eventually made of W H Goss himself in 1906, shortly before his death. Contrary to popular belief that he was so conceited that he made one of himself in large numbers, it was not his wish to be depicted in this way. It was only in his old age that enforced feebleness prevented him from standing up to his sons who organised the modelling of him as a good sales line.

Up until 1881 when he emigrated to America, the chief artist and modeller was W W Gallimore, except for the three years 1863-6 when he was induced to go to Ireland to work for the Belleek factory, taking the highly prized and secret Goss recipes with him, in particular the wafer thin eggshell method. After losing his right arm in a shooting accident, he returned to Stoke and worked with his left arm, and was said to have modelled even better than before!

After 1881 Joseph Astley became Goss's chief designer until his death in 1902. Astley had carried on where Gallimore left off with the creation of parian busts, with his boss often putting the finishing touches to his designs. William really valued his work and respected his talent. The two men worked well together for 21 years, with Astley religiously carrying out William's every instruction. It was as though William had two pairs of hands.

The portrait busts were favourably criticized by *The Reliquary* and *Art Journal.* The editors of these journals happened to be William's closest friends, Llewellynn Jewitt and Samuel Carter Hall, of whom he made busts!

The high quality of the busts, individually made from moulds from the one original, included detail about the eyes which most factories tended to ignore, giving the appearance of the subject being blind. Not so with the Goss versions, for the factory strove to obtain a true likeness. Readers of *The Reliquary* were recommended to purchase a Goss bust of Mr Gladstone because 'it conveys to the eye a far more truthful, and eminently pleasing likeness of the great statesman, than has ever been produced either by painting, engraving or sculpture.' Admirers of Charles Swain were also advised to purchase the Goss version of this well loved poet, because of its truthful and intellectual likeness .

The main series had either a square two-step plinth, or a socle base, the latter sometimes mounted on an octagonal plinth. The square base bust would carry the name of the subject impressed on to the lower step, or impressed into the back of the shoulder. Early busts had a circular (or socle) plinth, and tended to be of classical subjects. Plinths were affixed solidly with slip, or loosely with a steel or brass nut and bolt.

All Goss busts and figurines have an air hole at the back, usually in the rear of the neck on busts and smaller figures, and half way down the back on larger subjects.

Very little unglazed parian was issued after the turn of the century, with the exception of the busts of W H Goss, Shakespeare, King Edward VII, Queen Alexandra, The Prince of Wales (1911) and Scott. The ivory porcelain used for the production of heraldic ware was of the same recipe, but glazed.

In Section A the busts listed have been separated into two categories:- ROYALTY on page 73 and OTHER SUBJECTS on page 75. All busts in Section A have square two step plinths unless otherwise stated and all dimensions refer to the height of the piece. Every bust is white parian and unglazed unless otherwise stated.

Christ, socle base 310mm

Christ square plinth 277mm

A rare bust of The Prince of Wales, later King Edward VII, wearing the Masonic Collar of Grand Master of the Grand Lodge of England. 520mm

1 ROYALTY   £   p

Queen Victoria in Mob-cap, socle/octagonal plinth   201mm   400.00
Impressed on plinth: Victoria R.   210mm   400.00
Impressed side or back: *Copyright as Act Directs W.H. Goss*   236mm   450.00
Stoke-on-Trent November 1886
An example of the 236mm size has been noted with
the ornate 3 step plinth used for
The Beautiful Duchess.

Queen Victoria in Mob-cap, square plinth   101mm   135.00
Impressed on plinth: *Victoria R.*   Unglazed   129mm   150.00
Impressed on side or back: *Copyright as Act directs* Glazed   129mm   150.00
W.H. Goss Stoke-on-Trent November 1886   150mm   200.00
                                                                    157mm   200.00

Some busts of Queen Victoria have a single frill to the front of
the bonnet, others have a double frill. Value unchanged

Queen Victoria- wearing Imperial Crown,
the top of which is extremely fragile   Two step plinth   180mm   400.00
Impressed on plinth: *Victoria R.*   Socle/octagonal plinth   245mm   500.00
Impressed side or back: *Copyright as Act directs*
W.H. Goss Stoke-on-Trent January 1887

(NB. The 180mm version has been found in bronze colour, of heavy
earthenware with a large metallic content and is believed to be a
forgery .)

Note: Should any of the above busts bear reference on the back to
Queen Victoria's Diamond Jubilee, it will indicate that they
are commemorative items and of higher value, say £30.00 extra.
Inscribed on back: *1896-7 Memorial of 60th year*
of reign of Her Majesty Victoria R.I.

Mary, Queen of Scots socle plinth   131 mm   250.00
Inscribed on back: *Mary Q. of Scots, Copyright.*
Pub. As Act Directs (See 54 Geo 111, C.56)
W.H. Goss Stoke-on-Trent 1st Dec R 1894

Prince of Wales later King Edward VII wearing Masonic
collar; sculpted by W.W. Gallimore   520mm   2500.00
Inscribed: *Published by Bro. J.S. Crapper PM, PPAGDC,*
Staffs and Bro. C. Marsh PM, PPSGW Staffs 35 Design Office
April 16th 1875 Registered

Prince of Wales later King Edward VII, square plinth   167mm   300.00
Impressed on plinth: *H.R.H. The Prince of Wales*
Impressed side or back: *Copyright as Act directs W.H. Goss*
Stoke-on-Trent November 1882

Queen Victoria, Mob Cap socle/octagonal plinth

Queen Victoria wearing Mob Cap

Queen Victoria Wearing Imperial Crown

The Prince of Wales

The Princess of Wales

King Edward VII

King Edward VII, socle plinth

Queen Alexandra, socle plinth

The Prince of Wales

Mary Queen of Scots

Ajax

Apollo, socle plinth

			£ p

Princess of Wales later Queen Alexandra, square plinth   176mm   300.00
Impressed on plinth: *H.R.H. The Princess of Wales*
Impressed side or back: *Copyright as Act directs W.H. Goss*
Stoke-on-Trent November 1882

King Edward VII square plinth   163mm   250.00
Impressed on plinth: *King Edward VII*
Impressed side or back: *Copyright as Act directs W.H. Goss*
Stoke-on-Trent, and sometimes the date *7 May 1901*

King Edward VII socle plinth   glazed   133mm   245.00
Inscribed on back: *Copyright. Pub. As Act Directs*   unglazed   137mm   245.00
(See 54 Geo 111, C.56) W.H. Goss Stoke-on-Trent 7 May 1901

Queen Alexandra socle plinth   132mm   265.00
Inscribed on back: *Copyright. Pub. As Act Directs*
(See 54 Geo 111, C.56) W.H. Goss Stoke-on-Trent 7 May 1901

Queen Alexandra square plinth   approx.   175mm   275.00
Impressed on plinth: *Queen Alexandra*
Impressed on side or back: *Copyright as Act directs*
W.H. Goss Stoke-on-Trent, and sometimes the date *7 May 1901*

Prince of Wales later King Edward VIII, bearing
details of Investiture, and mounted on column bearing arms   143mm   250.00
Inscribed on back: *Investiture of H.R.H. The Prince of Wales*
Carnarvon Castle 13 July 1911. Copyright. Pub. As Act Directs
(See 54 Geo 111, C.56) W.H. Goss Stoke-on-Trent 16 June 1911
As above but lacking Investiture details [2]   143mm   225.00

2 OTHER SUBJECTS

Adonis socle plinth   265mm   950.00
Impressed on back: *W.H. Goss*

Ajax socle plinth   330mm   1000.00
Impressed on back: *W.H. Goss*

Apollo socle plinth with some gilding   375mm   1000.00
Impressed on back: *W.H. Goss*

Beaconsfield,Earl of square plinth	(a)	104mm	160.00
Impressed on plinth: *Beaconsfield*	(b) glazed	154mm	160.00
I mpressed side or back: *Copyright as Act directs*	(c) unglazed	154mm	165.00
W.H. Goss Stoke-on-Trent August 1876 OR *1881*	(d) bronzed	154mm	100.00
	(e)	162mm	165.00
	(f)	360mm	950.00
(g) as (f) but with socle plinth added		410mm	1250.00

*Earl Beaconsfield Wearing
Coronet*

*Beaconsfield, square base
360mm*

Ludwig van Beethoven

Beaconsfield 154mm

Beaconsfield, socle plinth

*The Beautiful Duchess
Coloured, white plinth*

John Bunyan

Lord Byron

*Lord Byron socle/octagonal
plinth*

John Bright

Robert Burns, socle plinth

*Robert Burns, socle/ octagonal
plinth*

£ p

Beaconsfield - wearing coronet, square plinth   181mm   500.00
Impressed on plinth: *Beaconsfield*
Impressed on side or back: *Copyright as Act directs W.H. Goss*
Stoke-on-Trent August 1876

Beaconsfield socle plinth, glazed   111mm   145.00

Beautiful Duchess,The.	(a) White, on 3-step plinth	242mm	1100.00
The Duchess of Devonshire	(b) Coloured, on 3-step plinth	242mm	2250.00
	(c) White, socle/octagonal plinth	242mm	1250.00

Impressed on the 3 steps of plinth (a) and (b): *The Beautiful Duchess*
Impressed on back: *Copyright as Act directs W.H. Goss*
Stoke-on-Trent December 1876 or January 1877

NOTE: This bust stands on a separate highly ornate plinth,
impressed on one foot: *W. H. Goss* (Also found unmarked)

	(a) Unglazed, plain	135mm	300.00
	(b) Glazed, four coats of arms	135mm	150.00

Add the price of this plinth to that of the bust when present

Beethoven, Ludwig Van square plinth	glazed	116mm	185.00
Impressed on plinth: *Beethoven*	unglazed	116mm	185.00

Bright, John square plinth	glazed	165mm	185.00
Impressed on plinth: *Bright* and sometimes also on	unglazed	165mm	185.00

the rear of right shoulder
Impressed side or back: *Copyright as Act directs W.H. Goss*
Stoke-on-Trent August 1876

Bunyan, John square plinth	glazed	132mm	200.00
Impressed on plinth: *Bunyan*	unglazed	132mm	200.00
Impressed side or back: *Copyright as Act Directs*	coloured	132mm	400.00

W.H. Goss Stoke-on-Trent January 1884

Burns, Robert socle plinth	glazed	136mm	125.00
Impressed on back: *Robert Burns*	unglazed	136mm	125.00
		155mm	165.00

Burns, Robert socle/octagonal plinth	glazed	166mm	225.00
Impressed on plinth: *Robert Burns*	unglazed	166mm	225.00

See also 9D TERRACOTTA

Byron, Lord square plinth   170mm   245.00
Impressed on Plinth: *Byron*
Impressed side or back: *Copyright as Act directs W.H. Goss*
Stoke-on-Trent. March 30, 1881

77

Child – Grief

Child – mirth

Christ, square base

Clytie, sunflower model

Clytie, socle plinth

*Classical Lady, coloured,
butterfly on shoulder*

*Richard Cobden
four button waistcoat*

*Richard Cobden
two button waistcoat*

Lord Derby

Lord Derby socle plinth

*Classical Bust of Maiden
180mm*

Charles Dickens, 256mm

		£ p

Byron socle/octagonal plinth   193mm   275.00
Impressed on plinth: *Byron*

Byron socle plinth (Bust 162mm, plinth 50mm)   212mm   300.00

Cairns, Earl square plinth   172mm   350.00
Reputed to be, but unnamed

Children- A pair of busts, after the style of the 17th century
sculptor Francois Dugnesnoy, each with a cartouche affixed to the
front of the socle plinth (often missing for which deduct £100).
The cherub or cupid figures depicted on the
cartouches vary from model to model.

          (a) Mirth (Laughing)   210mm   350.00
   (b) Grief(Weeping and wearing shawl on head)   218mm   450.00

Christ   (a) socle plinth (base 85mm)   310mm   950.00
Impressed on plinth: *W.H. Goss*   (b) square plinth   277mm   950.00
Impressed on back: *W.H. Goss*

Classical Bust of a Maiden coloured, with butterfly upon shoulder.
Socle/octagonal plinth. Multi-coloured floral garland in
the hair. Early puce Goshawk. A similar bust was made by
Belleek, evidently after the Goss original   240mm   1750.00
Impressed on back: *W. H. Goss*

Classical Bust of a Lady with star in band around forehead.
Possibly Clytie or Miranda.   260mm   650.00

Classical Bust of a Maiden   180mm   450.00
Impressed on back: *W. H. Goss*
not yet recorded with a base.

Clytie socle plinth, sunflower model.
This bust is thought to repesent the daughter of
Mark Anthony and mother of the Roman Emperor Claudius.
Also known as Antonia.   215mm   750.00
Impressed: *W. H. Goss*   270mm   1000.00

Clytie socle plinth   275mm   1000.00
Impressed on back: *W. H. Goss*

Clytie square base (not seen by the author)   approx.   160mm   550.00
Impressed on back: *W. H. Goss*

Cobden, Richard socle plinth   (a)   Four Button Waistcoat   223mm   450.00
Impressed on base: *W.H. Goss*   (b)   Two Button Waistcoat   223mm   450.00

Giuseppe Garibaldi

William Henry Goss

General Gordon

William Ewart Gladstone

Gladstone, socle plinth

Gladstone, square base on socle plinth 445mm

Earl Granville

William Court Gully

Samuel Carter Hall

George Fridrick Handel

Lord Hartington, socle plinth

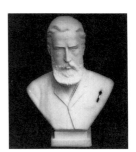

Lord Hartington

		£ p

Dawson, George socle plinth   215mm   450.00
See also 9D TERRACOTTA

Derby socle plinth   105mm   165.00
Impressed: *Copyright as Act Directs W. H. Goss*
Stoke-on- Trent Aug 1878

Derby square base   105mm   150.00
Impressed on base: *W.H. Goss*

Derby square plinth   115mm   160.00
Impressed on plinth: *Lord Derby*
Impressed side or back: *Copyright as Act*
Directs W. H. Goss Stoke-on-Trent August 1876

Derby, Earl of square plinth   glazed 160mm   175.00
Impressed on plinth: *Derby*   unglazed 160mm   175.00
Impressed side or back: *Copyright as Act directs W.H. Goss*
Stoke-on-Trent August 1876

Dickens, Charles socle plinth   256mm   750.00
Impressed: *W.H. Goss*

Dickens, Charles socle plinth - Goss & Peake   650mm 6500.00
Incised in manuscript in W.W. Gallimore's own hand
on the back of the bust: *Published as the Act directs (see Geo. 111,*
C.56) By Goss & Peake 12 October 1867 W. W. Gallimore ft
See frontispiece illustration

Giuseppe Garibaldi   174mm   550.00
Impressed on plinth: *Giuseppe Garibaldi*
Incised on rear in W.H. Goss's own hand:
Published as the Act directs under the Superintend J.A.P.
McBride

Gladstone, William Ewart square base   125mm   140.00
Impressed: *W. H. Goss*

Gladstone socle plinth   (a) With younger features   125mm   185.00
Impressed side or back: (b) With older features   130mm   185.00
Copyright as Act directs W.H. Goss
Stoke-on- Trent August 1876.

Gladstone square plinth   164mm   170.00
Impressed on plinth: *Gladstone*
Impressed side or back: *Copyright as Act directs W.H. Goss*
Stoke-on-Trent August 1876

A fine bust of Samuel Carter Hall, 376mm on socle plinth. Hall was editor of The Art Journal *in the 1870s and a close friend of William Henry Goss.*

Washington Irving. A fine 420mm bust on socle plinth.

		£ p

Gladstone square base on socle plinth   445mm   950.00
Impressed on base: *Gladstone*
Impressed on back: *Copyright as Act directs W.H. Goss*
Stoke-on- Trent November 30, 1889

Godiva, Lady square plinth
(Goss Record,9th Edition: Page 29)
Impressed on plinth: *Lady Godiva*
Inscribed on back: *Lady Godiva. Copyright, Pub.*
As Act Directs (See 54 Geo 111, C.56) W.H. Goss
Stoke-on- Trent 1st Oct R 1902

(a) White unglazed	110mm	125.00
(b) White glazed	110mm	125.00
(c) Coloured	110mm	285.00

Godiva, Lady socle/octagonal plinth   210mm   375.00
Incised on front of base: *Lady Godiva*
Impressed on back: *Copyright as the Act Directs*
W.H. Goss Stoke-on-Trent November 1891

Gordon, General square plinth   189mm   295.00
Impressed on plinth: *Gordon*
Impressed side or back: *Copyright as Act directs W.H. Goss*
Stoke-on-Trent January 1885

Goss, William Henry square plinth [2]   glazed 160mm 220.00
Impressed on plinth: *W.H. Goss*   unglazed 160mm 210.00
First sold in 1906 upon the death of W.H. Goss

Granville, Earl square plinth   glazed 176mm 185.00
Impressed on plinth: *Granville*   unglazed 176mm 185.00
Impressed side or back: *Copyright as Act directs W.H. Goss*
Stoke-on- Trent August 1877

for **Grief** see children

Gully, William Court square plinth   165mm   350.00
(Speaker, House of Commons 1895- 1905, and afterwards
first Viscount Selby)
Impressed on plinth: *W.C. Gully*
Impressed on back: *Copyright as The Act directs W.H. Goss*
Stoke-on-Trent August 1884
Inscribed: *Published by Wm. Workman, China Merchant, Whitehaven*

Hall, Samuel Carter socle plinth   376mm   3000.00

Handel, George Frideric square plinth   glazed 124mm 155.00
Impressed on plinth: *Handel*   unglazed 124mm 155.00

				£	p
Hartington, Marquess of square plinth	glazed	173mm		225.00
Impressed on plinth: *Hartington*	unglazed	173mm		225.00

Impressed on side or back: *Copyright as Act directs*
W.H. Goss Stoke-on-Trent March 30, 1886

Hartington socle plinth	125mm	225.00

Impressed on rear: *W.H. Goss*

Hathaway, Ann on two books

(Goss Record.9th Edition: Page 30) [2]	(a) White	75mm	95.00
	(b) White	100mm	110.00
	(c) Coloured	100mm	265.00

Inscribed on back: *Ann Hathaway. Copyright. Pub.*
As Act Directs (See54 Geo. 111, C.56) W.H. Goss
Stoke-on- Trent 1st DecR 1894
See also THIRD PERIOD 11 R for late examples of
busts of Ann Hathaway

Irving, Washington square plinth	325mm	1500.00

Impressed on plinth: *W. Irving*
Impressed on rear: *W.H. Goss*

Irving, Washington large bust on socle base.
This is one of the earliest and finest Goss busts
and modelled by a noted sculptor.

Incised: *MacBRIDE 1860*	420mm	2500.00

Jewitt, Georgiana socle/octagonal plinth	198mm	2250.00

The inscription on the back of this bust reads:'*Georgiana. The*
beloved wife of Edwin A.G. Jewitt, and daughter of William H.
Goss. She was born in London July 30, 1855, died at Matlock,
Nov. 3, 1889 and is buried in Winster Churchyard '.
The grave may still be seen today in the delightful Derbyshire
village of Winster.

Jewitt, Llewellynn socle plinth	380mm	3000.00

The inscription on the back of this bust reads: *This bust of*
Llewellynn Jewitt F.S.A . is made expressly for presentation
to his son Mr. Edwin Augustus George Jewitt on occasion
of his 21st birthday the 13th Oct. 1879 as a mark of the
the highest esteem for both by their devoted friend William Henry
Goss.
This bust was used as the frontispiece for *Ceramic Art in Great*
Britain, First Edition,1878, by Llewellynn Jewitt

Johnson, Dr. Samuel socle/octagonal plinth	190mm	450.00

Impressed on plinth: *Dr. Samuel Johnson*
Impressed on back: *Copyright as the Act directs W.H. Goss*
Stoke-on-Trent

Ann Hathaway, coloured

Washington Irving, square plinth

Dr Samuel Johnson socle/ octagonal plinth

Georgiana Jewitt

Llewellynn Jewitt

Sir Wilfred Lawson

Henry W. Longfellow

Unknown Dignitary possibly Earl Cairns

John Milton

John Milton, socle base

Thomas Moore

Wolfgang Amadeus Mozart

			£ p
Johnson, Dr. Samuel socle/octagonal plinth	glazed	195mm	450.00
Unnamed Bust	unglazed	195mm	450.00
Impressed on back: *W. H. Goss*			

For **Lady Godiva** see **Godiva**

Lawson, Sir Wilfrid square plinth   170mm   375.00
Impressed on plinth: *Sir Wilfrid Lawson*
Impressed side or back: *Copyright as Act directs W.H. Goss*
Stoke-on- Trent August 1880
Inscribed on-back: *Published by Marshall China Showrooms*
37-39-41 Scotch Street Carlisle

Longfellow, Henry W. square plinth   185mm   325.00
Impressed on plinth: *Longfellow*
Impressed side or back: *Copyright as Act directs W.H. Goss*
Stoke-on-Trent March 30th 1882

Mendelssohn, Felix square plinth	glazed	125mm	325.00
Impressed on plinth: *Mendelssohn*	unglazed	125mm	325.00

Milton, John square plinth	unglazed	125mm	175.00
Impressed on plinth: *Milton*	glazed	165mm	195.00
Impressed side or back: *Copyright as Act directs*	unglazed	165mm	195.00
W.H. Goss Stoke-on-Trent January 1884			

Milton, John socle plinth   210mm   225.00
Impressed on rear: *W.H. Goss*

for **Miranda** see bust of a Classical Lady

for **Mirth** see children

Montefiore, sometimes **Montifiore, Sir Moses** with hat   130mm   225.00
Impressed on plinth: *Sir Moses Montefiore*
Impressed side or back: *Copyright as Act directs W.H. Goss*
Stoke-on-Trent August 1882

Montefiore, Sir Moses without hat, square plinth   123mm   195.00
Impressed on plinth: *Sir Moses Montefiore*
Impressed side or back : *Copyright as Act directs W.H. Goss*
Stoke-on-Trent August 30. 1882

The above Montefiore Models can usually be found
inscribed on the back: *Pub. by W. Ballard*
Royal Albion Stationery Bazaar, Ramsgate.

Moore, Thomas square plinth	glazed	170mm	265.00
Impressed on plinth: *Thomas Moore*	unglazed	170mm	265.00
Impressed side or back: *Copyright as Act directs W.H. Goss*			
Stoke-on-Trent March 30. 1881			

Sir Moses Montefiore with Hat

Sir Moses Montefiore without Hat

Napoleon

Sir Stafford Northcote

Ophelia socle plinth

Pallas Athena socle plinth armour and helmet gilded

Lord Palmerston socle base 165mm

Lord Palmerston socle base 223mm

Lord Palmerston socle base and fluted column

Lady Godiva, white

Lady Godiva socle/octagonal plinth

Sir Isaac Pitman

				£ p
Mozart, Wolfgang Amadeus square plinth		glazed	118mm	175.00
Impressed on plinth: *Mozart*		unglazed	118mm	175.00
Napoleon	(a) square tapered plinth, unglazed		142mm	100.00
	(b) plinth only glazed		142mm	100.00
	(c) completely glazed		142mm	110.00

NOTE: This bust normally carried the arms of St. Helena, and
the above prices are for this model. Examples have been
found bearing the arms of Napoleon I, which would increase
the above values by £30.00 [2]

Northcote, Sir Stafford square plinth		glazed	169mm	225.00
Impressed on plinth: *Sir S. Northcote*		unglazed	169mm	225.00

Impressed side or back: *Copyright as Act directs W.H. Goss
Stoke-on- Trent November 3rd 1881*

Ophelia socle plinth	250mm	1000.00

Impressed on rear: *W.H. Goss*
See also 9B FIGURES

Pallas Athena socle plinth. The larger size has armour and	248mm	1000.00
helmet gilded, with the face tinted in natural colours	300mm	1500.00

Impressed on rear: *W.H. Goss*

Palmerston Lord socle plinth (unnamed)	165mm	185.00
Impressed on the back of the smaller bust: *W.H. Goss*	223mm	185.00

Copyright, and incised in manuscript on back of the larger:
Published by W.H. Goss Copyright.

Palmerston socle plinth and fluted column (unnamed)	240mm	195.00
Impressed on the back of the smaller bust: *W.H. Goss*	333mm	225.00

Copyright, and incised in manuscript on back of the larger:
Published by W.H. Goss Copyright.

Peeping Tom square plinth			
(Goss Record. 9th Edition:	(a) White glazed	115mm	95.00
Pages 29 & 30)	(b) White unglazed	115mm	95.00
	(c) Coloured	115mm	185.00

Impressed on plinth: *Peeping Tom of Coventry*
Inscribed on back: *Peeping Tom of Coventry Copyright Pub.
As Act Directs (See 54 Geo. 111, C.56) W.H. Goss
Stoke-on- Trent 22 Jany 1893*

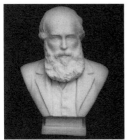

Lord Salisbury

Lady Godiva, coloured

Peeping Tom, coloured

Sir Walter Scott wearing Jacket and Cravat

Sir Walter Scott, socle/octagonal plinth

Sir Walter Scott

Sir Walter Scott, Tartan Plaid

Shakespeare, socle/octagonal pinth

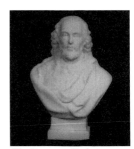

The Davenant Shakespeare

Shakespeare from The Monument, coloured

The Chandos Shakespeare

The Rysbrack Shakespeare

£ p

Pitman, Sir Isaac. This bust is an apparent anomaly. Sculpted   275mm   400.00
by T. Brock, R.A. in London in 1887, it has an unusual square
plinth, and carries the GOSS ENGLAND mark. The original
Goss bust was given to Pitman in 1887. He was knighted in 1894
so this late example was produced after that date. Though not
typical of the Goss factory, it was probably bought in and the bust
seen would appear to be the subject of a special order, as few
busts were produced after the turn of the century. In view of its
early date it is included in this section [3]
Impressed on plinth: *Sir Isaac Pitman*
Incised on back: *T. Brock RA, SC London 1887*

Salisbury, Marquess of square plinth	glazed	163mm	225.00
Impressed on plinth: *Salisbury*	unglazed	163mm	225.00

Impressed side or back: *Copyright as Act directs W.H. Goss*
Stoke-on-Trent December 29 1887

Scott, Sir Walter square plinth	glazed	176mm	175.00
Impressed on plinth: *Sir Walter Scott*	unglazed	176mm	175.00

Impressed side or back: *Copyright as Act directs W.H. Goss*
Stoke-on-Trent March 30. 1880

Scott, Sir Walter socle plinth, and wearing tartan plaid   135mm   45.00
Impressed on back or base: *W.H. Goss*

Scott, Sir Walter socle plinth, and wearing jacket, waistcoat
and cravat   138mm   95.00
Impressed on back: *Scott*

Scott, Sir Walter socle/octagonal plinth, and wearing jacket,
waistcoat and cravat   168mm   225.00
Impressed on back: *Scott*

Shakespeare from the monument, socle plinth   unglazed   100mm   80.00
Impressed on back: *From the Monument at Stratford-on-Avon 1616*

Shakespeare from the monument, socle/octagonal plinth.
Incised on back in manuscript: *From the Monument at*
Stratford-on-Avon. 1616.

(a) Unglazed	165mm	175.00
(b) Coloured	165mm	225.00

Sister Dora

Robert Southey

Robert Southey,
socle/octagonal plinth

Charles Swain

Sir William Wallace

H M Stanley

William Wordsworth

The Veiled Bride

Venus de Milo

John Wesley

Virgin Mary

Black Bust of Wesley

£   p

Shakespeare from tomb, mounted upon two books
(Goss Record. 9th Edition: Page 30) [2]
Inscribed on the back: *Copied from the Monument erected by*
Shakespeare's family in the Church at Stratford-on-Avon.

(a)	White	75mm	60.00
(b)	White	102mm	70.00
(c)	Coloured	102mm	85.00
(d)	White	158mm	85.00
(e)	Coloured	158mm	125.00
(f)	Black	158mm	110.00
(g)	White	200mm	135.00
(h)	Coloured	200mm	165.00

Shakespeare - The Chandos socle plinth   125mm   160.00
Incised in manuscript on back: *The Chandos Shakespeare*   135mm   165.00

Shakespeare - The Davenant square plinth   115mm   120.00
Impressed on plinth: *The Davenant Shakespeare*

Shakespeare - The Rysbrack   224mm   125.00
Impressed on bust, rear: *W. H. Goss*
This model is the unnamed Goss version of Shakespeare, but is the
likeness created by Rysbrack. It has been seen mounted on a square
pillar,and also on a fluted column impressed: *W. H. Goss*, but these
are believed to have been matched subsequently, and that the
original base is a socle plinth.

See also THIRD PERIOD 11R. for late examples of busts of
Shakespeare.

Sister Dora square plinth   174mm   250.00
Impressed on plinth: *Sister Dora*
Impressed on side or back: *Copyright as Act directs W.H. Goss*
Stoke-on-Trent November 1888

Southey, Robert square plinth   180mm   145.00
Impressed on plinth: *Southey*
Incised in manscript on back: *From the Drawing by Hancock (1796)*
Impressed on back: *W.H. Goss*

Southey, Robert socle/octagonal plinth.   205mm   195.00
Impressed on plinth: *Southey*
Incised in manuscript on back: *From a drawing by Hancock (1796)*
Impressed on back or side: *Copyright as Act directs W.H. Goss*
Stoke-on-Trent March 30, 1880

Stanley, Sir Henry Morton socle/octagonal plinth   212mm   750.00
Impressed on plinth: *H. M. Stanley*
Impressed on back: *Copyright as Act Directs W. H. Goss*
Stoke-on-Trent March, 1878

		£ p

Swain, Charles socle plinth — 283mm — 1750.00
Incised in manuscript on side or back: *Published as the Act
directs by R.R. Bealey, Manchester July 1870*
Impressed on back: *W.H. Goss*
See also 9D TERRACOTTA.

Veiled Bride, The after the original marble bust by — 270mm — 1000.00
Raphael Monti, socle plinth
Impressed on rear: *W.H. Goss*

Venus de Milo socle plinth — 273mm — 1250.00
Impressed on rear: *W.H. Goss*

Virgin Mary socle plinth — 650.00
Impressed on rear: *W.H. Goss*

Wallace, Sir William socle plinth — 134mm — 395.00
Inscribed on back: *Sir William Wallace. Copyright.
Pub. As Act Directs (See Geo. 111, C.56)
W.H. Goss Stoke-on-Trent 22 Jan Y 1903*

Webb, Captain Matthew — 230mm — 750.00
Impressed on rear; *W.H. Goss*

Wesley, John square plinth — unglazed — 168mm — 195.00
Impressed on plinth: *Wesley* — glazed — 168mm — 195.00
Impressed side or back: *Copyright as Act directs W.H. Goss
Stoke-on-Trent*

NOTE Black Basalt busts of Wesley were also made — 154mm — 110.00
but these, whilst being perfect smaller replicas of the
above, carry no manufacturer's identification mark.
The author definitely believes them to be products
of the Goss factory.

Wordsworth, William square plinth — 164mm — 185.00
Impressed on plinth: *Wordsworth*
Impressed side or back: *Copyright as Act directs W.H. Goss
Stoke-on-Trent March 30, 1880*

The Veiled Bride, socle plinth 270mm

Pallas Athena socle plinth 248mm

B Figures

William Henry Goss's extensive education and instruction in the arts influenced the products of his pottery from the start in 1858. The long reign of Queen Victoria had led to a very peaceful and stable era in fashions and art, and made the nation feel secure in the permanency of its beliefs and tastes, and this was reflected in Staffordshire china. The new parian medium was readily approved of by the Queen, and manufacturer's top ranges were aimed at the middle classes who were emulating the upper classes in the collection of marble statues.

William Goss had a desire to create shapes of beauty, mostly relating to known subjects in order to teach the general public an appreciation of art, history and culture. He felt, as head of his firm, and of better education and intellect than most, that he had a responsibilty to educate others.

As a student he had studied art at Somerset House from the age of 16 to 19 years, and his love of art led him to model superb classical figures, in the popular fashion of that time, of partly clothed mythical figurines in a variety of poses, often taken from classical mythology. A lady holding an asp aloft was Cleopatra; a robed woman, deep in thought with a dagger partly concealed in her dress, was the Shakespearian character Tragedy. A young woman praying is thought to be the Virgin Mary. Not all figurines were plain; some were coloured or were trimmed with colours, particularly gold, rose and turquoise, these being William's favourite colours.

In 1862 he won the much desired award of a medal at the Great International Exhibition for his display of parian and figurines. Many laudatory articles and engravings of his exhibits appeared in journals such as *The Illustrated London News* and Cassells' *Illustrated Family Paper*. Cassells wrote on November 15th, 1862, when examining an exhibit belonging to Goss of Stoke, 'It is necessary to glance at our engraving to perceive with what exquisite taste this manufacturer has worked out the several designs he produced in fictile wares. Here, classic forms blend harmoniously with the more ordinary forms in use in our domestic life... With the parian statuettes, the perfection of art manufacture seems certainly to have been reached.'

The two largest and most important figurines are Leda and the Swan, and Wood Nymph (holding a kid), of which coloured examples are dated 1866. Figurines made and sold in pairs were usually only factory marked on one of the pair. Almost all these were First Period and production had ceased well before 1900. The only figures listed on sale in the editions of *The Goss Record* were St Cuthbert of Durham and the coloured statues of the Trusty Servant and William of Wykeham, the latter two of which could only be obtained from the Winchester Agency during the Second Period. The same exclusivity applied during the First Period when Goss's friend, the first Winchester agent, William Savage, stocked his products.

The Lincoln Imp was available during the First and Second Periods, in both brown and white, in a variety of sizes.

Many figurines have gilded edges to their robes, usually brushed, a process first used by Copeland and then by Goss of having the gilding brushed across every 2mm so as to give a bright gilded appearance over a matt line of gilding. The brush marks remain visible, the whole leaving a distinctive striped effect.

Often figures were highlighted with William Henry Goss's favourite colour, turquoise blue, and occasionally also red. The robes of some figures were, more rarely, decorated with spots or dots of turquoise blue enamel, covering the entire garment and are particularly attractive. Sometimes faces and hair would be lightly tinted in correct pastel shades, the beautiful figurines of Leda and the Swan, and Wood Nymph holding a kid being the best examples.

Prices should be increased by at least £100 for the presence of gilding, £200 for brushed gilding and/or blue highlighting, and £250 for blue enamel dots or coloured faces and/or hair.

Some figurines are also jewelled. This is a process, not of insetting gem stones, (although, confusingly this is also called jewelling as described in the introduction to 9.C. ORNAMENTAL AND DOMESTIC), but of richly decorating ware, in the case of the Goss factory figurines, with a dot, usually in turquoise blue enamel, and surrounding this with decorative gilding and sometimes other colours, predominantly red.

Jewelling is usually found on the shoulders and around the base of robes on Goss figurines.

This distinctive decoration, used by no other factory on parian statuettes, makes Goss figurines easy to recognise, especially when otherwise unmarked, as often only one of a pair were marked, and many pairs have been separated over the years.

All figures in this section are white parian, unglazed and bear the impressed W H Goss mark unless stated otherwise.
The miniature male form is described as a figure and the female form as a figurine

Classical group of a young male figure looking down upon a reclining nude maiden with dying swan at her feet.

A magnificent jewelled comport and stand inset with stones. Part of a dinner service made by Copeland for the Shah of Persia around 1850. It was still in existence in the 1970s when this photograph was taken. The service was said to have been designed and modelled by William Henry Goss. Note the similarity of the precious stone arrangement and design to that of Goss' own vases inset with stones.

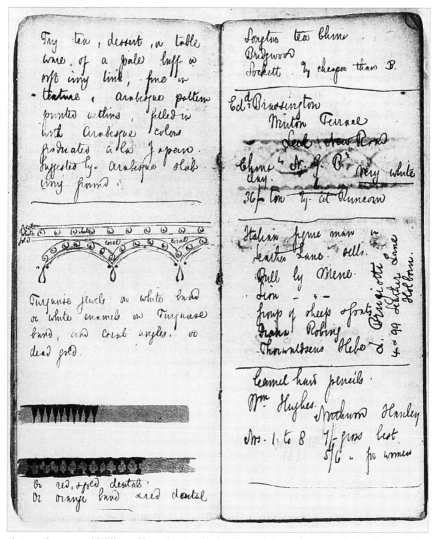

A page from one of William Henrys' recipe books. Centre left can be seen a design for turquoise jewels on a white band.

		£ p
Angel at annunciation standing with hands clasped in front	318mm	400.00
Angel holding shell in left hand	318mm	400.00
Angel kneeling, holding large shell (stoup) . A reproduction of St. John's Church Font, Barmouth	148mm	375.00
Bather nude, in pensive mood, seated on rock, White (a)	220mm	350.00
Decorated with turquoise jewels and brushed gilding (b)	220mm	600.00
Bather seated on a draped rock, holding conch shell with fishnet draped over knees and purse on ground.	240mm	500.00
Bather nude, seated on stump with drape over left knee, wearing bonnet	280mm	450.00
Bather nude, standing holding drape over right shoulder and supporting a basket of fruit on the left shoulder. approx 300mm		400.00
Bather nude, standing, probably Venus at bath	390mm	1000.00
Bather nude, standing by stump and holding an apple in right hand	390mm	1000.00
Bathers, a pair seated on rocky bases, nude.		
(a) wearing cap, right hand holding drape	200mm	350.00
(b) holding shell in right hand and drape in left	200mm	350.00
Blind Highlander and Lass with dog gazing up, with bonnet on paws, on circular base	315mm	850.00

Bride of Abydos, The
Embossed on front of plinth: *The Bride of Abydos*   535mm 1750.00
Inscribed: *Published as the Act directs (See 54 Geo 111, C.56)*
By Goss & Peake Stoke upon Trent September 12, 1867

Bull, John
Impressed: *W H Goss Sons Ltd*   165mm Unpriced
(In bisque, and almost certainly a forgery)

The Captive Cupid a winged putto, feet chained
with metal chains, holding bow, other arm to eye, weeping

(a) White unglazed	215mm	300.00
(b) Some colouring	215mm	400.00
(c) White unglazed, without wings	218mm	250.00

for Caskets see GOSS, EVANGELENE and CHERUB

Angel holding Shell

Angel at annunciation

Bather. Partly draped. Seated on rock

Bather nude seated on stump

Bather nude probably Venus at bath

Blind Highlander and Lass, with dog at feet

Cherub standing, foot on book, holding state

Cherub standing, holding palette in left hand

Classical Group, young male and nude maiden

Angel kneeling holding large shell (St John's Font)

The Boot Black

The Crossing Sweeper

£ p

Cherub The naked child, sleeping on a coverlet edged in gold
and stippled with purple dots, draped on the lid of an oval
casket; head resting on a basket of multi-coloured flowers.
The lid decorated around the top with turquoise jewels, and
around the edge with turquoise jewels and orange diamond
shapes. The casket decorated around the top with a white
ruche pattern in relief, interspersed with orange and gold
triangular shapes, and with turquoise jewels around the
bottom edge.   Length   130mm   750.00

Cherubs - a pair
  (a) Cherub standing on circular base, right foot on book, left
       hand holding compasses, pencil and slate   235mm   350.00
  (b) Cherub standing on circular base holding palette in left
       hand   210mm   350.00

Child kneeling on cushion, at prayer
  (a) White, glazed or unglazed   165mm   500.00
  (b) Coloured, the decoration is Third Period [3]   165mm   750.00

see Page 120 for an illustration

Child Girl, seated on circular base, holding open book
and crying   150mm   400.00

Children, Happy and Unhappy, The. A pair of figures from
originals by M. Simonis of Brussels, shown at the Great
Exhibition of 1851
  (a) Happy Child, holding toy Punch   approx.   150mm   500.00
  (b) Unhappy Child, having broken drum   143mm   500.00

Children Standing Beside Pillar Boxes - a pair
  (a) Boot Black   210mm   750.00
  (b) Crossing Sweeper (also found glazed)   224mm   750.00
       Both impressed LETTERS and incised in manuscript
       on the back of the pillar boxes:
       Published as the Act directs by W.H. Goss Stoke-on-Trent
       1 Dec 1873 Copyright.
NOTE: This pair, originally published in 1873 as unglazed
figures were re-issued in the latter days of the firm, but in
colour. In the earlier models, the pillar box has a loose top, always
missing, and more rarely a fixed top, while in the later models
it is always fixed.
  (a) Boot Black, coloured[3]   210mm   1400.00
  (b) Crossing Sweeper, coloured [3]   224mm   1400.00

See also Section 9D for TERRACOTTA version
of the Crossing Sweeper.

Classical Lady, partly draped,
seated on triangular base

Child, partly draped standing
with foot on stool

Child seated on Rock

The Devil looking over
Lincoln

Lady Godiva on Horseback,
white

Lady Godiva on Horseback,
coloured

Figurine standing with arms
crossed over breast

Winged Putto, The Captive
Cupid (Bow missing)

Child Kneeling on a Cushion

Ophelia

The Bride of Abydos

Little Red Riding Hood

		£	p

Children - a pair
    (a) Partly draped, standing with foot on stool   210mm   375.00
    (b) Seated on rock   210mm   375.00

Chimney Sweeps boys
    (a) Standing against street bollard, on base, brush under right
         arm; left hand to mouth, shouting his trade   185mm   1200.00
    (b) Standing against street bollard, on base, holding hat in right
         hand; brushes under left arm   195mm   1200.00
The above two figures are a pair, one usually unmarked, the other
inscribed on the base below the bollard at the rear: *W.H. Goss*

Chimney Sweep boy, sack over shoulder
    (a) White glazed or unglazed   292mm   850.00
    (b) Coloured, decoration probably late [3]   292mm   1500.00

Classical Figurine holding Child Playing Horn
    seated on lion rug, on oval base   275mm   850.00

Classical Figurine Comedy lady holding mask away from face
                 (a) White   328mm   450.00
                 (b) With some colour   328mm   600.00
                 (c) Earthenware   328mm   350.00

Classical Figurine Tragedy lady with dagger
                 (a) White   320mm   450.00
                 (b) With some colour   320mm   600.00
                 (c) Earthenware   320mm   350.00
The above two figurines are a pair. The (b) versions
both have edges of garments decorated in brushed gold
scrollwork pattern with red jewels in the scrollwork, the
pattern bordered each side with lines of turquoise, and
brushed gilding to outer edges of garments.
Comedy has a hair garland of gold edged ivy leaves with
turquoise berries, and a necklet of gold jewels with
turquoise beads.
Tragedy has a hair bandeau of brushed gold and turquoise
beads, and is holding a dagger of brushed gold .

Classical Figurine holding pitcher aloft with right arm;   345mm   400.00
left arm extended downwards and holding a fold of her drapes

Classical Figurine holding pitcher aloft with left arm;   345mm   400.00
right arm resting across her body, with the hand supporting the
drapes at her breast

(The above two figurines are a matching pair)

Classical Figurine
Comedy holding mask

Classical Figurine
Tragedy with dagger

Figurine, Lady playing Lyre

Classical Figurine, holding
Pitcher aloft

Classical Figurine, right hand
on head

Figurine, looking to Dexter,
right hand on stump

Figurine, hands partly
outstretched

Figurine, Seasons, holding
drape on head

Figurine, Meditation with
hand under chin

Classical Figurine, right hand
on head, turquoise jewels

Figurine, Seasons, holding
sheaf of wheat aloft

Classical Figurine, holding a
Child playing horn

£   p

Classical Figurine nude holding basket aloft with left arm,
    right arm holding a drape over her right shoulder.
  (a) Basket full of solid matter - possibly dough,
    with grapes and vine leaves in hair   260mm   400.00
  (b) Basket full of grapes with more grapes and
    vine leaves in hair than in (a)   260mm   400.00

Classical Figurine right hand on head, turquoise jewels on dress,
brown hair   380mm   500.00

Classical Group of a young male figure looking down upon a
reclining nude maiden with dying swan at her feet, all on a rocky
base
Impressed: *W.H. Goss*   Length 395mm Height 280mm   1250.00

Classical Lady partly draped, seated on large triangular shaped
base (similar to Eve at the Fountain by Edward Bailey)   270mm   1250.00

Classical Figurines seated, on large bases
  (a) Looking to dexter, with two money sacks, book and scroll
    at feet   350mm   450.00
  (b) Pensive mood, right hand under chin   350mm   450.00
  (c) Looking to sinister, holding scissors in right hand with
    hammer and chisel at feet   350mm   450.00

Cleopatra seated on draped tree stump holding aloft an asp.
On oval base   White (a)   240mm   750.00
    Decorated with turquoise jewels and brushed gilding (b)   240mm 1000.00

for **Comedy** see CLASSICAL FIGURINE COMEDY

Cupid asleep lying on a bed with bow and arrow. (a) 270mm x   140mm   550.00
Some colouring and gilded   (b) 280mm x   145mm   650.00
Impressed in manuscript: *Pub. as Act directs W.H. Goss*
Stoke-on-Trent 15th May 1867

Cuthbert of Durham, St.   134mm   400.00
(Goss Record. 9th Edition: Page 15) [2]
Inscribed on plinth, front: *St. Cuthbert* in Gothic script
and *Durham*

Devil and Witch Looking Over Lincoln,The (a) White 147mm   95.00
Impressed in Gothic script around   (b) Brown 147mm 100.00
front and side faces of the plinth:
The Devil Looking Over Lincoln

Evangeline Goss Lying on a shaped Casket (a)

Evangeline Goss natural coloured child blue dots gilded (e)

Evangeline Goss, on cushion white, blue trim, gilded (d)

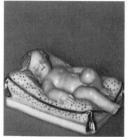

Evangeline Goss, natural coloured child, crimson jewels, blue trim, gilded (g)

Evangeline Goss, white, on casket (b)

Cherub on lid of oval casket, coloured

Mr Punch

Lincoln Imp

Lincoln Imp on Pedestal

Wood Nymph (holding a Kid) coloured

Leda and the Swan, coloured

Shepherd Boy holding a horn

£   p

Fairy reclining in sleep, nude, natural colour, double wings, hands clasped behind head, brown hair caught in a multi-coloured snood of flowers, gilded star on forehead, lower limb drape with brushed gilding to edges, turquoise blue waist cord with gilded tassels, three porcelain back hooks for suspending the model. Found unmarked but with all the hallmarks of Goss, as to familiar colours, gilding and execution   Length   225mm   600.00

Figurine holding trumpet-shaped posy holder   300mm   350.00

Figurine Affection, standing with hand on breast. Gown   345mm   400.00
edged in gold.

Figurine Meditation, standing in pensive mood with hand
under chin. Gown edged in gold   345mm   400.00

Figurine with dove feeding from sea-shell   320mm   525.00

Figurine with hands partly outstretched   325mm   400.00

Figurine standing, looking to dexter at right hand and holding
lamp, whilst right hand holding gathered folds of garments to
chin   330mm   400.00

Figurine standing, playing Lyre. Some colouring   340mm   450.00

Figurine standing with arms crossed over breast,
naked except for drapes covering legs   345mm   450.00

Figurines a pair, each holding a baby
   (a) Baby in left arm, basket of bull rushes in right arm   375mm   450.00
   (b) Baby in right arm, robes gathered with left arm   365mm   450.00

Figurines - a pair - **Seasons**
   (a) Holding sheaf of wheat aloft, turquoise jewels,
       brushed gilding   340mm   500.00
   (b) White unglazed   340mm   350.00
   (c) Holding drape on head with left hand and edge of cloak
       with right hand. Turquoise jewels, brushed gilding   340mm   500.00
   (d) White unglazed   340mm   350.00

Figurine looking to dexter, with right hand on stump   320mm   400.00
possibly Venus after Bertel Thorweldsen

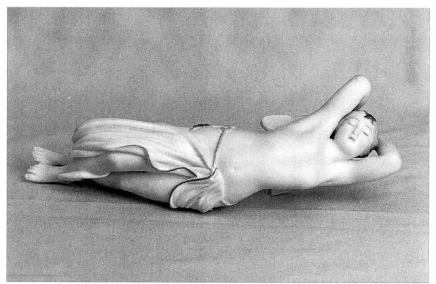

Fairy reclining in sleep, obverse

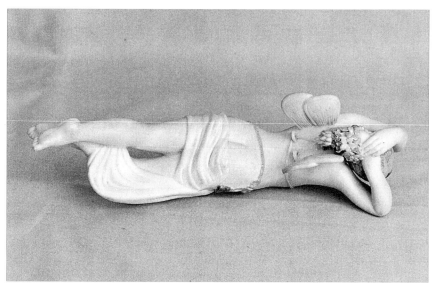

Reverse

£   p

Godiva, Lady, on horseback
(Goss Record. 9th Edition: Pages 29 & 30)
Impressed on plinth: *Lady Godiva* and *Copyright as*
Act directs. W.H. Goss Stoke-on-Trent 1st October 1902
Inscribed on the base: *W. H. Goss Lady Godiva*, on the 112mm
version. Also found with *August 1876* or *October 1880* on the
165mm size, and impresed *W. H. Goss* on the base in addition.
Sometimes found inscribed: *From the figure in Maidstone*
Museum, Maidstone

(a)	White	112mm	400.00
(b)	White	133mm	400.00
(c)	White	165mm	450.00
(d)	White	182mm	650 00
(e)	Coloured	182mm	950.00

Goss, Evangeline the child sleeping on a cushion either forming
the lid of a casket, white or coloured, or as a solid-based item
(Illustrated in Goss Record. 8th Edition: page 4. Bottom right.)

(a) Coloured, forming removable lid to casket	Length 135mm Height	95mm	295.00
(b) As (a) but all white unglazed	Length 145mm Height	95mm	400.00
(c) White, on cushion.	Length 135mm Height	55mm	325.00
(d) White, on cushion, blue trim	Length 135mm Height	55mm	325.00
(e) As (a) but natural coloured child turquoise jewels, jewelling and gilded	Height	95mm	400.00
(f) Natural coloured child on cushion, blue trim and gilded	Length 135mm Height	55mm	425.00
(g) As (d) but with crimson jewels on cushion	Height	55mm	450.00

Dr. Kenealy caricature head modelled as a spillholder
Incised in manuscript on the base in W.H. Goss's own hand:
'Dew-drops ' copyright Published as the Act directs (see
54 Geo 111, C.56) W.H. Goss Stoke-on-Trent
5th November 1875   130mm   275.00

Dr. Kenealy caricature figure standing and holding top-hat
and umbrella, as spill-vase and match-holder
Incised in manuscript on the base: *'Dewdrops'* and on the back:
Pub . as Act directs by W.H. Goss See 54 Geo . 111 C.56,
5th November 1875 Copyright.   188mm   450.00

Dr. Kenealy Jug depicting Dr Kenealy as a lion on
circular plinth holding a shield
Sir Roger Tichborne and Magna Charta Defended
Umbrella handle. Unmarked, Unique.   210mm   950.00

Lady holding a kid, The Wood Nymph	(a) White	435mm	1250.00
Inscribed:*Published as the Act directs*	(b) Coloured	435mm	2250.00
(See 54 Geo 111, C.56) by W. H. Goss	(c) Cream glazed		
Stoke upon Trent November 18 1866	earthenware	435mm	350.00

A Pair of bathers seated on rocky bases

A Pair of figurines each holding a baby

Shakespeare standing leaning on lectern

Venus emerging from two shells

Virgin Mary

The Trusty Servant implements, alternative version

Dr Kenealy Spill and Match holder

Dewdrops, Dr Kenealy Spillholder

Dr Kenealy Jug 210mm

The Trusty Servant and William of Wykeham

			£	p

Leda and the Swan   (a) White   430mm   1250.00

Inscribed: *Published as the Act directs*   (b) Coloured   430mm   2250.00

(See 54 Geo 111, C.56) by W.H. Goss   (c) Cream glazed

Stoke upon Trent November 18 1866   earthenware   350.00

(handwritten: (D) MAJOLICA 3500.00 (2004))

The above two figurines are a pair and can sometimes
be found marked *Goss & Peake*. Experimental examples
were produced in cream earthenware with a heavy glaze
and cream colouring and decorated with wide gilded decorative
bands, with turquoise jewels and other motifs. These did not go into
full time production, perhaps because of their lack of delicacy.
They weigh very lightly and are somewhat crude.

(handwritten: ? Really)

Lincoln Imp In high relief on beakers.
See L. 11 DOMESTIC and UTILITY WARES

Lincoln Imp Miniature version on sconce of frilled candle
holder. See L.14 DOMESTIC and UTILITY WARES

Lincoln Imp
(Goss Record. 9th Edition: Page 22)
Incised in manuscript on back: *The Imp of Lincoln*
From the carving in the Angel Choir at Lincoln Cathedral,
and intended as a wall hanging decoration.

(a) White	44mm	100.00
(b) White	80mm	55 00
(c) Brown	80mm	65.00
(d) White	110mm	45.00
(e) Brown	110mm	55.00
(f) White	120mm	65.00
(g) Brown	120mm	75.00
(h) White	145mm	85.00
(i) Brown	145mm	135.00

These pieces often appear unmarked. Whilst some are from Goss
moulds they cannot be properly considered as such and are
worth approximately £ 15.00
NOTE: Some of the above models are also found glazed, usually
with Blackpool Arms and are worth half the above prices.

Lincoln Imp seated on column
Impressed on base of column: *The Imp of Lincoln*

(a) White unglazed	114mm	95.00
(b) White glazed plinth, usually with matching arms	114mm	120.00
(c) Brown	114mm	165.00

Little Red Riding Hood   270mm   750.00
Impressed: *W. H. Goss*

The W.H.Goss prizewinning entry in the International Exhibition, London 1862. Approximately fifty per cent of the items exhibited are still known to exist and are listed in this Encyclopaedia.

Tazza (missing) supported by a group of three carytids from the W.H. Goss Prizewinning entry in The International Exhibition, London 1862. Photograph: Paul Dobson

Shepherd Boy playing a flute, 305mm

£   p

Ophelia   535mm   1750.00
Embossed on front of plinth: *Ophelia*
Inscribed: *Published as the Act directs (see 54 Geo 111,*
C.56) By Goss & Peake Stoke upon Trent September 12, 1867
See also 9A BUSTS

for Nude female sitting on rock coloured with holes in base
(for flower arrangement).
see THIRD PERIOD 11R FIGURES AND ANIMALS.

Punch, Mr   295mm   1500.00
The three-quarter length figure resting on a base consisting of
four volumes of *Punch* and backed by two more.
Usually impressed: *Copyright as Act Directs*
Incised: *W. H. Goss,* and *1861* in Roman numerals
Possibly made in 1861 to commemorate 20 years of publication of *Punch*

Shakespeare
Full length figure from monument in Westminster Abbey,   (a)   145mm   295.00
standing, leaning on a lectern.   (b)   180mm   325.00
   (a) also seen with the Third Period Goss England Mark

Shepherd Boy holding horn, wearing hat and sheepskin trousers,   280mm   950.00
sitting on a stone wall, flask by right elbow; bare footed; one
foot on the wall, the other on ground

Shepherd Boy wearing goat skin trousers, and playing a flute,   305mm   750.00
on naturalistic base.
Impressed: *W. H. Goss*

Tazza supported by a group of three caryatids, decorated with
gilded edges and turquoise jewels.
This group was originally the centrepiece of
W. H. Goss exhibit at the International Exhibition
held in London in 1862 (see illustrations on pages 116 and 117).
The one example of this group known has the tazza
missing but is almost certainly the original
from the exhibition and unique.   Estimated overall height 465mm   3000.00

for Tragedy see CLASSICAL FIGURINE TRAGEDY

                                                    £   *p*

Trusty Servant, The [2]   202mm   2500.00
Inscribed on base: *A piece of antiquity painted on the wall adjoining to the kitchen of Winchester College.*
Inscribed in manuscript on front of column:

> *A Trusty Servant's Portrait would you see,*
> *This Emblematic Figure well survey;*
> *The Porker's Snout - not Nice in diet shews;*
> *The Padlock Shut - no Secrets He'll disclose;*
> *Patient in the Afs - his Master's wrath will bear;*
> *Swiftness in Errand the Staggs Feet declare;*
> *Loaded his Left Hand - apt to labour Saith;*
> *The Vest - his Neatnefs; Open hand-his Faith;*
> *Girt with his Sword, his Shield upon his Arm,*
> *Himself and Master He'll protect from harm.*

Variations of the implements held by the Trusty Servant can be found - see illustrations pages 112 and 114

William of Wykeham [2]   202mm   2500.00
Inscribed on front: *William of Wykeham founder of Winchester College 1393.*

The above two are a Winchester pair in full colours.
William of Wykeham carries a removable crozier with a wire stem without which the figure is incomplete. This crozier bears the Rd. No.208046 which dates the first year of manufacture to 1893

See also the story of the Winchester Goss Agencies on page 285

Venus emerging from between two large shells, supported by dolphins. Unglazed or part glazed   175mm   550.00
SEE ALSO FIGURINE LOOKING TO DEXTER

for **Virgin Mary** see WOMAN PRAYING

Woman Praying standing, possibly the Virgin Mary   275mm   400.00

Child kneeling on a cushion, at prayer, The Third Period coloured variety with crimson cushion is shown here. Height 165mm

A beautiful study of a Classical Figurine holding a child playing a trumpet seated on a lion rug on an oval base. Height 275mm

Chimney Sweep Boy with sack over shoulder. This subject was modelled in the First Period, white unglazed, and in the Third Period brightly coloured 292mm.

C Ornamental and Domestic

Apart from the range of busts and figures, the factory, under the managment of the founder, produced many other wares. These included a variety of artistically tasteful wares: scent bottles with pierced sides (the scent was contained in the outer hollow rim of the round pierced bottles), large wall plaques, flagons and flasks, and wall vases with faces in relief.

The most costly wares were the jewelled vases and scent bottles, which were made up until 1885. The jewels were, in most cases, paste which had their colours enhanced by being placed into hollows coloured with the Goss enamels. These processes were patented in 1875, and were a successful improvement on the methods used by the Sevres factory whose enamel jewels frequently rubbed off. Real jewels notably emeralds, rubies and pearls were used on certain precious pieces.

Pieces in this chapter usually bear impressed marks, sometimes with the addition of a Goshawk. In order to avoid confusion or duplication, nothing which could be expected to be found in another chapter has been listed in this section, but those pieces also produced during the First Period have been marked thus [I] in other chapters.

THE BULLOCK AND SHEEP GROUP AND FIGHTING BULLS PLAQUE

Albert Loring Murdock, a native of Boston, Massachusetts, discovered around 1860 that liver, then only given to animals, was the life saving treatment for pernicious anaemia. Murdock perfected a potion which he called Murdock's Liquid Food to treat this disease. He expanded his business, eventually supplying almost every drug store in the USA and many in Europe and the Orient. Every two years he went to Europe to maintain his agencies. Murdock owned a Victorian oil painting by W. Watson of a typical highland cattle scene which he used as an advertisement for his liquid food.

He wanted an advertising piece made for use in retail shops and contacted the Goss factory to whom he had been recomended for the fineness of its porcelain.

William Henry Goss made an oval plaque in bas-relief depicting two bulls fighting from the painting (page 124) and also a figure group of a bullock and sheep standing on an oval base (page 126). Murdock chose the lattter and this group was made in some quantity and supplied to him in Boston for his use in retail outlets that stocked his liquid food.

Goss subsequently used the plaque in his exhibition on the occasion of His Majesty George V and Queen Mary's visit to the Potteries in 1913. Only one specimen is known and the piece is believed to be unique, although it seems to have been used as the prototype of a large terracotta representation of the bulls that overhung the entrance of Murdock's office in Boston.

The chosen group of a bullock and two sheep on an oval plinth, was produced with the printed advertising slogan on the side of the beast MURDOCK'S LIQUID FOOD IS CONDENSED BEEF, MUTTON &

FRUITS. It is surprising that William undertook the order, considering his dislike of advertising. Murdock and Goss, both eccentrics, became good friends and were regularly in contact with one another.

Murdock was a very generous and charitable man, who built and ran a free 175 bed hospital for the poor women and children of Boston. He also sent free cases of his liquid food to the Civil War wounded. Yet a member of his family can recall him as stingy! He was married with two sons and his unfulfilled ambition was to have a daughter, so he much admired Goss for having four beautiful girls. He particularly liked the youngest, Florence, and asked William if he could adopt her, pay her school fees and bring her up as his own. This offer was, no doubt, firmly rejected.

Murdock remained in contact with Florrie, as she was called, by sending her letters and postcards from his travels all over the world, and when, by chance, he returned to Stoke in 1905, he found a beautiful, mature, composed young woman in her thirties and was amazed to find her still single. She had had many suitors and offers of marriage, but had declined them all. Murdock had lost his wife and he proposed to Florrie, who eventually accepted. They married on St. Valentine's Day in 1906, one month after her father's death. Albert Murdock was older than her father! In his wedding photograph he had white hair and long grey whiskers. Life with him looked to be a life of luxury. Their honeymoon was a six month world tour including Paris, New York, California and Japan. But Murdock's real ambition was realised when they had a daughter in 1907.

Murdock died aged 82 years old, when his daughter was still only 5. His headstone holds pride of place in a South Hingham, Massachusetts cemetery, and his home, Maple Hall, still stands nearby.

Examples of the bullock and sheep group often come to light in the USA, but a purported group with a pig has yet to be seen.

All pieces in this section are white parian unglazed unless stated otherwise. Almost all carry the W H Goss impressed mark, often very difficult to see, and sometimes the gosshawk mark in addition.

The Fighting Bulls plaque

The magnificent Alhambra Vase 516mm

The Alhambra Vase

Noah's Ark

Bird, Wren on Edge of Nest

Bird on Tree Stump

Bird, Falcon on rock, Inkwell

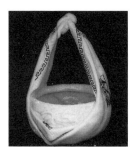

Birds Nest in a Napkin

Cockatoo, sitting on perch on rocky base

Bullock and Sheep Group Reverse

Bullock and Sheep Group

Dolphin, Inkwell

Guillemot Egg, open and closed

Bear and Ragged Staff, coloured chain and harness

C. Ornamental and Domestic

£　p

The Alhambra Vase - after the Alhambra Palace at Granada,
Spain. Probably the most dramatic and valuable First Period
piece produced. William Henry Goss was fascinated with Moorish
design and made a copy of this fabulous multi-coloured winged
vase in earthenware especially for the 1861 Crystal Palace Exhibition.
The vase adorned the mantlepiece of his cottage in Barthomley,
Cheshire, a photograph of which can be seen on page 119
of *William Henry Goss* by Lynda and Nicholas Pine.
An Illustration showing the decoration of the vase in more
detail may be found on page 125. Unique.　　516mm　Unpriced

The Ark (Noah's) - an excellent model of The Ark, with every
plank detailed, and a decorated rubbing straight; the
superstructure interior decorated in turquoise blue, with a pitched
roof, and open at the stern end. Unique.
Impressed: sans-serif mark and brown Goshawk, but without
W. H. Goss printed beneath it　　Length 150mm Height　80mm　3000.00

Basket, Fruit Glazed, with acanthus-leaf pattern and strap
handle　　　　　　　　(a) Length 215mm Height　145mm　300.00
　　　　　　　　　　　(b) Length 195mm Height　130mm　300.00

Basket, Fruit Glazed, fluted with turquoise strap
handle　　　　　　　　　　　　　　Length　120mm　150.00

Basket, Dutch style blue coral handle, multi crested
　　　　　　　　　　Length 215mm Width　130mm　400.00
　　　　　　　　　　Length 215mm Width　140mm　400.00
(Illustrated. Goss Record. 8th Edition: Page 4. Upper Shelf.)

Basket, Posy Glazed. Fluted sides with twisted handle (Illustrated
Goss Record. 8th Edition. Page 4, at bottom)
　　　　　　　　　　Length 140mm Height　105mm　450.00

See also Basket 11 S THIRD PERIOD for late examples

Bear and Ragged Staff
(Goss Record, 9th Edition: Page 31)
Impressed on top of plinth: *Warwick*
Inscribed in the base: *Copyright. Pub. As Act Directs*
(See 54 Geo. 111, C.56) W.H. Goss Stoke-on-Trent 7 May 1898

(a) White unglazed [2]　　　　　　　　　　　90mm　200.00
(b) White glazed with shield and arms [2]
　　(Add £100.00 for Warwick Arms)　　　　　90mm　200.00
(c) White unglazed with gilded harness and chain [2]　90mm　250.00
(d) White unglazed, coloured harness and chain, plain base [2] 90mm　300.00
(e) White unglazed with brown harness, yellow chain and
　　green and yellow striped base　　　　　　90mm　395.00
(f) Beige with brown harness and green and yellow striped
　　base. Glazed or unglazed　　　　　　　　90mm　450.00
(g) Brown unglazed　　　　　　　　　　　　90mm　350.00
(h) Brown and coloured unglazed　　　　　　90mm　450.00

Early Jug. Acanthus Leaf Pattern

Sugar Basin. Turquoise jewels in relief

Cream Jug, Sea-urchin turquoise jewels in relief

Fruit Basket with Flutes and Strap handles

Basket with Coral handle Dutch style

Basket with Acanthus Leaves and Strap handles

Eggshell Cup with twig handle and feet

Eggshell Cream jug

Posy Basket, fluted, twisted handle

Eggshell Tea Pot with raised floral decoration

Eggshell Cup and saucer with raised floral decoration

Bowl, fluted, inscribed Homeopathic Medicine

		£ p
Bird a wren standing on the edge of a nest, coloured light blue inside	70mm	325.00

Bird on Tree Stump as posy vase   approx 100mm   250.00

Bird, Falcon, on a rock as inkwell   125mm   300.00

Bird's Egg Apart from the named Guillemot's Egg with a
pointed end, for which see 10E HISTORIC MODELS,
there is also a similar sized sea-bird egg with a rounded
base. Both varieties were produced in beige, blue, green and pink
speckled colourings.   (a) Closed, coloured   95mm   80.00
                          (b) Closed, white   95mm   85.00
                          (c) Open, to hang as posy vase   83mm   85.00

Bird's Nest in Napkin
    (a) White glazed with and without arms   185mm   375.00
    (b) Forget-Me-Nots covering piece   185mm   550.00

Bowl and Lid circular. The body formed from pink rose petals
trimmed with green leaves. The lid has a rosebud knop   Dia.   73mm   100.00

Bowl (heavy), slightly fluted edge; Dia. 90mm   Height   52mm   75.00
decorated with two primrose sprays (Rd. No.25947)

Bowl fluted,inscribed *HOMOEOPATHIC MEDICINE*
with measurement scale on the inside and pattern around
outside of body. All decorations in sepia. Unique.   70mm   195.00

For **Brooches** see FLORAL DECORATIONS 9C ORNAMENTAL AND DOMESTIC

Bowl, Pierced
A latticed window bowl with turned over rim.
(Illustrated Goss Record.8th Edition: Page 4,
Middle Shelf)   Dia.   140mm   300.00

Bullock and Two Sheep on oval plinth   148mm   1250.00
Inscribed with the following advertising slogan on one side
of the Bullock: *Murdock's Liquid Food is Condensed Beef,*
Mutton & Fruits.
Impressed on the base: *Copyright as Act directs.*
W.H. Goss Stoke-on-Trent 1st September 1882
See also the story of this group in the introduction to this chapter.

Butter Dish circular ***WASTE NOT*** in relief around the rim.   Dia 142mm   75.00

*Elephant with Howdah on
oval base*

*Elephant with Howdah,
no base*

The Fighting Bulls Plaque.

Fox and its Prey

Game Pie Pin oval box and lid

*Imperial Crown on tasselled
cushion, gilded*

Early Sheep

Squirrel beside tree-trunk

Swan

*Hand as Ring Tree, natural
colour, blue cuff*

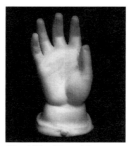

*Hand Ring Tree, white
glazed*

Hand holding Bag Vase

£   p

Cockatoo sitting on perch on rocky base, open at top as vase. Glazed.

                                          270mm   600.00

Comport with three 50mm short legs .
Floral decoration of nasturtiums, with star pattern
centrally, in bas-relief inside bowl.   Dia. 224mm Height   170mm   125.00

Cream Jug and Sugar Basin sea-urchin design.

	Jug Height 60mm	Bowl Dia.	100mm	
	(a) White glazed		Each	100.00
	(b) Some turquoise colouring		Each	100.00

Cream Jug and Sugar Basin with vertical turqoise jewels in relief

                                   Basin Dia.   100mm   50.00
                                   Jug Height   60mm   50.00

Cream Jug. Glazed, having acanthus leaf pattern in low relief.
Many variations of pastel coloured decoration predominently
pink, blue and green, both to handle and body can be found as
well as plain white, in addition to inscriptions in Gothic script.
'A PRESENT FROM ' or 'FROM '   75mm   95.00

Cream Jug. Unglazed, with two cherubs in high relief, grape and
vine decoration in low relief   90mm   100.00

Cream Jug and Sugar Basin.

folded leaves with butterfly	(a) Cream Jug	Length 100mm	200.00
handles sometimes enameled.	(b) Cream Jug	Length 115mm	200.00
	(c) Sugar Basin	Length 100mm	200.00
	(d) Sugar Basin	Length 140mm	200.00

Crown, Imperial, on square tasselled cushion, the
tassels at each corner joined by gilded cord. The crown
pierced and gilded.

                  Height 45mm Width 60mm Length   60mm   450.00

Dog Bowl. Illuminated lettering in relief around rim:
Quick at Work, Quick at Meals   Dia.   210mm   125.00

Dolphin on seaweed base with flat scallop shell dish supported
on raised tail   90mm   250.00

Dolphin - Tail uppermost on small round hollow plinth,
presumably for use as posy holder or inkwell   98mm   225.00
One example seen has an early puce Goshawk mark without
lettering and the registration mark for 1874. Found either
white or tinted pink glazed, after Belleek. The other has only
the serif impresed mark.

Leaf Pattern Cream Jug

Leaf Pattern Sugar Basin

Sark Milk Churn, early

Bowl, Pierced

Pierced Comport

Pierced Dish 242mm

*Pin Cushion blue shell
pattern*

Pin Cushion A Present
from Crystal Palace

*Pierced Dish, beige, coloured
floral decoration*

*Keystone of the Kingdom,
Lord Beaconsfield*

*Monmouth Mask,
The Knight*

*Monmouth Mask,
The Miller*

£   p

Eggshell Porcelain Tea Service
Cups, saucers, plates and jugs, bearing only the
impressed W.H. GOSS mark. Cups and saucers are very
fine wafer-thin glazed parian ware with apple blossom, violets,
fuchsia, periwinkle or vine and grape decoration in bas-relief.
Belleek later used the same design.

		£ p
Cup with twig handle and three feet	60mm	165.00
Cup and saucer Taper	65mm	75.00
	80mm	100.00
Cream Jug blue handle	65mm	110.00
Milk Jug	70mm	110.00
Sucrier on three legs, with pierced cover and fruit knop surrounded by open lattice work	92mm	400.00
Plate. Crested, glazed, violets in relief Dia.	148mm	100.00
Plate. Round, unglazed Approx. Dia.	200mm	150.00
Bread or Cake Plate. Oval, unglazed Max. width	215mm	225.00
Tea Pot and Lid. three feet (Also found gilded)	130mm	450.00
Tea Pot and Lid. flat base moulded fuchsias in relief see illustration page 128	126mm	450.00

One unique set has been decorated with butterflies in relief
and apple blossom in relief and has forged Chamberlain
Worcester marks concealing the impressed W.H. GOSS

Tea Pot		130mm	1000.00
Sucrier and cover on three legs		92mm	350.00
Milk Jug on three legs		76mm	350.00
Cup and saucer	Dia.	138mm	350.00

Cup and Saucer, bagware with gilded trim.
No other decoration in relief. Glazed   55mm   95.00

Elephant with Howdah on oval base
  (a) White glazed   153mm   800.00
  (b) Some colouring, pink or green blanket   153mm   1500.00
  (c) Earthenware   160mm   700.00

Elephant with Howdah. No base, coloured, unmarked   140mm   1500.00

For **Ewer,** early, see **Vases**

Coloured Box and lid with floral decoration (4)

Turquoise/white Bowl and lid with floral decoration (3)

Patterned Bowl and lid with fixed floral spray (5)

Coloured Puff Box with floral decoration (2)

Puff Box and lid with floral decoration (1)

Bowl and patterned lid with large floral spray (3)

Puff Box and lid with floral decoration (1)

Box and lid with floral decoration (6)

Floral decoration in Bowl (8)

Early Lozenge Vase, Oval mouth floral decoration

Lozenge Vase, Oval mouth with floral decoration

Pendant Cross, Ivy decoration, brown (13)

134

FLORAL DECORATIONS

Brooches were a successful line for the factory and these were sometimes affixed to the sides of First Period lozenge and other vases. They were also affixed to the tops of powder bowls and puff boxes, which were often highly decorative with fern and similar patterns in relief and usually multi-coloured in pastel shades, blue, green, pink and yellow predominating.

Floral decorations were used in the Third Period and are often finished in lustre. Certainly anything with a lustre finish would only have been produced during that period.

Specific items are listed below but generally a floral decoration affixed to a piece would add some £50-£75.

BOWLS AND BOXES				£ p
1 Puff box and lid,white, with a large spray of coloured flowers				
affixed to lid.	Dia. 82mm Height	47mm		75.00
Several variations including:				
Zinnia, periwinkle and carnation				110.00
Three primroses				110.00
2 Puff Box and lid coloured, with a single rose as knop; petals				
mostly white, with the innermost ones tinted yellow				
	Dia 80mm Height	50mm		75.00
3 Circular box and lid with fern and similar pattern in relief and				
criss-cross brooch as a knop.	Dia. 70mm Height	70mm		
Also brooch knop without criss-cross centre on this version				
(a) White				200.00
(b) Coloured				
(i) green and white bowl and lid				300.00
(ii) turquoise and white bowl and lid				300.00
4 Box and lid, floral knop; leaf green and orange leaf patterns in				
relief	Dia. 100mm Height	75mm		250.00
5 Circular taper box and lid with pattern in relief and floral spray				
as a knop.	Dia. 100mm Height	75mm		150.00
6 Circular box and lid, white, patterned in relief and with floral				
spray as a knop.				
(a)	Dia. 102mm Height	70mm		75.00
(b)	Dia. 110mm Height	55mm		95.00
7 Circular box and lid, fern pattern in relief in green,				
coloured brooch as knop, orange and green in relief on the				
box	Dia. 100mm Height	98mm		350.00

CROWN STAFFORDSHIRE TYPE FLORAL SPRAYS, BOWLS OR BASES

8 (a) Three yellow roses in bud on long stems, with small			
flowers at the base Dia. 43mm Height	75mm		85.00
(b) Mother of pearl lustre, assorted flowers [3]	45mm		65.00
(c) Floral decoration inset, into lip-salve pot base	40mm		65.00
9 Four red or yellow/pink tulips and leaves on circular base; four			
tiny forget-me-nots on the green moss-like base.			
Dia. 53mm Height	77mm		95.00

Pendant Cross, Lily of the Valley, white (15)

Pendant Cross, mixed floral, white (16)

Pendant Cross, mixed floral, black unglazed (14)

Lily of the Valley (53)

Daisies and Anemones, coloured (55)

Red Grapes with Green Vine Leaves, Oval, coloured (37)

Three Rosebuds, oval, coloured (51)

Petunias and Leaves, tied with ribbon (28)

Forget-me-not spray, oval, coloured (43)

Roses, oval bouquet tied with ribbon, coloured (34)

Daisy and Forget-me-nots, oval, coloured (46)

Rose and Lily of the Valley buds, oval spray, coloured (47)

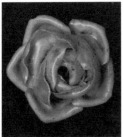

Pink Rose (52)

Carnation, two tone, coloured (33)

Daisy with buds and leaves, circular, coloured (38)

Speedwell, Petunia and Daisy, coloured (45)

Violets with scarlet, yellow Primroses, circular (42)

Double Daisy, circular, coloured (32b)

Poppy, Speedwell and Petunia, triangular, coloured (44)

Rose, Forget-me-nots and speckled buds, circular (48)

Anemone with yellow Primroses, circular (31)

Roses, two with three in bud and Forget-me-nots (54)

Roses, Forget-me-nots on criss cross background, coloured (39)

Petunia, Rose and Forget-me-nots, oval, coloured (30)

*Daisy and Forget-me-nots,
white (21)*

*Petunia, Rose and Forget-me-
nots, white (19)*

*Rose with speckled buds,
round, white (23)*

*Oval spray of Violets, white
(20)*

*Rose, Snowdrops and Forget-
me-not spray, oval (24)*

*Rose with speckled buds, circu-
lar, coloured (49)*

*Forget-me-not circle,
coloured (29)*

*Daisy Zinnia and Rose,
coloured (35)*

*Violet with buds and foliage,
oval, coloured (36)*

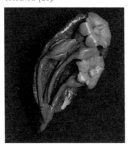

*Spray of yellow Primroses,
oval (41)*

*Wild Anemone spray, oval,
coloured (40)*

*Forget-me-not spray, oval,
coloured (43)*

                                                              £   p

10 Four daisies with long stems and green leaves on circular
     base (two yellow, one pink, one purple) . One tiny flower
     between each stem, all on green moss-like base.
                               Dia. 55mm Height   98mm   95.00

FLORAL JEWELLERY - PENDANTS, ETC.

11 Pendant, in form of a Cross with Clematis decoration in gold.
     Unglazed, (Red Goshawk) .   80mm   165.00
12 Pendant, white glazed, with roses and speckled buds.   56mm   150.00
13 Pendant, in form of a Cross with ivy decoration, unglazed
     brown (Red Goshawk).   80mm   200.00
14 Pendant, in form of a Cross with roses, forget-me-nots
     peonies in relief. Unglazed black.   90mm   165.00
15 Pendant, in form of a Cross with lily of the valley in relief.
     White glazed.   80mm   175.00
16 Pendant, in form of a Cross with roses, daisy, lily of the valley
     and forget-me-nots in relief.   (a) White unglazed.   80mm   175.00
                                 (b) Fully coloured   80mm   225.00
17 Stick Pin, blue forget-me-nots, pink buds, green leaves.   80mm   95.00
18 Earrings, to match above stick pin. Priced as a pair.   20mm   125.00

BROOCHES

Some thirty-five different designs were made, some white unglazed and others
coloured and glazed. As well as being produced during the First Period, some of
these designs were re-introduced during the 1920s in the Second Period. After manufacture, the brooches were casually stored and little care was taken to see that they
remained perfect. Exceptionally, light damage would not affect the values quoted
here as all brooches are chipped to some extent. All dimensions of brooches are
diameter or length, whichever is the greatest.

Brooches, white unglazed

19 Petunia, rose and forget-me-nots, oval   47mm   85.00
20 Spray of three violets, oval   58mm   95.00
21 Daisy and forget-me-nots, oval   47mm   75.00
22 Rose and speckled buds, oval   50mm   85.00
23 Rose and speckled buds, circular   45mm   85.00
24 Rose snowdrops and forget-me-not spray, oval   50mm   95.00
25 Forget-me-not spray, oval   50mm   75.00
26 Forget-me-nots in border of leaves, circular   50mm   85.00
29 Forget-me-nots, circular   42mm   85.00
48 Rose, Forget-me-nots and speckled buds, circular   50mm   75.00

Brooches, white glazed

27 Scarab   40mm   85.00

Stick pin and earrings to match, Forget-me-nots (17/18)

Scarab, Brooch, white glazed (27)

Crown Staffordshire type floral spray, two tulips on a base

Late Floral Brooch inset into Lip-salve pot base, lustre (8)

Late floral spray planted in bowl (8)

Crown Staffordshire type floral spray, four daisies (10)

Delicate Limpet shell on Coral tripod

Brown Mushroom, green grass to stem base

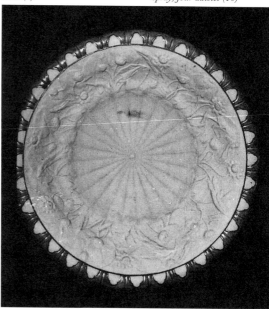

Plate, Water Lillies pattern in relief, Dia. 200mm

Brooches, coloured glazed

			£ p
28	Petunias and leaves, tied with ribbon, oval	66mm	85.00
29	Forget-me-nots circular	42mm	85.00
30	Petunia, rose and forget-me-nots, oval	47mm	85.00
31	Anemone with yellow primroses, circular	40mm	90.00
32	Daisy, circular, coloured purple, green centre (a) single	30mm	85.00
	(b) double	37mm	85.00
33	Carnation, two-tone, circular	45mm	80.00
34	Bouquet of roses, tied with ribbon, oval	60 and 70mm	85.00
35	Daisy, zinnia and one or two roses, circle	60mm	90.00
36	Violet with buds and foliage, oval	58mm	75.00
37	Bunch of red grapes and vine leaves with trailing creepers, oval	46mm	80.00
38	Daisy with buds and leaves, circular	40mm	75.00
39	Roses and forget-me-nots on criss-cross background, circular.	50mm	130.00
40	Wild anemone spray, oval	60mm	110.00
41	Spray of yellow primroses, oval	55mm	100.00
42	Violets with scarlet and yellow primroses, circular	45mm	150.00
43	Forget-me-not spray, oval	45 and 55mm	85.00
44	Poppy, speedwell and petunia, triangular	40mm	75.00
45	Speedwell, petunia and daisy, triangular	40mm	85.00
46	Daisy and forget-me-nots, oval	50mm	85.00
47	Rose (pink or yellow) and lily of the valley buds, oval	50mm	85.00
48	Rose (pink or yellow) forget-me-not and speckled buds, circular	50mm	85.00
49	Rose and speckled buds, circular	40mm	95.00
50	Large initial F on lily of the valley, roses and forget-me-nots on criss-cross background	80mm	175.00
51	Three rosebuds on leaf base, tied with ribbon, oval	70mm	95.00
52	Rose, pink	40mm	150.00
53	Lily of the valley, pink, oval	50mm	165.00
54	Roses, two, with three in bud and forget-me-nots	65mm	95.00
55	Daisies and anemones	60mm	85.00

Brooches, Terracotta

56 Terracotta base with floral brooch of forget-me-nots and roses	55mm	125.00

Fox and Its Prey a rooster, on oval plinth. Height 90mm Length   200mm

(a) parian		300.00
(b) earthenware		145.00

For **Fruit Basket.**
see Basket

Game Pie oval pin box with pheasant and ferns decoration on lid and ivy around base.   Length   95mm   125.00

Hand Glazed. A ring tree.

(a) White	95mm	100.00
(b) White, blue button	95mm	110.00
(c) Natural colour, blue cuff	95mm	125.00

£ p

Hand Glazed, holding bag vase.
Some fine gliding and turquoise cord and button. 122mm 125.00

Japan Ewer
Unglazed with ring of turquoise jewels below neck, the
body decorated with two buff coloured transfers of a
radiating Grecian figure on a chariot drawn by three
horses rearing before an arc of eight stars; possibly
Apollo the Sun God riding his chariot. 200mm 250.00
This was an experimental piece

For **Jewelled Ware** see Introduction to 9B FIGURES and VASES INSET WITH
STONES

Keystones of the Kingdom, The being almost life-size
heads of
    (a) **Lord Derby** 450.00
    (b) **Lord Beaconsfield** 450.00
Impressed on back: *Copyright as Act Directs W.H. Goss*
Stoke-on- Trent August 1880
These Heads are mounted on keystone shaped slabs.
Dimensions. Height 300mm; Width 175mm reducing to 144mm
See also 9D TERRACOTTA.
An advertising leaflet was issued with those models and is
valued at £60.00. See page 57

Lion, and Mouse group on ornamental base, with bamboo
poles at rear. The lion is trapped in netting which is usually
found disintegrated Length 150mm Height 180mm 600.00

Lithophane A wafer-thin porcelain circle depicting an
art nouveau style girl with a star in her hair. Dia. 89mm 3000.00
Signed and dated *J.A. 1888* Joseph Astley, chief
modeller at the time). Unique.

Milk Can unglazed, early, with coloured spray of flowers
in bas-relief on both sides. Similar to the First Period
Sark Milk Churn. Marked No. 885X 64mm 1500.00

for **Mirror in ornate frame** see 9C WALL PLAQUES

Monmouth Masks [2]
(Goss Record. 9th Edition: Page 23)
Inscribed: *Model of Mask from Geoffrey of Monmouth's Study*
at Monmouth.
Although there are actually three masks in Geoffrey of
Monmouth's study: the Miller, the Knight, and the Angel, only
the former two have so far been found reproduced by Goss:

					£	p
The Miller	(a)	White glazed	81mm	275.00
	(b)	White unglazed	81mm	275.00
	(c)	Brown	81mm	350.00
	(d)	White	95mm	350.00
	(e)	Brown	95mm	400.00
	(f)	White glazed	115mm	500.00
	(g)	White unglazed	115mm	500.00
	(h)	Brown	115mm	500.00
The Knight	(a)	White glazed	80mm	275.00
	(b)	White unglazed	80mm	275.00
	(c)	Brown unglazed	80mm	350.00
	(d)	White unglazed	96mm	350.00
	(e)	Brown unglazed	96mm	400.00
	(f)	White glazed	115mm	500.00
	(g)	White unglazed	115mm	550.00
	(h)	Brown unglazed	115mm	500.00

Mushroom Brown unglazed, with green grass around base
of stem [2]. Unique.   60mm   275.00

for **Noah's Ark** see Ark

for **Oval Plaques** see Wall Plaques

Pierced Dish in imitation basket-work, oval, glazed with
a coat of arms in base of dish, usually of Boston.   Length   242mm   150.00
Alternatively, with beige ground and coloured floral
decoration around border   Length   242mm   175.00

for **Pinbox and lid,** see CHERUB, and GOSS, EVANGELINE

Pin-cushion holder with three sprays of coloured
thistles or seagulls   (a)Dia.   57mm   65.00
                                                        (b)Dia.   75mm   75.00

Pin-cushion A round, glazed porcelain base with blue shell pattern,
to be filled with sawdust and top covered in velvet. Inscribed
in Gothic lettering 'A PRESENT FROM '   (a) Dia.   70mm   85.00
                              Plain white (b) Dia.   70mm   45.00
                                             (c) Dia.   97mm   85.00

Pin-cushion A round unglazed porcelain bowl with two bands
of turquoise and A PRESENT FROM THE CRYSTAL.
PALACE in orange capitals around top, and moulded leaf
pattern to lower half.   95mm   85.00

£   p

Plaque. Fighting Bulls (Illustrated, Goss Record. 8th Edition: Page 4, Top Shelf) This unique plaque is based on a Victorian Highland cattle painting by W Watson, a Liverpool animal and landscape painter who worked from 1866 - 1872
The picture was used as part of an advertisement by Albert Loring Murdock of Boston Massachusetts (See introduction to this section page 123). This plaque is First Period and was made by William Henry Goss either for himself or for Murdock. Alternatively, it could well have been a prototype that was rejected in favour of the bullock and sheep group (see page 126). It was later used in an exhibition at Stoke on Trent town hall in 1913 on the occasion of their Majesties King George V and Queen Mary's visit to the Potteries. Only one specimen is known and the piece is believed to be unique. It depicts two bulls fighting, in bas-relief and is unglazed. the border is perfectly plain. [2]   335mm x   275mm   2500.00

see also WALL PLAQUES

PLATES

Plates Circular. The following various early unglazed plates, measuring about 345mm in diameter were produced. Some were left completely white while others had the wording, coat of arms or other decoration in colour. The most common is the Winchester plate, which often bears the inscription: *Designed and Published by W. SAVAGE* on the back often without the W.H. Goss impressed mark.

Manners Makyth Man
Embossed around rim, with Arms of Bishop William of Wykeham centrally and his See at the bottom.

(a) White	345mm	225.00
(b) Coloured	345mm	300.00

Domus Eleemosynaria Nobilis Paupertatis (sic)
Embossed around rim with **Arms of St. Cross Hospital Winchester,** centrally
Translation: ALMS HOUSE OF THE NOBLE POOR

(a) White unglazed	345mm	225.00
(b) White or cream glazed	345mm	185.00
(c) Coloured	345mm	300.00

Eat Thy Bread with Thankfulness
embossed around rim

(a) White	345mm	225.00
(b) Coloured	345mm	300.00

£   p

A Little Cheese if you Please
embossed around rim - White   345mm   200.00

Think Thank and Thrive
embossed around rim [2]
(Illustrated. Goss Record. 8th Edition: Page 4)

(See also Platters)	(a) White		345mm	185.00
	(b) Coloured		345mm	285.00

A Merry Christmas
 inscribed in a ribbon on a circular plate, with magenta border,
and in the centre a coloured bouquet of holly, ivy and mistletoe
      Dia.   218mm   750.00

Christmas Pudding Plate
with holly decoration around rim

	(a) White	Dia.	348mm	225.00
	(b) Coloured	Dia.	348mm	350.00

Plate, Toft style with glazed recessed centre and heavy
relief decoration around wide unglazed rim   Dia.   200mm   150.00

Plate Celandine pattern, in relief   Dia.   227mm   100.00

Plate Nasturtium pattern, in relief   Dia.   227mm   100.00

Plate Water Lillies pattern, in relief   Dia.   200mm   100.00

Plate circular, wavy edge with vine and grape decoration
in low relief, found both marked and unmarked

	(a) Coloured with gilt rim.	Dia.	175mm	150.00
	(b) Gilded around edges of leaves.	Dia.	210mm	110.00
	(c) Ungilded.	Dia.	210mm	90.00
	(d) Coloured with gilt rim.	Dia.	220mm	180.00

Plate pierced, with piercings left in place, with pink band as
decoration. The body is of cream earthenware, and a matching
comport, also pierced, was made of three twisted cornucopia, with fruit and
foliage at the base of the legs, which open up to a triangular pierced
base to support the plate.
This plate may also be found with an early transfer of
a child in the centre for which add £50.00   Plate Dia.   225mm   90.00
         Comport Height 170mm Dia.   245mm   125.00

Plate square pierced with piercings removed with a ring of oval medallions around
rim. Creamware and glazed.

	(a) Plate		Dia.	220mm	90.00
	(b) Comport circular	Height 170mm Dia.		240mm	125.00
	(c) Comport oval	Height 65m Length		290mm	125.00

St. Cross Hospital,
Winchester plate Dia. 345mm

Plate Dia. 345mm with
proverb

Winchester plate
Dia. 345mm

Oval Plate: Think, Thank
and Thrive

Oval Platter: Give Us This
Day Our Daily Bread

Oval Platter: Where Reason
Rules The Appetite Obeys

Early Plate with Glazed
Recessed Centre

Unglazed plate with vine and
grape pattern in relief

Christmas pudding plate
coloured Holly Dia. 348mm

Pierced plate Dia. 225mm

Pierced plate, coloured with
medallions in relief Dia. 225mm

Japan Ewer with Grecian
decoration

146

£   p

Plate, pierced with linked chain decoration in relief
Bournemouth coat of arms in centre. This is from the same
mould as that used for the comport featured in the 1862
International Exhibition. (See page XX)   Dia.   234mm   125.00

Plate, flat with curved edge in typical first period style.
This plate may be found inscribed: (a)*The Alms Houses of Noble Poverty*
in illuminated gothic script surrounding the arms of St Cross Hospital,
surmounting the badge of Bishop Fox.
For this inscription and decoration add £150.
(b) *Manners Maketh Man* in illuminated gothic script surrounding
William of Wykeham coloured likeness.
For this inscription and decoration add £100
                                  Dia.   117mm   25.00

Platters Oval Bread 310mm x 250mm which appear (a)
unglazed with coloured lettering and (b) glazed with plain or
coloured lettering, and with arms or other motif central .
     (a) *Where Reason Rules, The Appetite Obeys* embossed around rim.   145.00
     (b) *Give Us This Day Our Daily Bread* embossed around rim .   125.00
White or cream glazed.

Platters almost Oval 328mm x 245mm carrying the *Think,*
Thank and Thrive wording embossed around the border are
found with two differing types of lettering
                 (a)White unglazed   175.00
                 (b) White, coloured lettering, glazed or unglazed   225.00

Sark Milk Churn parian with small handle and gilded acanthus
decorations in relief and bearing in gilded lettering *Souvenir de*
Sercq in gilt script. It has no lid   64mm   300.00

Scent Bottle circular and pierced, with an openwork twisted
stopper. Richly gilded with a wide turquoise band around the
circular scent tube, which can be found with plain edge, or
decorated with turquoise jewels. This item is
jewelled and set with tiny gilt stones set around a central ruby.
Originally supplied in a fitted leather case lined with purple
velvet, for which add £350.00   120mm   1500.00

Scent Bottle with decoration in relief of crown over cipher in
orange colour. Floral cartouche, oval, on reverse. Unglazed.
Can be found unmarked and uncoloured   130mm   400.00

Sheep lying down, identical to those featured in the Bullock and
Sheep group. (See also 101 Animals and Birds)
This same sheep re-appeared some half a century later, this time
glazed and on an oval plinth as one of the series of animals produced
in the 1920s. [2]   Glazed or unglazed   115mm   200.00

Winchester flagon patterned in relief, blue trim, gilded handle

Lithophane

Wall Plaque, with bust of Shakespeare in bas relief

Winchester flagon

Jewelled scent bottle in original fitted leather case

Vase, oval, flat faced, wreath surround, rectangular base

First Period Scent bottle with Crown over Cipher

Rare vase 293mm, flying cherubs in relief

Unique vase jewelled and set with stones

Vase, round, flat faced, wreath surround, rectangular base, round mouth

Unique jewelled vase, octagonal, raised ivy leaf pattern and set with stones

Unique jewelled vase with oviform body and pedestal foot and inset with stones

148

£   p

SHELLS:

for Second Period shells see SECOND PERIOD 10K ORNAMENTAL

Limpet [2]
An extremely fine glazed limpet shell mounted on a coloured
coral tripod base, an example of eggshell porcelain.
(Illustrated. Goss Record. 8th Edition: Page 4. Bottom Shelf
front)   66mm   200.00

Limpet [1]
Eggshell porcelain on three coral legs   60mm   150.00

Nautilus
(a) large glazed and crested version [2] (See 10K.5
    Miscellaneous)   155mm   195.00
(b) As (a) in Earthenware   155mm   125.00
(c) a finer smaller, glazed, uncrested version tinted in pink   95mm   375.00
    (Illustrated. Goss Record. 8th Edition: Page 4. Middle
    Shelf). [2] This is an example of Goss eggshell porcelain.
(d) very fine decorated with pink dots, also egg shell porcelain   95mm   325.00

Oyster
On red coral base identical to that of the Nautilus shell gilded
and with large frills to shell.   90mm   200.00

Whelk
(a) a single glazed whelk shell supported on a coral and
    rock base   Length   144mm   200.00
(b) a single glazed whelk shell supported on a red
    coral base   Length   120mm   200.00
(c) a group of three glazed whelk shells mounted on a stone
    base and having coloured coral between the shells   Length   137mm   325.00
(d) one large whelk shell supported by three smaller ones,
    standing on four coral legs (Glazed)   Length   185mm   350.00
(e) seven whelk shells on rocky base surrounding the nautilus
    shell, the latter supported on coral   Length   200mm   950.00

A single glazed Whelk shell supported on a red coral base 120mm

A fine eggshell porcelain Nautilus shell with pink tinted porcelain 95mm

			£	p
Squirrel standing beside a hollow tree-trunk, glazed and unglazed. Trunk glazed inside for use as a posy vase		117mm	200.00	

for **Sugar Basins**
see also **Cream Jugs** in this section

for **Sucrier** see EGGSHELL PORCELAIN

Swan	(a)		60mm	125.00
Can be either a cream jug or posy	(b)		73mm	125.00
holder. Occasionally found	(c)		94mm	125.00
with arms or decorations to rear.	(d)	Glazed	130mm	175.00
Same value.	(e)	Unglazed	130mm	175.00
	(f)	Glazed	135mm	175.00
	(f)	Cream glazed	135mm	125.00

for **Swan posyholder** on ashtray base see SECOND PERIOD
10I ANIMALS & BIRDS CHAPTER.

for **Tea service** see EGGSHELL PORCELAIN, and CREAM JUGS,
and SUGAR BASINS

for **Trinket Box and Lid** see CHERUB, and GOSS, EVANGELINE

Urn, covered and base plate decorated with bacchii in relief
and with rams head handle   Height 110mm   Dia. of bowl   140mm   250.00

VASES

Vase, Bulbous With cup top and strap handle
Turquoise trim to cup top and handle. Two purple transfers of
Oxford High Street, believed to be an early experimental piece
unglazed [1]. Unique.   135mm   300.00

Vase Round, flat faced, turquoise or plain leaves on border,
oval base and mouth   120mm   100.00

Vase Round, flat faced, wreath surround in blue or plain;
rectangular base and round mouth   107mm   100.00

Vase Oval, flat faced, wreath surround, rectangular base and oval mouth	(a)	115mm	100.00
	(b)	120mm	110.00
	(c)	170mm	125.00
with floral brooch affixed to front	(d)	170mm	175.00

Vase Oval, flat faced, wreath surround with 2 angular
handles each incorporating a small circular finger
grip decorated with blue dots   165mm   100.00

Vase, whorl pattern in relief
No 980X

Ewer, rounded handle
No 889X

Ewer, flat handle
No 889X

Vase, fluted, with three bands
of turquoise jewels

Vase with vertical flutes and
rich floral pattern No 895X

Vase, dove in circle and leaves,
white

Vase, green and beige
decoration No 891X

Vase, coloured flowers in relief,
taper stem No 881X

Pompeian Vase, with coloured
Grecian scenes

Vase, round, flat faced, oval
base and mouth

Three Whelk Shells on base

Three Whelk Shells on coral
base

		£ p
Vase, rectangular, flat faced, knurled edges, diamond mouth.	137mm	95.00

Vase decorated with flying cherubs in relief and two gargoyles
on shoulder. Exhibited at International Exhibition 1862.   293mm   1500.00
See illustration page 116. Unique.

Vases, inset with real stones
These are probably the finest and most beautiful pieces ever
produced by the Goss factory. William H. Goss carried out
hundreds of experiments in order to perfect the parian body,
which the author considers to be among the finest ever
produced. Into this he set stones; some semi-precious, others
glass, in the most attractive and decorative way. He patented
this process which was the object of widespread acclaim, for
nobody had yet been able to successfully produce high quality
work of this nature, although many, even Sevres, had tried .
Only a few examples of ware inset with jewels are known to exist; all
known are illustrated in this Chapter.

(a) **Vase** with oviform body, and pedestal foot, having 597 stones
    coloured green, red, yellow and magenta set amongst jewelling
    and rich and ornate gilding. Goshawk mark. Unique.   155mm   4000.00

(b) **Vase** octagonal with two shaped handles. Raised ivy leaf
    pattern, richly gilded and inset with 740 magenta and
    green stones and jewelling. Unique.   240mm   4000.00

(c) **Vase** with body tapering upwards and everted crinkled rim
    and two pierced knurled handles. Beautifully decorated
    on beige ground set with red, yellow and green stones
    and jewelled. Glazed interior. Unique.   170mm   2500.00

(d) **Scent Bottle** See pages 147 and 148

Vases A number of early parian vases 70-385mm in height
were produced, each unique. Illustrations of these may be
found in the engraving of W.H. Goss's exhibit for the
International Exhibition of 1862 (illustrated on page 116)
All unglazed except one, numbered 888

Some specific known examples are given here:

(a) **Vase** Having multi-coloured sprays of flowers in relief on both
    sides of body, and two gilded bands around narrow taper stem.
    Inscribed on base: *881X*. Unique.   96mm   2000.00

Oval plaque 'Can't you talk'

Oval plaque Oakley Coles

Oval plaque J.S. Crapper

Oval plaque Robert Garner

*Oval plaque Rev. Lovelace
Stamer*

*Oval plaque The Prince of
Wales*

*Two Housemartins on nest
shaped wall pocket*

Humming Bird wall vase

Florence Goss wall vase

*Wall name plate decorated with scrolls, jewelled and surrounded by turquoise.
The name Georgiana in flowers and foliage. Glazed. 190mm x 83mm*

Oval plaque mirror

	£	p

(b) **Ewer** glazed, vertical blue lines, raised pattern on vertical white stripes (numbered 888). Unique.   67mm   2000.00

(c) **Vase** Whorl pattern in relief with lines of alternate turquoise jewels and gilding
Inscribed on base: *890X*. Unique.   70mm   2000.00

(d) **Vase** Having vertical green leaves around hase, and beige and green decoration to body.
Inscribed on base: *891X*. Unique.   122mm   2000.00

(e) **Ewer** Having vertical blue lines and raised ivy leaf pattern with two horizontal bands of turquoise jewels enclosed by gilded bands. One shaped handle to side, rounded or flat   70mm   2000.00
Inscribed on base: *889X*. Unique.

(f) **Vase** Having vertical flutes with rich multi-coloured floral pattern around bulbous centre.   100mm   2000.00
Inscribed on base: *895X*. Unique.

(g) **Vase** Fluted pattern in relief with three horizontal bands of turquoise jewels enclosed by gilded lines. Ivy pattern in relief at neck. Unique.   70mm   2000.00

(h) **Vase** of Pompeian slender form and having Grecian scenes in light pastel shades. Unique.   385mm   2000.00

(i) **Vase** Unglazed, no colouring or gilding, having a dove in a circle within crossed sprays of leaves .   130mm   750.00

Wall plaque large upright oval, with bust of Shakespeare in bas-relief centrally   Height 435mm Width   390mm   650.00
Impressed: *W.H. Goss*

Wall Plaques, Oval, upright. A number of these were produced with busts in bas-relief centrally. The plaques were normally edged in richly gilded acanthus leaves with red berries, and surmounted by a porcelain ribbon bow trimmed in turquoise The subjects are raised from a cream ground. The title for each will be found lightly impressed under the subject.

(a)	**Oakley Coles**	200mm	650.00
(b)	**J-S. Crapper**	200mm	650.00
(c)	**Robert Garner**	200mm	650.00
(d)	**William Ewart Gladstone**	190mm	650.00
(e)	**The Prince of Wales** (later King Edward VI I)	200mm	650.00
(f)	**Eugene Rimmel**	200mm	650.00
(g)	**The Rev Sir Lovelace Stamer,** Bart	200mm	650.00
	For examples found uncoloured	200mm	450.00
(h)	**Wall Plaque, Oval, horizontal etc. Child with**		
	Large Dog with title on front: *can't you talk* Length	180mm	650.00
(i)	With a **mirror** enclosed in the oval surround White glazed	230mm	350.00

Wall vase, Beaconsfield
(Disraeli)

Wall vase, Beaconsfield
(Disraeli)

Wall vase, John Bright

Wall vase, Derby

Wall vase, Derby

Wall vase, Granville

Wall vase, Georgiana Jewitt

Wall vase, Georgiana Jewitt

Wall vase, W. H. Goss

Wall vase, Acanthus Leaves
only

Wall vase, Gladstone

Wall vase, George Dawson

The above wall plaques were commissioned and published by J.S.
Crapper, a colleague of W.H. Goss, and the following is impressed
on the reverse, in addition to W.H. Goss:

Plaques (a) (b) and (h)

COPYRIGHT
as the Act directs
(See 54 Geo iii, c56)
J S Crapper
Hanley
1st May 1876

Plaques (e) and (f)

COPYRIGHT
as the Act directs
(See 54 Geo iii, c56)
William H Goss
Stoke-on- Trent
May 1st 1876

Plaques (c) (d) and (g)

Copyright as the Act directs
W.H. Goss
Stoke on Trent
January 1877

Wall Vases   £   p

(a) **Child's Head** with radiating hair and feathers. The face is that
    of Florence, William Henry Goss's youngest daughter.   125mm   250.00
    Impressed on back: *Copyright as Act directs*   150mm   275.00
    W.H. Goss Stoke-on-Trent January 30 1882   190mm   300.00
    Usually glazed, but occasionally unglazed.

(b) Heads of the following in high relief on front of a glazed or
    unglazed oval wall-pocket, with plain, blue, or green background
    and acanthus leaf surround, with the name of the subject usually
    found impressed on the front at the base of the oval mount:-

Beaconsfield (Disraeli)
John Bright
George Dawson
Earl of Derby
Gladstone
William Henry Goss
Earl Granville
Georgiana Jewitt

White, glazed or unglazed	180mm	295.00
Part-coloured, glazed	180mm	395.00

One of a series of eight oval wall plaques, 230mm high with acanthus leaves and berries encircling a mirror and surmounted by a ribbon. Unusually for this series, this particular piece is white glazed.

£ p

(c) As (b) but without head, i.e. a wall-vase decorated with turquoise blue acanthus leaves. 180mm 350.00

(d) **A Humming Bird** taking nectar from a passion flower, and with a nest above containing three eggs in the surrounding foliage. Glazed
Impressed on back: *Copyright as Act directs W.H. Goss Stoke-on-Trent January 1888* 257mm 300.00

(e) **Two House Martins** on nest-shaped wall pocket, decorated with fern leaves on front, and a snail shell at the bottom.
Impressed on back: *W.H. Goss*   Overall Height 235mm
                                                  Overall width   180mm   450.00

Winchester Flagons These are a pair, unglazed, carrying coloured likenesses in bas-relief of:

(a) **The Trusty Servant** fully coloured version can be found decorated with brushed gilding 160mm 550.00

(b) **William of Wykeham** white and coloured. The coloured version is marked, and the white is unmarked, but the same mould. 160mm 550.00

Many of these appear unmarked and may possibly have been made by the Goss factory. Similar flagons were made by Davenport, Copeland and other factories for William Savage, the first Winchester Agent. Unmarked varieties would be worth £200.00 - £400.00 depending on size and desirability.

Winchester Flagon (Unmarked) patterned in relief, turquoise blue rim and base, gilding to rim and handle 150mm 350.00

Winchester Flagons with completely gilded handles and decorated on each side with three hand painted swallows in various stages of flight. These are a unique pair, probably painted by Eva Adeline Goss, daughter of William Henry Goss.
Both impressed: *W H Goss* 153mm 950.00
each

Winchester Quart
Inscribed: *Model of the Winchester Quart temp Q. Elizabeth*
Carries an embossed Crown and *1601 E.R.* on its side.
Almost certainly the prototype piece from which the second period example was made.
Impressed: *W H Goss* and *by Wm Savage*. Unique. 85mm 950.00

Wall Name Plate
Personalised ornamental name plate made for William Henry Goss's eldest daughter. Decorated with gilded scrolls, jewelled, and surrounded by turquoise. The name Georgiana in flowers and foliage. Glazed. Unmarked. Unique Length 190mm Height 83mm 2000.00

Pompeian vase with Grecian scenes in light pastel shades 385mm

A magnificent jewelled vase with oviform body and pedestal foot and inse with 597 stones. 155mm The word jewelled refers to the application of coloured dots and rich gilding as well as decoration with stones.

A beautiful octagonal jewelled vase decorated in raised Ivy leaf pattern with 740 magenta and green stones inset and richly jewelled 240mm

D Terracotta

In 1856 a valuable deposit of red clay was found in the Stoke area giving birth to the red clay tile industry. One manufacturer involved in this trade was a Mr Peake who entered into a brief partnership with W H Goss in 1866-7. It was short lived due to Peake's own financial difficulties and lasted for less than a year.

The partnership concentrated on the production of terracotta ornamental and utility ware, marked GOSS & PEAKE in fine black lettering. Terracotta manufactured after the partnership dissolved was marked W H GOSS. Few of the utility items such as tobacco jars with lids are to be found perfect today as they were made to be used. Decorations on these heavy wares included transfers of Egyptian and Greek influence in black, red, yellow and green, and amusing cartoons in black silhouette.

The transfers applied to Goss terracotta wares always match exactly when applied around a curved body, whereas those of other factories do not.

Wares marked GOSS & PEAKE are more desirable, being scarcer in number, and £30.00 should be added for this mark.

Terracotta was produced in The Potteries between 1867 and 1876 and Goss appeared to be one of the few factories to mark their wares. Probably for this reason much unmarked terracotta is hopefully, but incorrectly attributed to Goss.

Terracotta Jardinière and base plate

Terracotta spill holder, cartoons

Terracotta Cambridge Jug with hinged Pewter lid

Terracotta Vase, cartoons and patterned

Terracotta spill holder, patterned

Terracotta Vase, slender waisted, patterned

Terracotta Keystone of the Kingdom, Lord Beaconsfield

Terracotta Keystone of the Kingdom, Lord Derby

Terracotta bust of Burns

Terracotta comport patterned

Terracotta jug, with thumb rest

Terracotta Tobacco jar. Patterned

Terracotta Tobacco jar. Patterned

Terracotta Tobacco jar. Cartoons

Terracotta Tobacco jar. Cartoons

Black enamelled Terracotta vase, with stencilled Classical figures

Terracotta bag-vase, Barbados transfer

Terracotta vase and stopper, Cartoons

		£ p
Busts (a) **Robert Burns** socle/octagonal base	170mm	450.00
(b) **George Dawson** socle base, dated 1871	280mm	600.00
(c) **Charles Swain** socle base	280mm	600.00

See also FIRST PERIOD 9A BUSTS for white parian varieties

Cambridge Jug sometimes with hinged pewter lid

Overall height (a)	117mm	125.00
(b)	135mm	125.00

Candle Holder		150.00

Candlesticks	per pair	198mm	375.00

Coffee Pot and lid		125mm	175.00

Comport	Dia. 245mm	115mm	175.00

Crossing Sweeper in varied brown shades; the Child standing beside a Pillar Box with impressed word LETTERS and a loose lid; incised in manuscript on the back of the Pillar Box: *Published as the Act directs by W. H. Goss, Stoke-on-Trent 1 Dec 1873 Copyright*, and impressed below: *WETLEY BRICK AND POTTERY CO. LIMITED. W.K.*

	224mm	350.00

See also FIRST PERIOD 9B FIGURES for white parian variety

Jardinière normally found with an unmarked base plate, but correct

	190mm	200.00

Jug sometimes with hinged pewter lid	Approx.	330mm	135.00
with hinged thumb lever; sometimes with		180mm	150.00
thumb rest affixed to top of handle		190mm	165.00

Spill Holder	112mm	125.00
	130mm	125.00

Tea Pot	Length	150mm	175.00

Tobacco Jar with damper and lid.	105mm	125.00
These are relatively common	155mm	125.00
	132mm	125.00

A Black-enamelled Terracotta Vase having Classical Figures stencilled around the body.

	180mm	400.00

Vase, Bag with pictorial view of *The Cassino, Barbados Aquatic Club*, and *Arms of Barbados* on the reverse.

	50mm	125.00

Vase slender waisted, patterned	120mm	125.00
	140mm	125.00
	210mm	150 00

		£ p
Vase bulbous bottom glazed interior	140mm	150.00
Vase bulbous bottom , narrow neck	240mm	150.00
Vasc and stopper usually missing, and base plate	250mm	150.00

The Keystones of the Kingdom
being almost life-size heads mounted on keystone shaped
slabs of
  (a) Lord Derby
  (b) Lord Beaconsfield
Impressed on back: *Copyright as Act directs W.H. Coss*
Stoke-on-Trent August 1876
One example also has additionally impressed on the back
WETLEY BRICK AND POTTERY CO. LIMITED. W.K.
thus posing the question as to whether they were all
made by this firm.
Height 321mm; Width 195mm reducing to 150mm   Each   500.00
See also FIRST PERIOD 9C ORNAMENTAL for an unglazed
white parian variety. An advertising leaflet was issued with
these models and is valued at £80.00 (see page 57)

A rare terracotta bust of Robert Burns on
socle/octagonal plinth. Height 170mm

10 The Second Period
1881-1934

Period Symbols

Where a shape was known to have been made during more than one period, the number in brackets after its entry denotes the other period(s) during which it was manufactured .

The First Period	**[1]**	**1858-1887**
The Second Period	**[2]**	**1881-1934**
The Third Period	**[3]**	**1929-1939**

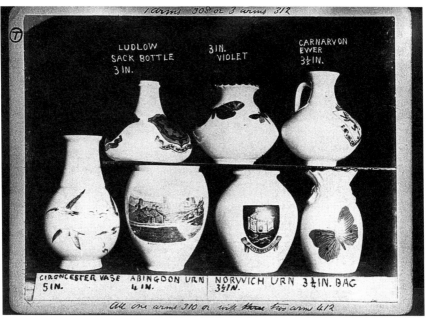

Photograph sent by Adolphus Goss to agencies to assist them in ordering.

Five of the earliest models to be produced. Top row: York Roman Vessel, Windsor Urn, Scarborough Kettle, Elizabethan Jug and Jersey Milk Can and Lid.

E   Historic Models and Special Shapes

The majority of models in this section were manufactured during the Second Period between 1888 and 1929. However, certain shapes, especially the larger versions, were test-marketed during the First Period up to seven years earlier, and more popular lines continued for four years into the Third Period after the sale of the pottery in 1929. Numbers in square brackets throughout the listing indicate other periods where particular models were known to have been in production. It is possible to tell by the thicker feel and slightly gritty texture plus the more yellow hue of the porcelain, if a piece was made pre-1888. Thereafter, the quality of china, enamel and gilt improved drastically and became consistent. Second Period named models are very much whiter in appearance and the quality is excellent. The original factory photograph on page 171 shows an example of armorial ware made from 1929 to 1934. The named models are the most widely known of all the factory's products and they dominated production for the larger part of its existence. This chapter will probably be the most important to collectors because it contains the six hundred plus models which are most avidly collected. Cottages, Fonts, Animals and Crosses are also models, but due to their importance will be found under their own sub-headings.

Two sets of values are given where applicable, one for any arms and the other for matching arms . For example, an Exeter Vase with the Arms of Exeter will be worth very much more than one with, say, City of Edinburgh arms. No general percentage can be added for matching arms as examples vary so much in rarity. Many collectors prefer to have the correct arms on a model and where possible these are stated. Where there are no arms for a particular model, such as the Ashley Rails Urn, the nearest town or the local agency in this case Christchurch or New Milton (Manor of New Milton) is considered correct. If a model relates to a specific person rather than a place, such as Dorothy Vernon's Porridge Pot, then the arms of that person is to be preferred . Ethnic shapes such as the Welsh Leek, Welsh Picyn, Welsh Milk Can etc relate to the Principality as a whole and not just to one town. Any Welsh arms can be considered matching although the true correct arms are the Arms of Wales. Foreign models such as the Norwegian Dragon and Horse shaped Beer Bowls and Bucket are matching with the arms of Norway and also with those of any Norwegian town. Matching arms also include the arms of any school, hospital, or nobleman relevant to the respective town of the model concerned. Nearby towns and correct county arms will attract premiums ranging from ten per cent to fifty per cent to be added to the price given with any arms. For the values of the various arms and decorations to be found on any piece of Goss see the Price Guide's companion volume - The Price Guide to Arms and Decorations on Goss China by Nicholas Pine (Milestone Publications).

Occasionally, the factory would apply the incorrect model name to the base of a model. This does not alter the value of such a piece either upwards or downwards.

The factory produced large size models during the First Period, but smaller models were introduced during the Second Period by Adolphus Goss due to the demand by agents for less expensive, more easily transportable stock.

Some models are listed with only one price. This is where the item is known only with or without matching arms as the case may be. For instance, the Alderney Fish Basket appears only with the matching arms of Alderney so no price is given for a variety with any other arms.

Larger models normally have two or three coats of arms and therefore no additional premium should be added in such cases. Where the larger size of a model carries only one coat of arms then a £5 - £10 deduction should be made. Some models bear four or five coats of arms for which a premium of some £20.00 should be added. Variations from this rule are indicated separately in this section.

The factory Sales director and chief representative, Adolphus Goss, a pioneer photographer, always carried a set of agents cards to assist in ordering. These would be photographs of a selection of Goss models. During the First and Second Periods the pieces depicted were not numbered but during the latter part of the Second Period and during the Third Period each model was allocated a number.

These numbers were not reproduced on the models themselves with the exception of nine of the very latest models which were numbered as follows:-

Roman Vase	783
Cirencester Roman Urn	784
Tuscan Vase	785
Priests House Prestbury	786
Ramsgate Urn	787
Ramsgate Romano – British Ewer	794
Ramsgate Romano – British Jug	795
The Maple Leaf of Canada	813
Isaac Waltons Cottage (large)	834

Two vases were also numbered (see 10K4 ORNAMENTAL ARTICLES) and are given here for completeness of numbering.

Oviform Vase	849
Classical Shaped Vase	850

The inscription on each model is given in italics in this encyclopaedia in every case. There is no inscription if none is stated.

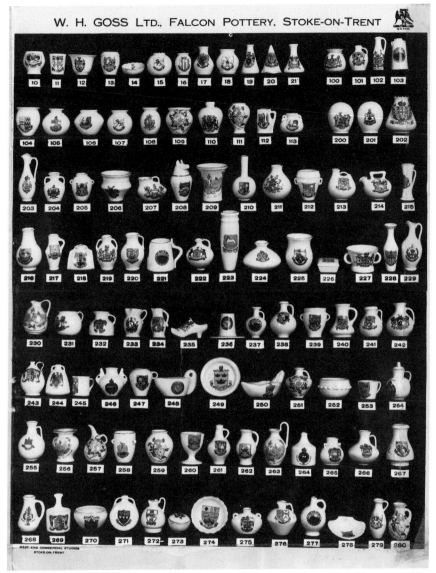

A selection of Second Period Goss models and shapes sold during the Second Period between 1929 1934 displayed on an agents ordering card

Aberdeen Bronze Pot

Abergavenny Ancient Jar

Abingdon Roman Vase

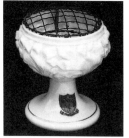

Acanthus Rose Bowl

Alderney Fish Basket

Alderney Milk Can and Lid

Alnwick Celtic Sepulchral Urn

Amersham Leaden Measure

Ancient Costril or Pilgrims Bottle (League model)

Antwerp Oolen Pot

Appleby Elizabethan Bushel Measure

Arundel Roman Ewer

Models which bear no arms are included in the first column and are marked thus †.
All dimensions refer to the height unless otherwise stated.
Where no price is given, no piece exists in that particular category

Model			With any Arms £ p	With Matching Arms £ p

for ABBOT BEERE'S JACK
see Glastonbury (Abbot Beere's) Jack

for ABBOT'S CUP, FOUNTAINS ABBEY
see Fountains Abbey, Abbot's Cup

Model			With any Arms	With Matching Arms
ABERDEEN BRONZE POT		63mm	10.00	30.00
(Goss Record. 8th Edition. Page 4)		89mm	23.00	34.00
Inscribed: *Model of Bronze Pot*	multi-crested	133mm	38.50	65.00

found in Upperkirkgate Aberdeen May 31st, 1886.
Containing 12267 silver pennies.
(Can be found with inscription omitting reference to the pennies) .
See also POSTCARDS Chapter 5.

| Variation with unusually short legs attached to the large size pot, multi-crested | | 110mm | 75.00 | |

Matching Arms: *ARMS OF ABERDEEN*

ABERGAVENNY ANCIENT JAR		54mm	9.25	25.00

(Goss Record. 8th Edition. Page 29)
Inscribed: *Model of Ancient Jar found at*
Abergavenny. Rd. No. 633432.
Matching Arms: *ABERGAVENNY* OR *SEAL OF ABERGAVENNY*

ABINGDON ROMAN VASE		95mm	32.00†	95.00

(Goss Record. 8th Edition: Page 16)
Inscribed: **Model of Roman Vase dug up at The Abbey, Abingdon.**
Incorrectly described as the Abingdon Roman Urn
in the 8th edition of The Goss Record
Matching Arms: *ABINGDON* OR *ARMS OF ABINGDON*

ACANTHUS ROSE BOWL	with wire cage	130mm	155.00	
(Goss Record. 8th Edition: Page 45)	without wire cage	130mm	80.00	

Inscribed: *The Acanthus Rose Bowl.*
Rd. No. 633431
This model was originally sold with a
wire cage which is often missing nowadays.
It has no correct arms.

Ashbourne Bushel

Ashley Rails Roman Urn

Avebury Celtic Urn

(Cup of) Ballafletcher

*Barnet Stone
White and Brown*

Bartlow Ewer

Bath Ancient Roman Cup

Bath Bronze Roman Ewer

Bath Roman Ewer

Bath Roman Jug

Bath Urn

Beachy Head Lighthouse

Model		With any Arms £ p	With Matching Arms £ p

ALDERNEY FISH BASKET　　　　　　　40mm　　　　　　　65.00
(Goss Record. 8th Edition. Page 17)　　　58mm　　　　　　　80.00
Inscribed: *Model of Alderney Fish Basket*
Matching Arms: *ALDERNEY*

ALDERNEY MILK CAN and lid　　　　　70mm　　　　　　　77.50
Inscribed: *Alderney Milk Can*　　　　　　108mm　　　　　　80.00
This model is incomplete without it's lid.　140mm　　　　　　80.00
Price £15.00 in all three sizes
Matching Arms: *ALDERNEY*

ALNWICK CELTIC SEPULCHRAL URN　68mm[1]　　25.00　　55.00
(Goss Record. 8th Edition. Page 30)
Inscribed: *Model of Celtic Urn dug up at Alnwick.*
Matching Arms: *ALNWICK*

AMERSHAM LEADEN MEASURE　　　48mm　　17.00　　55.00
(Goss Record. 8th Edition. Page 17)
Inscribed: *Model of Leaden Measure circa 1682, found in the Old Lock up in the Town Hall, Amersham. Rd. No. 626749.*
Matching Arms: *AMERSHAM*

for AMPHORA VASE
see Greek Amphora Vase or
ORNAMENTAL 10K chapter

ANCIENT COSTRIL or **PILGRIMS BOTTLE**　(a) 56mm　　　77.50
(Goss Record 9th Edition. Pages 22, 28, 40 and　(b) 56mm　　　95.00
Plate B)
Inscribed: *Model of Ancient Costril or Pilgrims' Bottle. Rd. No. 526384. This model is only issued to Members of the League and cannot be bought*
This model was first introduced bearing **The League of Goss Collectors** motif (a), and re-introduced later bearing the **International League of Goss Collectors** motif (b) .

for ANCIENT STONE VESSEL, DOVER CASTLE
see Dover Mortar

for ANCIENT TYG (One Handle)
see Staffordshire One Handled Tyg

for ANCIENT TYG (Two Handles)
see Staffordshire Two Handled Tyg

Model		With any Arms £ p	With Matching Arms £ p

for ANGLO-SAXON CINERARY URN
see King's Newton Anglo-Saxon Cinerary Urn

ANTWERP OOLEN POT	(a) I coat of arms 70mm	10.00	30.00
(Goss Record. 8th Edition. Page 42)	(b) 3 coats of arms 70mm	20.00	38.50

Inscribed: *Model of Oolen Pot 16th century.*
Found inside a Caisson at Antwerp. Now in Liebaert
Museum at Ostend. Rd. No. 495668.
Matching Arms: *ANTWERPEN OR PROVINCIE ANTWERPEN*

APPLEBY ELIZABETHAN BUSHEL MEASURE

(Goss Record. 8th Edition: Page 36)	Dia. 59mm	22.00	38.50

Inscribed: *Model of Elizabethan Bushel Measure now*
in Appleby Moot Hall.
Matching Arms: *APPLEBY*

ARUNDEL ROMAN EWER	55mm	15.00	30.00
(Goss Record. 8th Edition: Page 34)	102mm	30.00	47.00

Inscribed: *Model of Roman Ewer, found at*
Avisford Hill, Arundel.
Matching Arms: *ARUNDEL.*

ASHBOURNE BUSHEL	Dia. 51mm	16.00	30.00

(Goss Record. 8th Edition: Page 18)
Inscribed: *Model of Ashbourne Bushel. Rd. No. 450628.*
Matching Arms: *ASHBOURNE*

ASHLEY RAILS ROMAN URN	108mm	65.00	77.50

Inscribed: *Model of Roman Urn found at Ashley Rails,*
New Forest. Copyright.
Matching Arms: None, but any of the following may
be considered local: *MANOR OF NEW MILTON,*
CHRISTCHURCH, LYMINGTON OR *RINGWOOD.*

for ASHMOLEAN VASE, GNOSSUS
see Gnossus Ashmolean Vase

for ATWICK VASE
see Hornsea Roman Vase

AVEBURY CELTIC URN	105mm[1]	30.00	65.00

(Goss Record. 8th Edition: Page 36)
Inscribed: *Model of Celtic Urn, dug up nearAvebury.*
Matching Arms: *CALNE, MARLBOROUGH* OR *DEVIZES*

for AYSGILL URN
see Hawes Ancient British Urn

Model			With any Arms £ p	With Matching Arms £ p
(CUP OF) BALLAFLETCHER		95mm	65.00	105.00

(Goss Record. 8th Edition: Page 24)
Inscribed: *Model of the Lhannan Shee (Peaceful Spirit) Cup of*
Ballafletcher in the possession of J. C. Bacon Esq Seafield,
Isle of Man. Rd. No. 448432.
Matching Arms: *DOUGLAS, ISLE OF MAN*
OR *ANY ISLE OF MAN ARMS* for which £30 should be added

for BARGATE, SOUTHAMPTON
see Southampton, Bargate

BARNET STONE	(a) White†	172mm	125.00	
(Goss Record. 8th Edition:Page24)	(b) Brown†	172mm	165.00	

Inscribed on base: *Barnet Stone Rd . No. 489664.*
Inscribed on front: *Here was fought the famous Battle*
between Edward the 4th and the Earl of Warwick April
the 14th ANNO 1471 in which the Earl was Defeated
and Slain.
Inscribed on reverse: *From St. Albans VIII*
miles 3/4. Left side: *To Hatfield VII miles 3/4.*
Right side: *This was erected 1740.*

for BARROW'S MONUMENT
see Sir John Barrow's Monument, Ulverston.

BARTLOW EWER	104mm[11	42.00	55.00

(Goss Record. 8th Edition: Page 22)
Inscribed: *Model of Roman Bronze Ewer. Found in 1835 at*
Bartlow Hills. Near Saffron Walden.
Matching Arms: *SAFFRON WALDEN*

BATH ANCIENT ROMAN CUP	102mm	95.00	160.00

(Goss Record. 8th Edition: Page 31)
Inscribed: *Model of Ancient Roman Cup found at Bath.*
Rd. No. 543009.
Matching Arms: *BATH*

BATH BRONZE ROMAN EWER	120mm[1]	38.50	55.00

(Goss Record .8th. Edition: Page 31)
Inscribed: *From Bronze original found in Roman Bath*
at Bath.
(An example has also been seen erroneously inscribed
as a Bartlow Ewer)
See also POSTCARDS Chapter 5
Matching Arms: *BATH*

Model		With any Arms £ p	With Matching Arms £ p
BATH ROMAN EWER	63mm	7.50	22.50
(Goss Record. 8th Edition: Page 31)	130mm	24.50	38.50

Inscribed: *Model of Roman Ewer in Dorset Museum Found in Bath.*
The original of this model is in Dorset County Museum, Dorchester and was chosen by that town's agent, J T Godwin as a local model (see *Goss Record 8th Edition* page 61) Dorchester could therefore possibly be considered as being correct arms.
Matching Arms: *BATH*

BATH ROMAN JUG With one or two coats of arms 150mm[1]		55.00	95.00
With three coats of arms 150mm[1]		65.00	110.00

(Goss Record. 8th Edition: Page 31)
Inscribed: *Model of Roman Jug found at the Roman Bath at Bath.*
Matching Arms: *BATH*

BATH URN	75mm[1]	30.00	47.00

(Goss Record. 8th Edition: Page 31)
Inscribed: *The Bath Urn from original in Museum.*
Matching Arms: *BATH*

for BATTLE OF LARGS MEMORIAL TOWER
see Largs Memorial Tower

BEACHY HEAD LIGHTHOUSE (a) Brown band	125mm	65.00	95.00
(Goss Record. 8th Edition: Page 34) (b) Black band	125mm	65.00	80.00

Inscribed: *Model of Beachy Head Lighthouse. Rd. No. 622475.*
The black band version also found with a brown rim around the top, below the lantern
Matching Arms: *EASTBOURNE* (with or without addition of the words BEACHY HEAD)

This exact model also appears as the extremely rare DUNGENESS LIGHTHOUSE only one example of which has been found

Model		With any Arms £ p	With Matching Arms £ p

BECCLES RINGERS JUG 87mm 250.00 600.00

Inscribed on base: *The Ringers Jug in Beccles Parish Church.*
The original was made by Samuel Stringfellow, Potter.
Inscribed on the side with the ringers verse: *When I*
am fill'd with Liquor strong, Each Man drink once & then
ding dong. Drink not to much to Cloud your Knobs. Least
you forget to make the Bobbs, a gift of JOHN PATTMAN Beccles
Impressed: *(1827)*.
Very rare; only seen bearing matching arms until 1990,
when a model was found bearing the Hastings crest and the usual
(1827) impressed, but with no inscriptions on the base or side.
Matching Arms *ANCIENT SEAL OF BECCLES*

BETTWS-Y-COED ANCIENT BRONZE KETTLE 73mm 20.00 34.00
(Goss Record. 8th Edition: Page 38) 114mm 34.00 55.00
Inscribed: *Model of Ancient Bronze Kettle dug up near*
Bettws-y-Coed 1877. Rd. No. .543011.
Matching Arms: *BETTWS-Y-COED*

BIDEFORD ANCIENT MORTAR 42rnm 22.00 34.00
(Goss Record. 8th Edition: Page 20)
Inscribed: *Model of Ancient Mortar dredged out of the*
Torridge at Bideford. Rd. No. 622407.
Matching Arms: *BIDEFORD*

for BLACK AND BROWN CUP
see Newcastle (Staffordshire) Cup

BLACKGANG CANNON Length 95mm 14.50 24.50
(Goss Record. 8th Edition: Page 26)
Inscribed: *Model of Ancient Cannon found on the beach at*
Blackgang Chine, 1. W. Rd. No. 554472.
Matching Arms: *BLACKGANG*

BLACKGANG TOWER, ST. CATHERINE'S HILL 112mm 38.50 65.00
(Goss Record. 8th Edition: Page 26)
Inscribed: *Model of Tower on St. Catherine 's Hill, Blackgang,*
1. W. Built in 1323 by W. De Godyton for a chantry priest to
sing mass for the souls of mariners and in the tower a light was
placed to warn ships off this dangerous coast. Rd. No. 630366.
Matching Arms: *BLACKGANG*

BLACKPOOL TOWER
(Goss Record. 9th Edition: Page 21 & Plate J) 118mm 34.00 65.00
Inscribed: *Model of Blackpool Tower.*
Matching Arms: *BLACKPOOL.*

Beccles Ringers Jug

Bettws-y-Coed Ancient Bronze Kettle

Bideford Ancient Mortar

Blackgang Cannon

Blackgang Tower St Catherine's Hill

Blackpool Tower

Bognor Lobster Trap

Bolton Abbey Wine Cooler

Boston Ancient Ewer

Boulogne Milk Can and Lid

Boulogne Sedan Chair

Boulogne Wooden Shoe

Model			With any Arms £ p	With Matching Arms £ p

BOLTON ABBEY WINE COOLER Dia. 68mm 25.00 55.00
(Goss Record. 8th Edition. Page 38)
Inscribed: *Model of Wine Cooler at Bolton Abbey.*
Rd. No. 633428.
Matching Arms: *BOLTON ABBEY*

BOSTON ANCIENT EWER 70mm 16.50 47.00
(Goss Record. 8th Edition: Page 28)
Inscribed: *Model of Ancient Ewer now in Boston Museum.*
Rd. No. 594871
Matching Arms: *BOSTON*

BOULOGNE MILK CAN and lid 74mm 30.00 47.00
(Goss Record. 8th Edition: Page 42)
Inscribed: *Model of Boulogne Milk Can. Rd. No. 521974.*
The model is incomplete without its lid, value £ 15.00
Matching Arms: *BOULOGNE-SUR-MER*

BOULOGNE SEDAN CHAIR (a) 69mm 40.00 80.00
(Goss Record. 8th Edition. Page 42) (b) 69mm 300.00†
Inscribed: *Model of Sedan Chair used by the Countess*
of Boulogne. XVII Century. Rd. No. 539423.
In the 8th Edition of the Goss Record (Page I) a
version specially decorated in turquoise blue is
advertised (b). The author has seen only one example.
This model has very fragile handles. With one of
these broken it would be worth only one-quarter of
its perfect price.
Matching Arms: *BOULOGNE-SUR-MER*

BOULOGNE WOODEN SHOE Length 118mm 34.00 80.00
(Goss Record. 8th Edition: Page 42)
Inscribed: *Model of wooden shoes worn by the*
fisherwomen of Boulogne sur Mer and Le Portal.
Rd No. 539421.
Matching Arms: *BOULOGNE-SUR-MER*

BOURNEMOUTH ANCIENT BRONZE
  MACE HEAD 80mm 27.50 42.50
(Goss Record. 8th Edition: Page 22)
Inscribed: *Model of Ancient Bronze Mace Head circa A.D. 300.*
Found in Kings Park, Bournemouth. Rd. No. 613962.
Matching Arms: *BOURNEMOUTH*

Bournemouth Ancient Bronze
Mace Head

Bournemouth Ancient
Eygptian Lamp

Bournemouth Pilgrim
Bottle

Bournemouth Pine Cone

Bournemouth Bronze Urn

Brading Stocks

Brading Roman Ewer

Braunton Lighthouse

(The Nose of) Brasenose

Bridlington Elizabethan
Quart Measure

Bristol Puzzle Cider Cup

British Six Inch Shell

182

Model			With any Arms £ p	With Matching Arms £ p

BOURNEMOUTH ANCIENT EGYPTIAN LAMP   Length   105mm   20.00   47.00
(Goss Record. 8th Edition: Page 23)
Inscribed: *Model of Ancient Egyptian Lamp Circa B. C.*
100 to A.D. 100. Found at Southbourne, Bournemouth.
Rd. No. 638371.
Matching Arms: *BOURNEMOUTH*
With Egyptian Arms add £ 20.00

BOURNEMOUTH PILGRIM BOTTLE   90mm   22.00   40.00
(Goss Record. 8th Edition: Page 23)
Inscribed: *Model of Pilgrim Bottle (circa 600A.D.) Found at*
Southbourne, Bournemouth 1907. Rd. No. 562740.
See also Chapter 5 Postcards for a postcard
advertising this model.
Matching Arms: *BOURNEMOUTH*

BOURNEMOUTH PINE CONE   90mm   16.50   22.00
(Goss Record. 8th Edition: Page 23)
Inscribed: *Pine Cone. Rd. No. 559524.*
Matching Arms: *BOURNEMOUTH*

BOURNEMOUTH BRONZE URN   52mm   16.00   25.00
(Goss Record. 8th Edition: Page 23)
Inscribed: *Model of Ancient Bronze Urn in the Museum of the*
Royal Bath Hotel, Bournemouth. Rd. No. 489583.
Matching Arms: *BOURNEMOUTH*

BRADING STOCKS   Length   87mm   155.00   300.00
Inscribed: *Model of The Stocks, Brading, I. O. W.*
Copyright.
The stocks are unglazed Brown on a white glazed base.
Matching Arms: *THE KING'S TO WN OF*
BRADING, SEAL OF BRADING OR *ANCIENT*
ARMS OF BRADING

BRADING ROMAN EWER   (a)   70mm   10.50   23.00
(Goss Record. 8th Edition:Page26)   (b)   125mm[1]   17.00   26.00
    (c)   125mm[2]   17.00   26.00
Inscription [1]: *Model of ewer found on site of Roman Villa*
Inscription [2]: *Model of Ewer Found on Site of Roman Villa*
Brading 1. of W.
Also known as the Isle of Wight Roman Ewer by J.J. Jarvis
in The Goss Record. As it is not so named on the piece itself
the author prefers to call it the Brading Ewer.
Either *THE KING'S TOWN OF BRADING, SEAL OF*
BRADING OR *ANCIENT ARMS OF BRADING*
may be considered as Matching Arms.

The Nose of Brasenose with flat back and pointed nose. This unique model was produced especially for William Huntley's son, Noel who attended Brasenose College, Oxford.

Model		With any Arms £ p	With Matching Arms £ p

for BRAMPTON WARE MUG
see Chesterfield Brampton Ware Mug

(THE NOSE OF) BRASENOSE   104mm   30.00   40.00
(Goss Record. 8th Edition: Page 31)
Inscribed: *The Nose of Brazenose, Oxford.*
Brasenose is frequently spelt Brazenose.
The Matching Arms are *BRAZENOSE COLLEGE, OXFORD*
OR *ARMS OF THE CITY OF OXFORD.*

(THE NOSE OF) BRASENOSE   98mm†   125.00
Second variety with a flat back and pointed nose.
Inscribed: *H.N.W. Goss 20/11/19*
Impressed: *W H Goss*
Unique example; probably a prototype for the Second
Period model, except that it is too late. It has a flake chip
to the side of the nose.The model was listed in *The Goss Record*
8th Edition, and this 1919 example was made for William
Huntley's son, Huntley Noel William Goss, who
attended Brasenose College, Oxford.

BRAUNTON LIGHTHOUSE   133mm   650.00   850.00
Inscribed: *Model of Braunton Lighthouse near*
Westward Ho. Copyright.
The third rarest lighthouse, it has a grey roof.
Matching Arms: *WESTWARD HO.*

for (OLD) BRAZIER AT TRESCO
see Tresco Old Brazier

BRIDLINGTON ELIZABETHAN QUART
  MEASURE   50mm   16.00   30.00
(Goss Record. 8th Edition: Page 38)
Inscribed: *Model of Elizabethan Quart Measure now in*
"The Old Bayle Gate", Bridlington. Rd. No. 509868
and with E.R. 1601 embossed on the side.
Also found with *Rd. No. 500865*
Matching Arms: *BRIDLINGTON*

BRISTOL PUZZLE CIDER CUP   51mm   34.00   65.00
(Goss Record. 8th Edition: Page 22)
Inscribed: *Model of Puzzle Cider Cup made at the Bristol Pottery*
1791. Now in Bristol Museum. Rd. No. 562739.
Matching Arms: *CITY OF BRISTOL*

for BRITISH CONTACT MINE OR BRITISH SEA MINE
see Contact Mine

British Tank

Brixworth Ancient Cup

Broadway Tower

Burton Beer Barrel

Bury St. Edmunds German Bomb

Bury St. Edmunds Kettle and Lid

Caerhun Roman Burial Urn 833

Caerleon Glass Lachrymatory or Tear Bottle

Caerleon Lamp

Cambridge Pitcher

Cambridge Roman Jug

Canary Porron

Model			With any Arms £ p	With Matching Arms £ p

BRITISH (SIX INCH) SHELL   110mm   65.00
(Goss Record. World War Edition. Pages 5 [illustrated]
and 7) . This model is COPYRIGHT but is not usually
so marked.
Inscribed: *Model of British 6in Inciendiary Shell.*
(Note misspelling of incendiary)
The value of any military crest is to be added to the price,
say £40.00-£100.00 depending upon rarity and suitability.
Correct Arms: *ANY ARTILLERY REGIMENT*

BRITISH TANK   Length110mm   65.00
(Goss Record. 9th Edition: Plate L)   (both moulds)
Inscribed: *Model of British Tank - "England Expects that*
every Tank will do its Damn'dest." Copyright.
Two versions can be found, one with sponson guns
pointing upwards, the other with sponson guns
pointing horizontally ahead. Both are of the same value.
Lincoln is where military tanks were first manufactured in 1916.
Matching Arms: (a) *CITY OF LINCOLN* OR
                ANCIENT ARMS OF LINCOLN   80.00
           (b) *TANK CORPS*   140.00

BRIXWORTH ANCIENT CUP   55mm   11.00   20.00
(Goss Record. 8th Edition: Page 30)
Inscribed: *Model of Ancient Cup found at Brixworth,*
Northamptonshire. Rd. No. 413199.
Matching Arms: *NORTHAMPTON*

BROADWAY TOWER	(a) White	75mm	140.00	190.00
(Goss Record. 8th Edition: Page 36)	(b) Grey†	75mm	195.00	
Inscribed: *Model of Broadway Tower.*	(c) Brown†	75mm	250.00	
Rd. No. 634630.				

Matching Arms: *BROADWAY*

| **BURTON BEER BARREL** | 60mm | 14.00 | 27.50 |
| (Goss Record. 8th Edition: Page 32) | 73mm | 19.00 | 28.00 |

Inscribed: *Model of Burton Beer Barrel.*
Matching Arms: *BURTON-UPON-TRENT*

BURY ST. EDMUNDS GERMAN BOMB   75mm   38.50   65.00
(Goss Record. 9th Edition: Page 28)
Inscribed: *Model of German Bomb dropped on*
Bury St. Edmunds from a Zeppelin 30 April 1915. Copyright.
This model has an extremely delicate handle
without which it is of little value.
Matching Arms: *BURY ST. EDMUNDS*

Model		With any Arms £ p	With Matching Arms £ p
BURY ST. EDMUNDS KETTLE and lid	76mm	27.50	47.00
(Goss Record. 8th Edition: Page 34)	121mm[1]	38.50	65.00

Inscribed: *Model of Roman Libation Vessel found at Suffolk.*
Now in Bury Museum.
This model is not complete without its lid,
worth £15 small and £20 large of the prices shown.
Matching Arms: *BURY ST. EDMUNDS*

for BURY ST. EDMUNDS LIBATION VESSEL
see Bury St. Edmunds Kettle

for CAERHUN BRONZE CROCHON
see Welsh Crochon

CAERHUN ROMAN BURIAL URN	54mm	21.50	40.00

Inscribed: *Model of Roman Burial Urn found at Caerhun*
(Conovium) in 1878 containing calcined female bones.
Copyright.
This model is the rarest of the smaller urns and is
numbered 833
Matching Arms: *CONWAY*

CAERLEON GLASS LACHRYMATORY

(or Tear Bottle)	86mm	12.00	

(Goss Record. 8th Edition: Page 29)
Inscribed: *Model of Glass Lachrymatory or Tear Bottle found in*
stone coffin. Discovered in the excavations for the railway, near
Caerleon, July 1847. Now in Caerleon Museum.
Rd. No. 559520.

Matching Arms:	(a) *CAERLEON*			38.50
	(b) *NEWPORT. MON.*			26.00

CAERLEON LAMP
(Goss Record. 8th Edition: Page 29)
Inscribed: *Model of Ancient Lamp in Museum at Caerleon*
(City of Legions, King Arthur's Capital).

Matching Arms:	(a) *CAERLEON*	Length	88mm	12.00	30.00
	(b) *NEWPORT. MON.*				19.50

CAMBRIDGE PITCHER	63mm	7.50	22.50
(Goss Record. 8th Edition: Page 17)	108mm	19.00	25.00

Inscribed: *The Cambridge Pitcher from the original in*
Archaeological Museum.
Matching Arms: *CAMBRIDGE*

Model		With any Arms £ p	With Matching Arms £ p
CAMBRIDGE ROMAN JUG	70mm	17.50	30.00
This model is not found named in the usual way,	76mm	17.50	30.00
but it is a well known shape produced by many	82mm	26.00	34.00
factories during Victorian and Edwardian times.	88mm	26.00	38.50
It is also one of the few Goss models not to be named	94mm	30.00	47.00
and the reader is referred to the illustration	120mm	30.00	47.00
for identification. See also 9D TERRACOTTA	130mm	34.00	50.00
Matching Arms: *CAMBRIDGE*	140mm	38.50	55.00
	155mm	50.00	60.00

for CANADIAN MAPLE LEAF
see (The) Maple Leaf of Canada

for CANARY ANCIENT COVERED JARRA
see Las Palmas Ancient Covered Jarra

for CANARY ANCIENT EARTHEN JAR
see Las Palmas Ancient Earthen Jar

for CANARY ANCIENT JARRA
see Las Palmas Ancient Jarra

CANARY PORRON	68mm	25.00	40.00

(Goss Record. 8th Edition: Page 42)
Inscribed: *Model of Canary Porron. Rd. No. 449120.*
This model is identical to the Gibraltar Alcaraza, but rarer,
so the inscriptions on all models found should be carefully
checked.
Matching Arms: *LAS PALMAS, GRAND CANARY*

for CANNON BALL
see Rye Cannon Ball

CANTERBURY JUG	113mm	20.00	28.00

(Goss Record. 8th Edition: Page 26)
Inscribed: *The Canterbury Jug.*[1]
Inscribed: *Model of Norman Jug found near the*
Cathedral, Canterbury and now in the museum [2]
Matching Arms: *CITY OF CANTERBURY*

CANTERBURY LEATHER BOTTLE	46mm	7.50	14.00

(Goss Record. 8th Edition: Page 26)
Inscribed: *Model of the Pilgrim 'Leather Bottell ' in*
Canterbury Museum. Rd. No. 392067.
Matching Arms: *CITY OF CANTERBURY*

Canterbury Jug

Canterbury Leather Bottle

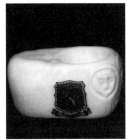

Capel Madoc Stoup

*Cardinal Beaufort's
Candlestick*

*Cardinal Beaufort's Salt
Cellar*

Carlisle Old Salt Pot

Carmarthen Coracle

Carnarvon Ewer

Castletown Cinerary Urn

(The) Cenotaph, Whitehall

Cheddar Cheese

Cherbourg Milk Can and Lid

190

Model			With any Arms £ p	With Matching Arms £ p

CAPEL MADOC STOUP   Length 80mm   30.00   77.50
(Goss Record. 9th Edition: Page 34)
Inscribed: *Model of Stoup from Capel Madoc near*
Rhayader removed to Dderw, circa 1855. Rd. No. 643962.
Matching Arms: *RHAYADER*

CARDINAL BEAUFORT'S CANDLESTICK   152mm[1]   115.00   235.00
(Goss Record. 8th Edition: Page 23)
Inscribed: *Model of Cardinal Beaufort's Candlestick.*
(1404-1447) .
Matching Arms: *CARDINAL BEAUFORT* OR
CITY OF WINCHESTER

CARDINAL BEAUFORT'S SALT CELLAR   70mm[1]   85.00   160.00
(Goss Record. 8th Edition: Page 23)
Inscribed: *Model of Cardinal Beaufort's Salt Cellar.*
(1404-1447).
Matching Arms: *CARDINAL BEAUFORT* OR
CITY OF WINCHESTER

CARLISLE OLD SALT POT   46mm   7.50   19.00
(Goss Record. 8th Edition: Page 18)
Inscribed: *Model of Old Salt Pot in Carlisle Museum.*
Rd. No. 403422.
The original of this model was actually a urinal.
Matching Arms: *CARLISLE OR CARLISLE ANCIENT*

CARMARTHEN CORACLE   Length 133mm[1]   65.00   125.00
(Goss Record. 8th Edition: Page 38)
Inscribed on the seat or base: *Model of Carmarthen Coracle.*
Pub. by E. Colby Evans Guildhall Sq. Carmarthen.
The arms can be found either inside or on base of this model.
Matching Arms: *CARMARTHEN*

CARNARVON EWER   63mm   16.00   22.50
(Goss Record. 8th Edition: Page 39)   82mm[1]   19.00   32.50
Inscribed: *From original found at Carnarvon. (Roman*
Segontium), now in Carnarvon Castle.
Matching Arms: *CARNARVON*

CASTLETOWN CINERARY URN   40mm   14.00   30.00
(Goss Record. 8th Edition: Page 24)
Inscribed: *Model of Cinerary Urn found at Gretch Veg 1. of*
Man Jany 1899. Now in Museum Castle Rushen Castletown
I. of Man. Rd. No. 599333.
Matching Arms: *TOWN OF CASTLETOWN*

*Cheshire Roman Urn
League Model, 1932*

Cheshire Salt Block

*Chester Roman Altar
League Model, 1931*

Chester Roman Vase

*Chesterfield "Brampton Ware"
Mug*

Chichester Roman Ewer

Chichester Roman Urn

Chicken Rock Lighthouse

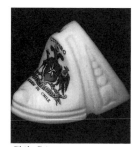

Chile Stirrup

Chile Hat

Chile Mate Cup

Chile Spur

Model			With any Arms £ p	With Matching Arms £ p

CENOTAPH, WHITEHALL   (a) White glazed   145mm   30.00   47.00
(b) White unglazed†   145mm   55.00
Inscribed: *The Cenotaph Whitehall.*
See also THIRD PERIOD 11.0 for later varieties.
Matching Arms: *WESTMINSTER* OR *CITY OF WESTMINSTER*

**for CHARLOTTE'S (QUEEN) FAVOURITE
WINDSOR KETTLE**
see Windsor Kettle

CHEDDAR CHEESE   (a) Yellow   62mm   34.00†   55.00
(Goss Record. 8th Edition: Page 31) (b) White glazed [3] 62mm   34.00   55.00
Inscribed: *Model of a Cheddar Cheese.*
Rd. No. 521975.
Also so named on side in Gothic script. For which add £10.00
Matching Arms: *CHEDDAR*

CHERBOURG MILK CAN and lid   65mm   24.50   77.50
(Goss Record. 8th Edition: Page 42)
Inscribed: *Model of Cherbourg Milk Can. Rd. No. 605734*
This model is not complete without its lid which is
worth £ 15.00 of the price shown .
Matching Arms: *VILLE DE CHERBOURG*

CHESHIRE ROMAN URN   90mm   400.00
Inscribed: *Model of Roman Urn found at Condate*
(Kinderton) Cheshire 1820. Copyright 1932. This model is only
issued to Members of the League and cannot be bought.
International League Model for 1932
Correct Arms: *INTERNATIONAL LEAGUE OF GOSS*
  COLLECTORS

CHESHIRE SALT BLOCK   80mm   28.50   40.00
(Goss Record. 9th Edition: Page 11 and Plate K)
Inscribed: *Model of Cheshire Salt Block. Copyright.*
Matching Arms: *CHESHIRE* OR *ANY*
CHESHIRE TOWN OR NOBILITY ARMS

CHESTER ROMAN ALTAR   117mm   150.00   800.00
Inscribed: *Model of Roman Altar found buried off Pepper*
Alley Chester 1861. This model is only issued to Members
of the League and cannot be bought. Copyright 1931.
International League Model for 1931
Correct Arms: *INTERNATIONAL LEAGUE OF GOSS*
  COLLECTORS

Model		With any Arms £ p	With Matching Arms £ p
CHESTER ROMAN VASE	59mm	7.50	16.50
(Goss Record. 8th Edition: Page 17)	89mm[1]	16.50	30.00
Inscribed: *Model of Roman Vase found at Chester from the original in Museum.*			
see also Chapter 5 POSTCARDS			
Matching Arms: *CHESTER*			
CHESTERFIELD BRAMPTON WARE MUG	93mm	65.00	80.00
(Goss Record. 9th Edition Page 13)			
Inscribed: *Model of "Brampton Ware " Mug found on a beam during repairs to roof of Chesterfield Church, the original being left by workman in 1750. Copyright.*			
Matching Arms: *CHESTERFIELD*			
for CHESTERFIELD MUG			
see Chesterfield Brampton Ware Mug			
CHICHESTER ROMAN EWER	63mm	7.50	16.50
(Goss Record. 8th Edition: Page 34)			
Inscribed: *Model of Roman Ewer in Chichester Museum. Rd. No. 403420.*			
Matching Arms: *CHICHESTER*			
CHICHESTER ROMAN URN	81mm[1]	24.50	34.00
(Goss Record. 8th Edition: Page 34)			
Inscribed: *Model of Roman Urn found at Chichester now in the Museum.*			
Matching Arms: *CHICHESTER*			
CHICKEN ROCK LIGHTHOUSE	127mm	36.00	55.00
(Goss Record. 8th Edition: Page 26)			
Inscribed: *Model of Chicken Rock Lighthouse, Isle of Man. Rd. No. 602905.*			
Matching Arms: *ISLE OF MAN*			
CHILE HAT	Dia. 86mm	215.00	385.00
(Goss Record. 9th Edition: Page 37 and Plate O)			
Matching Arms: *RECUERDO DE CHILE*			
CHILE MATE CUP	60mm	100.00	180.00
(Goss Record. 9th Edition: Page 37 and Plate O)			
Matching Arms: *RECUERDO DE CHILE*			

Model		With any Arms £ p	With Matching Arms £ p
CHILE SPUR	Length 150mm	200.00	300.00

(Goss Record: 9th Edition: Page 37 and Plate N)
Matching Arms: *RECUERDO DE CHILE*

CHILE STIRRUP	50mm	100.00	190.00

(Goss Record. 9th Edition: Page 37 and Plate N)
Matching Arms: *RECUERDO DE CHILE*

N.B. The Chilean pieces do not carry the usual named model
inscriptions, but when bearing the arms of Chile titled
RECUERDO DE CHILE, they are inscribed above the arms
respectively, as follows:-
    CHURAYA (Hat)
    MATE (Cup)
    ESPUELA (Spur)
    ESTRIBO (Stirrup)

for CHIPPING NORTON FOURSHIRE STONE
see Fourshire Stone

CHRISTCHURCH ANCIENT BOWL	Dia. 60mm	10.50	30.00

(Goss Record. 8th Edition: Page 23 and the
advertisement on page 65)
Inscribed: *Model of Ancient Bowl found near Christchurch,*
Hants. Rd. No. 639534.
Matching Arms: *CHRISTCHURCH*

CHRISTCHURCH PRIORY CHURCH NORMAN TOWER
(Goss Record. 8th Edition:

Page 23), and the advertisement	(a) White glazed†	123mm	55.00
on page 65)	(b)White unglazed†	123mm	80.00
	(c) Grey†	123mm	85.50
	(d)Brown†	123mm	155.00

Inscribed: *Model of Norman Tower, Priory Church*
Christchurch, circa 1100, built by Ralph Flambard Bishop
of Durham 1099-1128. Rd. No. 567379.
A descriptive leaflet was issued with this model
and is valued at £20.00 (see page 59)

CHRISTCHURCH ROMANO-BRITISH URN	52mm	9.00	27.50

(Goss Record. 8th Edition: Page 23, and the advertisement
on page 65)
Inscribed: *Model of Romano-Bntish Urn,found near*
Christchurch, Hants. Rd. No. 639533.
Matching Arms: *CHRISTCHURCH*

Christchurch Ancient Bowl

*Christchurch Priory Church
Norman Tower*

*Christchurch
Romano-British Urn*

*Cirencester Roman Ewer
League Model, 1918*

Cirencester Roman Ewer

Cirencester Roman Urn, 784

Cirencester Roman Vase

Cliftonville Roman Jug

Cliftonville Roman Vase

*Colchester Gigantic Roman
Wine Vase*

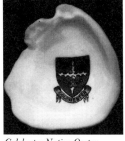

*Colchester Native Oyster
Shell*

*Colchester Roman Lamp
League Model, 1927*

Model			With any Arms £ p	With Matching Arms £ p

for CHRIST'S HOSPITAL WINE FLAGON
see London Christ's Hospital English Wine Flagon

CIRENCESTER ROMAN EWER   (a) 78mm   105.00
(Goss Record. 9th Edition: Pages 22, 41 and Plate C) (b) 78mm   125.00
Inscribed: *Model of Roman Ewer found at Cirencester.*
Issued to Members only & cannot be purchased. Copyright.
This model was first introduced bearing THE LEAGUE OF
GOSS COLLECTORS motif(a), and re-introduced in 1918
bearing the INTERNATIONAL LEAGUE OF GOSS
COLLECTORS motif (b) .

CIRENCESTER ROMAN EWER	(a) I Arms	115mm [1]	32.00	77.50
(Goss Record. 8th Edition: Page 22)	(b) 2 Arms	115mm [1]	40.00	80.00
Inscribed: *Model of Roman Ewer found at*	(c) 3 Arms	115mm [1]	47.00	95.00

Cirencester now in the museum.
Matching Arms: *CIRENCESTER*

CIRENCESTER ROMAN URN   165mm   87.00   225.00
This model is marked COPYRIGHT and numbered 784
(see Roman Vase 783 for comparison)
This model often appears in coloured lustre glaze and
uncrested
Matching Arms: *CIRENCESTER*

CIRENCESTER ROMAN VASE   80mm   10.50   30.00
(Goss Record. 8th Edition: Page 22 and   124mm   24.50†   30.00
advertisement Page 66)
Inscribed: *Model of Roman Vase found at Cirencester,*
now in the museum.
Matching Arms: **CIRENCESTER**

CLIFTONVILLE ROMAN JUG   180mm   175.00   235.00
Inscribed: *Model of Roman Jug found during excavations*
in Avenue Gardens, Cliftonville 1924.
Matching Arms: *MARGATE*

CLIFTONVILLE ROMAN VASE   70mm   195.00   275.00
Inscribed: *Model of Roman Vase found during excavations*   107mm   200.00   300.00
in Avenue Gardens, Cliftonville 1924.
Matching Arms: *MARGATE*

Model	With any Arms £ p	With Matching Arms £ p

**Colchester enthusiasts should refer to The Goss Record
8th Edition: Page 63 for a full page advertisement.**

COLCHESTER GIGANTIC ROMAN WINE VASE

(a) with one coat of arms	157mm	60.00	95.00
(a) with four or five coats of arms	157mm	80.00	125.00

(Goss Record. 8th Edition: Page 21)
Inscribed: *Model of Gigantic Roman Wine Vase in Colchester
Castle. Found in Castle Yard.*
Matching Arms: *COLCHESTER* OR *PORT OF COLCHESTER*

COLCHESTER NATIVE OYSTER SHELL   Width 68mm   14.50   23.50
(Goss Record. 8th Edition: Page 22)
Always appears unnamed.
Matching Arms: *COLCHESTER* OR *PORT OF COLCHESTER*
OR POSSIBLY *CINQUE PORT LIBERTY OF BRIGHTLINGSEA*
which was the place from which the oysters were caught.

COLCHESTER ROMAN LAMP   Length 100mm   200.00
Inscribed: *Model of Roman Lamp found at Colchester* Height 75mm
*Copyright 1927. This model is only issued to Members
of the League and cannot be bought.*
International League Model for 1927
Correct Arms: *INTERNATIONAL LEAGUE OF
  GOSS COLLECTORS*

COLCHESTER VASE (Cloaca)

(a) with one coat of arms	45mm	10.50	24.00
(a) with three coats of arms	45mm	12.50	29.50

(Goss Record. 8th Edition: Page 22)
Inscribed: *Model of Roman Vase found in the "Cloaca".
Now in Colchester Castle.*
Cloaca refers to the place where the original vase was
found. It is included with the model's name to distinguish
the piece from the Colchester Vase (Famous) .
Correct Arms: *COLCHESTER* OR *PORT OF COLCHESTER*

COLCHESTER ROMAN VASE (Famous)

(a)	44mm	7.50	17.50
(b)	90mm	15.50	38.50
(c) with one coat of arms	127mm	25.00	42.50
(d) with four coats of arms	127mm	35.00	55.00

(Goss Record. 8th Edition: Page 22)
Inscribed: *The Famous Colchester Vase in the museum.*
Famous refers to that part of the full name listed in
The Goss Record viz. Famous Roman Colchester Vase. . .
etc. and is quoted to distinguish this model from the
Colchester Cloaca Vase.
Matching Arms: *COLCHESTER*

Model		With any Arms £ p	With Matching Arms £ p

CONTACT MINE Length 73mm   215.00
(Goss Record. 9th Edition: Pages 22,41 and Plate C)
Inscribed: *Model of Contact Mine. Copyright. Issued to*
Members only and cannot be purchased.
International league Model for 1919.
Correct Arms: *INTERNATIONAL LEAGUE OF*
GOSS COLLECTORS (in Gothic script)

for CONWAY WELSH CROCHON
see Welsh Crochon

CORFE CASTLE CUP   62mm[1]   20.00   34.00
(Goss Record. 8th Edition: Page 20)
Inscribed: *Model of Ancient Cup dug up near Castle Corfe.*
Matching Arms: *CORFE-CASTLE*

CORNISH BUSSA   55mm   10.00   19.50
(Goss Record.8th Edition: Page 18)
Inscribed: *Model of Cornish Bussa. Rd. No. 594377.*
Matching Arms: *CORNWALL*

CORNISH PASTY
Inscribed: *Cornish Pasty. There are so many Saints in Cornwall*
that the Devil was afraid to cross the Tamar for fear of being
put into a Cornish Pasty. (Ancient Legend) .

Matching Arms: *CORNWALL*	Length		
(a) White glazed	82mm	47.00	77.00
(b) Yellow	82mm	70.00	120.00
(c) Yellow	87mm	75.00	120.00
(d) White glazed	87mm	47.50	77.50
(e) White glazed	110mm	60.00	80.00
(f) Yellow	110mm	80.00	135.00

CORNISH STILE	(a) White unglazed†	Length	95.00	
	(b) White glazed†	72mm	55.00	
	(c) Brown†		140.00	

Inscribed: *Model of a Cornish stile. Rd. No. 567378*
Variety (b) can be found with the Blackpool arms,
which would reduce its value by half.

for CORONATION CHAIR IN WESTMINSTER ABBEY
see Westminster Abbey Coronation Chair

for CORONATION CHAIR, PERTH
See Perth Coronation Chair

Colchester Vase (Cloaca)

*Colchester Roman Vase
(famous)*

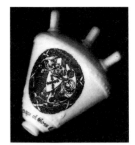

*Contact Mine
League Model, 1919*

Corfe Castle Cup

Cornish Bussa

Cornish Pasty

Cornish Stile

*Cuckfield Ancient
Bellarmine*

*Cumbrae, The Monument
Tomont End*

*Cyprus Mycenaean Vase
League Model, 1925*

Dartmouth Sack Bottle

Denbigh Brick

Model		With any Arms £ p	With Matching Arms £ p

for COSTREL
see Luton Bottle

for CRICKET STONE, HAMBLEDON
see Hambledon Cricket Stone

for CRONK AUST CINERARY URN
see Ramsey Cronk Aust Cinerary Urn

CUCKFIELD ANCIENT BELLARMINE	75mm	16.00	30.00

(Goss Record. 9th Edition: Page 29)
Inscribed: *Model of Ancient Bellarmine found in a pond at*
Horsgate, Cuckfield. Rd. No. 647236.
This model is similar to the Rochester Bellarmine
The effigy of a bearded man is embossed on the neck of this
model, also known as a Greybeard
Matching Arms: *CUCKFIELD*

CUMBRAE, THE MONUMENT, TOMONT END
(Goss Record. 8th Edition: Page 40)   Brown† 175mm   800.00
Impressed on front: *The Monument Towmontend*
Cumbrae.
There are several mis-spellings of Tomont End on the
Goss model

CYPRUS MYCENAEAN VASE   Dia. 90mm   215.00
Inscribed: *Model of Mycenaean Vase from Cyprus in*
British Museum. Copyright 1925. This model is only issued
to Members of the League and cannot be bought.
International League Model for 1925
Correct Arms: *INTERNATIONAL LEAGUE OF GOSS*
COLLECTORS

for DART SACK BOTTLE
see Dartmouth Sack Bottle

DARTMOUTH SACK BOTTLE	63mm	10.00	19.50
(Goss Record. 8th Edition: Page 20)	92mm[1]	17.00	22.50

Inscribed: *Model of Sack Bottle dredged from the Dart*
from the original in Exeter Museum.
This model depicts an embossed medallion with
Thos. Holdsworth, Dartmouth,1735 in relief.
He was the Governor of Dartmouth Castle at the time.
Matching Arms: *DARTMOUTH*
When matching arms are shown without a shield, as a
pictorial presentation: Add £10.00

Devizes Celtic Drinking Cup

Devon Cider Barrel

Devon Cooking Pot

Devon Oak Pitcher

Dinant Wooden Shoe

Doncaster Ewer

Doncaster Urn

Doncaster Vase

Dorchester Jug

Dorchester Roman Cup

*Dorothy Vernon
Porridge Pot*

*Dover Mortar
(or Stone Vessel)*

Model			With any Arms £ p	With Matching Arms £ p
DENBIGH BRICK	(a) White glazed	82mm[1]	77.50	140.00
(Goss Record. 8th Edition: Page 39)	(b) White unglazed	82mm	125.00	
	(c) Brown or red	82mm	275.00	

Inscribed: *Model of a Brick found at*
Denbigh Castle representing the Legend of
St. Hubert. Date about 1620.
Matching Arms:: *DENBIGH*

		With any Arms £ p	With Matching Arms £ p
DEVIZES CELTIC DRINKING CUP	63mm	11.00	27.50
(Goss Record. 8th Edition: Page 36)	82mm	20.00	33.00

Inscribed: *Model of Celtic Drinking Cup found at Devizes.*
Matching Arms: *DEVIZES*

		With any Arms £ p	With Matching Arms £ p
DEVON CIDER BARREL	60mm	15.00	30.00

Inscribed: *Model of Devon Cider Barrel. Copyright.*
This model is identical to the small version of the Burton
Beer Barrel but rarer.
Matching Arms: *DEVON* OR *ANY DEVONSHIRE ARMS*

		With any Arms £ p	With Matching Arms £ p
DEVON COOKING POT	46mm	15.00	30.00

Inscribed: *Model of Devon Cooking Pot. Copyright.*
This model is identical to the Manx Peel Pot but scarcer. ...so that
every apparent Peel Pot requires close examination.
Matching Arms: *DEVON* OR *ANY DEVONSHIRE ARMS*

NOTE: Almost always these two models are found with
arms of places in Devonshire, or rarely, Cornwall. The only
truly correct arms are those of Devon itself.

		With any Arms £ p	With Matching Arms £ p
DEVON OAK PITCHER	59mm	7.50	21.50
(Goss Record. 8th Edition: Page 20)	114mm[1]	20.00	33.00

Inscribed: *Model of Oak Pitcher peculiar to Devon.*
Matching Arms: *DEVON* OR *ANY DEVONSHIRE ARMS*

			With any Arms £ p	With Matching Arms £ p
DINANT WOODEN SHOE	Length	74mm	30.00	47.00

(Goss Record. 8th Edition: Page 42)
Inscribed: *Model of Wooden Shoe worn at Dinant.*
Matching Arms: *DINANT*

		With any Arms £ p	With Matching Arms £ p
DONCASTER EWER	67mm	23.00	38.50

Inscribed: *Model of Ancient Ewer found during alterations*
at Elephant Hotel,Doncaster, 1914. Copyright.
Matching Arms: *DONCASTER* OR *COUNTY BOROUGH OF DONCASTER*

		With any Arms £ p	With Matching Arms £ p
DONCASTER URN	39mm	15.50	36.00

Inscribed: *Model of Ancient Urn found in the Market Place*
Doncaster. Copyright.
Matching Arms: *DONCASTER* OR *COUNTY BOROUGH OF DONCASTER*

Model		With any Arms £ p	With Matching Arms £ p

DONCASTER VASE   78mm   17.00   38.50
Inscribed: *Model of Ancient Vase found in High St., Doncaster.*
Copyright.
Matching Arms: *DONCASTER* OR *COUNTY BOROUGH OF DONCASTER*

DORCHESTER JUG   50mm   7.50   19.00
(Goss Record. 8th Edition: Page 20 and also see full
page advertisement on page 61)
Inscribed: *Model of Old Jug found in North Sq., Dorchester.*
Matching Arms: *DORCHESTER*

DORCHESTER ROMAN CUP   51mm   7.50   21.00
(Goss Record. 8th Edition: Page 21)   82mm[1]   21.50   30.00
Inscribed: *Model of Roman Cup (Dorset Museum) found at*
Dorchester.
Matching Arms: *DORCHESTER*

DOROTHY VERNON'S PORRIDGE POT   72mm[1]   22.50   40.00
(Goss Record. 8th Edition: Page 18)
Inscribed: *Model of Dorothy Vernon's Porridge Pot.*
The inscription is normally in Gothic script on the reverse, but
when the model carries two crests it can be found around the
rim or neck.
Matching Arms: *SEAL OF DOROTHY VERNON*

DOVER MORTAR (or Stone Vessel)   51 mm   10.50   17.00
(Goss Record. 8th Edition: Page 26)
Inscribed: *Model of Ancient Stone Vessel from Dover Castle*
in Dover Museum. Rd. No. 390788.
This model is listed as DOVER MORTAR in the
8th Edition (page 26) and 9th Edition (page 20) of *The Goss Record.*
Matching Arms: *CINQUE PORT OF DOVER,*
TOWN OF DOVER OR VILLE-ET-PORTUS DOVER

DUNGENESS LIGHTHOUSE   125mm   550.00
Inscribed: *Model of Dungeness Lighthouse*
This model is actually the Beachy Head Lighthouse
re-titled, presumably for the local agent. It is the rarest
version of this lighthouse, only one example being reported.
It was probably produced as a prototype for the
Romney agent who failed to place an order.
Matching Arms: *THE LORDS OF THE LEVEL OF*
ROMNEY MARSH

Model		With any Arms £ p	With Matching Arms £ p

DURHAM SANCTUARY KNOCKER

(Goss Record. 8th Edition: Page 21)
Inscribed: *(The) Durham Abbey Knocker.*
Inscribed (g,h,i): *Durham Abbey Knocker Cup Rd. No. 245459*

(a) Flower holder, or hair tidy, white glazed Height 125mm		40.00†	
(b) Flower holder, or hair tidy, white unglazed Height 125mm		42.00†	
(c) Flower holder, or hair tidy, brown Height 125mm		55.00†	
(d) Flower holder, or hair tidy, gold front on brown. Probably an 1887 Golden Jubilee Edition. Height 125mm		117.00†	
(e) Flower holder, or hair tidy, brown with green tingeing	125mm	115.00†	
(f) Night-light with base	83mm	95.00	120.00
(g) Mug or cup	52mm	47.00	65.00
(h) Mug or cup	80mm	60.00	85.00
(i) Mug or cup	118mm	85.00	125.00

A descriptive leaflet can also be found with the above
items and is worth £25.00 see page 59. The brown example is
sometimes tinged with green to represent moss or ageing.
An additional £20.00 should be added to the matching arms
prices for examples bearing The Grey Towers of Durham Verse.
matching Arms: *CITY OF DURHAM* OR *COUNTY OF DURHAM*

DUTCH MILK CAN and lid

Inscribed: *Model of Dutch Milk Can Rd. No. 521974* (identical to Boulogne Milk Can)	74mm	65.00	125.00

This model is incomplete without its lid, value £ 15.00
Matching Arms: *HOLLAND* OR *ANY DUTCH TOWN*

DUTCH SABOT

DUTCH SABOT Length	82mm	25.00	40.00

(Goss Record. 8th Edition: Page 42)
Inscribed: *Model of Dutch Sabot.*
Matching Arms: *HOLLAND* OR *ANY DUTCH TOWN*

EDDYSTONE LIGHTHOUSE

Inscribed: *Model of Eddystone Lighthouse.*
Matching Arms: *PLYMOUTH, DEVONPORT*

OR *STONEHOUSE*	125mm	30.00	47.00

for EDDYSTONE SPANISH JUG

see Plymouth Jug

for EDINBURGH CASTLE, MONS MEG

see Mons Meg, Edinburgh Castle

Dutch Milk Can and Lid. Identical to the Boulogne Milk Can and Lid

	With any Arms £ p	With Matching Arms £ p
Model		

THE EGYPTIAN MODELS

These have been listed in numerical order where found numbered otherwise alphabetically. According to the 8th Edition of *The Goss Record* (page 42) models of the Egyptian Water Jar and the Great Pyramid were in the course of preparation at the time of going to press in 1913, but the Water Jar must have been in production in 1911 as it has been found carrying the G & M Coronation decoration. By the time the 9th Edition was published in 1921 these two models had been on sale for some time (page 37) and ten other models of ancient shapes were listed as being in preparation. The production of these models must arouse today's collectors' curiosity, but the discovery of the young King Tutankhamun's Tomb in 1922 was only the climax of many years aggressive investigation of the region by several teams of explorers. Indeed, from a commercial point of view, the Goss factory would have found it much more convenient had the tomb been discovered two or three years later as no sooner had the models made their appearance than interest in Egyptology began to wane.

The models 'in preparation' were given numbers and why 2,3,12,13,14 and 15 were not used can only be a matter for speculation. The most probable explanation is that around twenty designs were prepared for consideration by the Cairo Agent. He in turn selected the models thought to be most suitable, which he ordered and the rejected designs account for the missing numbers.

An Egyptian Lotus Vase was chosen in 1923 as the model for issue exclusively to members of the International League of Goss Collectors, and at around the same time two further models were issued by the Goss factory and these, together with the Wembley Lion, were put on sale at the 1924 and 1925 British Empire Exhibition.

CAIRO, PORT SAID, SAKKARA, EYGPT OR ALEXANDRIA may be considered matching on any Egyptian piece, the Flag of Eygpt may also be considered so.

EGYPTIAN CANOPIC JAR WITH ANUBIS HEAD No. 1			
(Goss Record. 9th Edition: Page 37)	76mm	110.00	125.00

Inscribed: *Model of Ancient Egyptian Canopic Jar with Anubis Head. No. 1 Copyright.*
A most unusual model. The Anubis head is detachable and the model is incomplete without this lid, which is worth £50.00.
See also THIRD PERIOD (S) for a later one-piece model, and also a one-piece version utilised as pepper or salt cellars.
Matching Arms: *EGYPT* OR *ANY EGYPTIAN ARMS*

EGYPTIAN KOHL POT No. 4	66mm	38.00	65.00
(Goss Record. 9th Edition: Page 37)			

Inscribed: *Model of Egyptian Kohl Pot. No. 4 Copyright.*
Matching Arms: *EGYPT* OR *ANY EGYPTIAN ARMS*

*Durham Sanctuary Knocker
Flower holder. Brown*

*Durham Sanctury Knocker
Cup. 118mm*

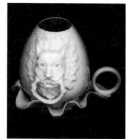

*Durham Sanctury Knocker
Night-light with base*

*Durham Sanctury Knocker
Mug*

Dutch Sabot

Eddystone Lighthouse

Egyptian Water Jar

*Egyptian Canopic Jar with
Anubis Head No. 1*

Egyptian Kohl Pot No. 4

Egyptian Kohl Pot No. 5

Egyptian Kohl Pot No. 6

Egyptian Alabaster Vase No.7

	With any Arms £ p	With Matching Arms £ p
Model		

EGYPTIAN KOHL POT No. 5   60mm   28.50   65.00
(Goss Record. 9th Edition: Page 37)
Inscribed: *Model of Ancient Egyptian Kohl Pot. No. 5 Copyright*.
Matching Arms: *EGYPT* OR *ANY EGYPTIAN ARMS*

EGYPTIAN KOHL POT No. 6   Dia.   70mm   25.00   65.00
(Goss Record. 9th Edition: Page 37)
Inscribed: *Model of Ancient Egyptian Kohl Pot. No. 6 Copyright*.
Matching Arms: *EGYPT* OR *ANY EGYPTIAN ARMS*

EGYPTIAN ALABASTER VASE No. 7   105mm   28.50   65.00
(Goss Record.9th Edition: Page 37)
Inscribed: *Model of Ancient Egyptian Alabaster Vase. No. 7
Copyright*.
Matching Arms: *EGYPT* OR *ANY EGYPTIAN ARMS*

EGYPTIAN ALABASTER VASE No. 8   105mm   34.50   65.00
(Goss Record. 9th Edition: Page 37)
Inscribed: *Model of Ancient Egyptian Alabaster Vase. No. 8
Copyright*.
Matching Arms: *EGYPT* OR *ANY EGYPTIAN ARMS*

EGYPTIAN ALABASTER BOWL No. 9   58mm   25.00   65.00
(Goss Record. 9th Edition: Page 37)
Inscribed: *Model of Ancient Egyptian Alabaster Bowl . No. 9
Copyright*.
Matching Arms: *EGYPT* OR *ANY EGYPTIAN ARMS*

EGYPTIAN WOODEN EWER No. l0   66mm   22.00   65.00
(Goss Record. 9th Edition: Page 37)
Inscribed: *Model of Ancient Egyptian Wooden Ewer. No. 10
Copyright*.
Matching Arms: *EGYPT* OR *ANY EGYPTIAN ARMS*

EGYPTIAN PORCELAIN EWER No. 1 1   58mm   30.00   65.00
(Goss Record. 9th Edition: Page 37)
Inscribed: *Model of Ancient Egyptian Porcelain Ewer. No. 11
Copyright*.
Matching Arms: *EGYPT* OR *ANY EGYPTIAN ARMS*

EGYPTIAN PORCELAIN BOTTLE No. 16   68mm   43.00   77.50
(Goss Record: 9th Edition: Page 37)
Inscribed: *Model of Ancient Egyptian Bottle. No. 16 Copyright*.
This is the rarest of the Egyptian models.
Matching Arms: *EGYPT* OR *ANY EGYPTIAN ARMS*

Egyptian Alabaster Vase
No. 8

Egyptian Alabaster Bowl
No. 9

Egyptian Wooden Ewer
No. 10

Egyptian Porcelain Ewer
No.11

Egyptian Porcelain Bottle
No. 16

Egyptian Lotus Vase
League Model, 1923

Egyptian Mocha Cup
(Bowl Shaped)

Egyptian Mocha Cup
(Egg-cup Shaped)

Elizabethan Jug

Ellesmere Ancient British
Canoe

Eton Vase

Exeter Flemish Goblet

Model		With any Arms £ p	With Matching Arms £ p

EGYPTIAN LOTUS VASE   80mm   215.00
Inscribed: *Model of Ancient Egyptian Lotus Vase. Copyright.*
Issued to members only & cannot be bought. 1923.
International League Model for 1923
Correct Arms: *INTERNATIONAL LEAGUE OF*
    GOSS COLLECTORS

EGYPTIAN MOCHA CUP (Bowl Shaped)	Named 40mm	10.50	55.00
Inscribed: *Model of Egyptian Mocha Cup.*	Unnamed 40mm	8.00	47.00

Rd. No. 572083
This model is not listed in any edition of *The Goss*
Record. It is described as Bowl shaped so as to distinguish
it from the Egg Cup shaped variety, also named
Egyptian Mocha Cup. This piece always appears to be
particularly finely modelled, the porcelain being very
thin and delicate . It is found both named and un-named .
Matching Arms: *EGYPT* OR *ANY EGYPTIAN ARMS*

EGYPTIAN MOCHA CUP (Egg Cup Shaped)	Named 52mm	16.00	55.00
Inscribed: *Model of Egyptian Mocha Cup.*	Unnamed 52mm	10.50	47.00

Rd. No. 572092.
This model is not listed in any edition of *The Goss*
Record. It is described as Egg Cup shaped so as to
distinguish it from the Bowl shaped version, also
named Egyptian Mocha Cup. It is found both named
and unnamed.
Matching Arms: *EGYPT* OR *ANY EGYPTIAN ARMS*

for EGYPTIAN ANCIENT LAMP
see Bournemouth Ancient Egyptian Lamp

for EGYPTIAN PYRAMID
see Great Pyramid

EGYPTIAN WATER JAR   56mm   7.50   40.00
(Goss Record. 9th Edition: Page 37)
Inscribed: *Model of Egyptian Water Jar. Rd. No. 569836.*
Matching Arms: *EGYPT* OR *ANY EGYPTIAN ARMS*

for ELIZABETHAN BUSHEL MEASURE
see Appleby Elizabethan Bushel Measure

Model		With any Arms £ p	With Matching Arms £ p

ELIZABETHAN JUG   95mm [1]   38.50   55.00
(Goss Record. 8th Edition: Page 43)
Inscribed: *The Elizabethan Jug.*
This model is listed as Miscellaneous in *The Goss Record*
under the heading at the end of the listing of special
historical shapes, that is, it was available to any agent
but was stocked with matching arms by the Stratford
on-Avon agent. It is difficult to find this model in fine
condition as it is First Period; indeed it was one of the
first models issued and the gilding and enamels of the
coats of arms are invariably worn. Few large size
models can have been manufactured after 1895 when
the newer models with specific local connections
became so much more popular. Frequently found
impressed W.H. GOSS only, i.e. without the
Goshawk.
Matching Arms: *QUEEN ELIZABETH*

ELLESMERE ANCIENT BRITISH CANOE
(Goss Record. 8th Edition: Page 31)

(a) White glazed	Length	149mm	56.50	80.00
(b) Brownt	Length	149mm	250.00	

Inscribed: *Model of Ancient British Canoe dug out of*
Whattall Moss near Ellesmere in 1864. Now in
Ellesmere Museum. Rd. No. 559521.
This model is listed as bearing no arms in the 9th
Edition of *The Goss Record*. After 1921, a white glazed
version of this model was issued and it is more
commonly seen bearing a coat of arms.
Matching Arms: *ELLESMERE*

for ENGLISH WINE FLAGON
see London Christ's Hospital English Wine Flagon

ETON VASE   86mm   10.00   21.50
(Goss Record. 8th Edition: Page 16)
Inscribed: *Model of Ancient Vase dredged out of the Thames*
near Eton. Rd . No. 539422.
This model is identical to the Greenwich Vase
Matching Arms: *FLOREAT ETONA (ETON COLLEGE)*
OR *WINDSOR* where it was sold.

Model		With any Arms £ p	With Matching Arms £ p

EXETER FLEMISH GOBLET   (a) 130mm   22.00   33.00
(Goss Record. 8th Edition: Page 20)   (b) 130mm   35.00   65.00
Inscribed: *16th Century Goblet found in well in Cathedral
Close Exeter.*
Matching Arms: *(a) EXETER, CITY OF EXETER,
COUNTY OF EXETER, CITY & COUNTY OF EXETER*
OR *CITY & COUNTY OF THE CITY OF EXETER.*
It can also rarely be found inscribed: *Similar ones are to
be seen in the Steen Museum, Antwerpen*
Matching Arms: *(b) ANTWERPEN OR PROVINCIE
ANTWERPEN*

EXETER VASE   63mm   7.50   19.00
(Goss Record. 8th Edition: Page 20)   101mm   23.00   33.00
Inscribed: *The Exeter Vase from the original in the Museum.*
Matching Arms: *EXETER, CITY OF EXETER,
COUNTY OF EXETER, CITY & COUNTY OF EXETER*
OR *CITY & COUNTY OF THE CITY OF EXETER.*

for FARM LABOURER'S BOTTLE
see Luton Bottle

for FEEDING BOTTLE
see Wilderspool Roman Tetinae

FELIXSTOWE ROMAN CINERARY URN   47mm   12.00   38.50
(Goss Record. 8th Edition: Page 34)
Inscribed: *Model of Roman Cinerary Urn circa A.D. 200. Found
at Felixstowe From the original in the possession of S.D. Wall,
Walton, Felixstowe. Rd. No. 638375.*
Matching Arms: *FELIXSTOWE, FELIXSTOWE U.D.C.
OR FELIXSTOWE & WALTON U.D.C.*

FELIXSTOWE ROMAN EWER   73mm   9.50   30.00
(Goss Record. 8th Edition: Page 34)   114mm   22.00   34.00
Inscribed: **Model of Roman Ewer found at Felixstowe, now in
Ipswich Museum**.
Matching Arms: *FELIXSTOWE, FELIXSTOWE U.D.C.
OR FELIXSTOWE & WALTON U.D.C.*

FENNY STRATFORD POPPER   58mm   19.00   47.00
(Goss Record. 9th Edition: Page 11)
Inscribed: *Model of one of the six Fenny Stratford Poppers
which are fired annually on the Patronal Festival St. Martins
Day, November 11th. Founded about 1730. Copyright.*
Matching Arms: *FENNY STRATFORD*

Exeter Vase

Felixstowe Roman Ewer

Felixstowe Roman Cinerary Urn

Fenny Stratford Popper

Fimber Ancient British Cinerary Urn. League Model, 1928

(Old) Flemish Melk Pot

Folkestone Saltwood Roman Ewer

Fountains Abbey Abbot's Cup

Fourshire Stone

Fraser Cuach

Froxfield Roman Bronze Drinking Bowl

Gibraltar Alcaraza or Spanish Carafe

Model		With any Arms £ p	With Matching Arms £ p
FIMBER ANCIENT BRITISH CINERARY URN	106mm		220.00

FIMBER ANCIENT BRITISH CINERARY URN   106mm   220.00

Inscribed: *Model of Ancient British Cinerary Urn found
at Fimber. Copyright 1928. This model is only issued to Members
of the League and cannot be bought.*
International League Model for 1928
Correct Arms: *INTERNATIONAL LEAGUE OF
GOSS COLLECTORS*

FISH BASKET
Early versions uncrested and without usual flat
surface on front to receive Arms. Simply named
MODEL OF FISH BASKET   63mm   38.50
See also Alderney, Guernsey, Jersey, Sark, and Welsh
Fish Basket

for FLEMISH GOBLET
see Exeter Flemish Goblet

(OLD) FLEMISH MELK POT   Max. Dia. 118mm   28.50   47.00
(Goss Record. 8th Edition: Page 42)
Inscribed: *Model of old Flemish Melk Pot.
Rd. No. 574598.*
The name of this model is spelt as above in the 8th
Edition of *The Goss Record* (page 42) and on every
model produced by the Goss factory. Melk being
Flemish for milk, it is obviously correct. However,
it is incorrectly spelt milk in the 9th Edition
(page 37).
Matching Arms: *ANTWERPEN, PROVINCIE ANTWERPEN* OR *OSTENDE*

for FLOATING MINE
see Contact Mine

for FLOWER HOLDER
see 10K ORNAMENTAL

FOLKESTONE SALTWOOD ROMAN EWER   88mm[1]   15.00   22.50
(Goss Record. 8th Edition: Page 27)
Inscribed: *From original found at Saltwood, now in
Folkestone Museum.*
Matching Arms: *FOLKESTONE* OR
CINQUE PORT OF FOLKESTONE OR *HYTHE*

Model		With any Arms £ p	With Matching Arms £ p
FOUNTAINS ABBEY, ABBOT'S CUP	44mm	7.50	23.00
	76mml 1]	23.00	34.00

FOUNTAINS ABBEY, ABBOT'S CUP   44mm   7.50   23.00
(Goss Record. 8th Edition: Page 38)   76mml 1]   23.00   34.00
Inscribed: *The Abbots Cup from the original at*
Fountains Abbey.
Also see POSTCARDS Chapter 5.
Matching Arms: *FOUNTAINS ABBEY*

FOURSHIRE STONE   118mm   65.00   80.00
(Goss Record. 8th Edition: Page 31)
Impressed on front: *The Fourshire Stone, Worcestershire.*
Impressed on left side: *Gloucestershire.* Impressed on right
side: *Oxfordshire.* Impressed on back: *Warwickshire.* Inscribed
on back: *Model of the Fourshire Stone near Chipping Norton.*
This stone marks the spot where the counties of Gloucester,
Oxford, Warwick and Worcester meet
This model has a delicate finial particularly prone to damage.
Matching Arms: *CHIPPING NORTON*

FRASER (FORT AUGUSTUS) CUACH   Length   104mm   21.00   55.00
(Goss Record. 9th Edition: Page 35)
Inscribed: *Model of Highland Cuach in possession of the*
Frazers at Fort Augustus. Rd. No. 633433.
Matching Arms: *LORD LOVAT*, who is head of the Fraser clan,
any other Highland arms are considered a good match.

for FRID STOL
see Hexham Abbey Frid Stol

FROXFIELD ROMAN BRONZE
DRINKING BOWL   Dia. 72mm   47.00   65.00
(Goss Record. 8th Edition: Page 36)
Inscribed: *Model of Roman Bronze Drinking Bowl found at*
Rudge near Froxfield, Wilts. A.D. 1725.
This model was originally sold without arms and
subsequently with those of MARLBOROUGH which are
considered matching.

HUNGERFORD ? [handwritten annotation]

for GERMAN INCENDIARY BOMB
see Maldon (Essex) German Incendiary Bomb

Model			With any Arms £ p	With Matching Arms £ p

GERMAN SMOKING PIPE

(*The Goss Record* 7th Edition 1910-11, page 56)

Although manufactured as an ornamental object, it merits inclusion in this section as an historic object or special shape. It consists of a wooden stem with a black Bakelite mouthpiece, a porcelain bowl and separate porcelain pipe, which bears the coat of arms. All these parts are joined by push-fitting into cork rings.

This must be one of the first examples of the use of bakelite which was invented by Leo Baekeland in 1909.

Matching Arms: *FRANCO-BRITISH EXHIBITION* 1908 for which it was first made. Also any *GERMAN* arms could be considered appropriate.

	Overall Length			
	252mm		77.00	115.00

for GERMAN ZEPPELIN BOMB

see Bury St. Edmunds German Bomb

GERRANS CELTIC CINERARY URN

(Goss Record. 8th Edition: Page 18)

Inscribed: *Model of Celtic Cinerary Urn found at Gerrans, Cornwall.*

With 1 coat of arms	57mm		10.50	17.00
With 1 coat of arms	127mm[1]		14.50	30.00
With 3 coats of arms	57mm		15.50	24.50
With 3 coats of arms	127mm[1]		23.00	38.50

Matching Arms: *PORTSCATHO* OR *FALMOUTH (LOCAL)*

GIBRALTAR ALCARAZA or
SPANISH CARAFE

(Goss Record. 8th Editiom Page 42)

Inscribed: *Model of Spanish Alcaraza from Gibraltar. Rd. No. 449120.*

This model can also be found inscribed Gibraltar Carafe and is identical to the Canary Porron

Matching Arms: *GIBRALTAR* OR *SPAIN*

	68mm		7.50	30.00

Glastonbury collectors should see the impressive two page advertisement in the Goss Record. 8th Edition: Pages 80-81

Where Glastonbury models carry matching arms, they are almost always inscribed on the base of the piece: *Arms of Glastonbury* or *Borough of Glastonbury* under the same arms.

German Smoking Pipe

Gerrans Celtic Cinerary Urn

Glastonbury (Abbot Beere's) Jack

Glastonbury Bronze Bowl

Glastonbury Vase

Glastonbury Roman Ewer

Glastonbury Ancient Salt Cellar

Glastonbury Terracotta Bowl

Gloucester Jug

Gnossus Ashmolean Vase League Model, 1920

Godalming Ancient Ewer

Gravesend Oriental Water Cooler

218

Model		With any Arms £ p	With Matching Arms £ p

GLASTONBURY (ABBOT BEERE'S) JACK 56mm 7.50 23.00
(Goss Record. 8th Edition: Page 32)
Inscribed: *Model of Abbot Beere's Jack from carving on*
St. Benedict's Church, Glastonbury. Rd. No. 382436.
Matching Arms: *ARMS OF GLASTONBURY (five versions)*

GLASTONBURY ANCIENT SALT CELLAR 82mm 21.00 42.50
(Goss Record. 8th Edition: Page 32)
Inscribed: *Model of Ancient Salt Cellar in Glastonbury*
Museum. Rd. No. 605731.
Matching Arms: *ARMS OF GLASTONBURY (five versions)*

GLASTONBURY BRONZE BOWL
(Goss Record. 8th Edition: Page 31)
Inscribed: *Model of Bronze Bowl from the Ancient British*
Lake Village near Glastonbury.
The largest version can be found with or without three
ball feet, and earlier models can be found uncrested.
One only example has been recorded in the smallest size
without ball feet. A small advertising leaflet was sold
with this model, see page 59.

Dia. (overall) 65mm Height 35mm		17.00	30.00
Dia. (overall) 127mm Height 80mm [1]		47.00	77.50

Matching Arms: *ARMS OF GLASTONBURY (five versions).*

GLASTONBURY ROMAN EWER 71mm 7.50 22.50
(Goss Record. 8th Edition: Page 32)
Inscribed: *Model of Ancient Roman Ewer found near*
Glastonbury. Rd. No. 382438.
Matching Arms: *ARMS OF GLASTONBURY (five versions).*

GLASTONBURY TERRACOTTA BOWL 36mm 7.50 19.00
(Goss Record. 8th Edition: Page 31)
Inscribed: *Model of Bowl from the Ancient British Lake*
Village near Glastonbury.
Matching Arms: *ARMS OF GLASTONBURY (five versions).*

GLASTONBURY VASE 45mm 7.50 21.50
(Goss Record. 8th Edition: Page 31)
Inscribed: *Model of Vase from the Ancient British Lake*
Village near Glastonbury.
Matching Arms: *ARMS OF GLASTONBURY (five versions).*

for GLEN DORGAL CINERARY URN
see Truro Glen Dorgal Cinerary Urn

Model		With any Arms £ p	With Matching Arms £ p
GLOUCESTER JUG	44mm	7.50	19.00
(Goss Record. 8th Edition: Page 22)	95mm[1]	19.50	28.50

GLOUCESTER JUG
Inscribed: *The Gloucester Jug from original in Museum.*
Matching Arms: *GLOUCESTER ANCIENT* OR *MODERN*

GNOSSUS ASHMOLEAN VASE	60mm		150.00

(Goss Record. 9th Edition: Pages 22,41 and Plate C)
Inscribed: *Model of Ancient Vase from Gnossus No. 110 in Ashmolean Museum. Issued to Members only & cannot be purchased. Copyright.*
International league model for 1920.
Correct Arms: *INTERNATIONAL LEAGUE OF
     GOSS COLLECTORS*

GODALMING ANCIENT EWER	55mm	17.00	47.00

(Goss Record. 8th Edition: Page 34)
Inscribed: *Model of Ancient Ewer found on Charterhouse Hill, Godalming, 31/3/1904, now in the museum. Rd . No . 630511.*
Matching Arms: *GODALMING* OR *CHARTERHOUSE*

for GOGARTH ANCIENT VASE
see Llandudno (Gogarth) Ancient Vase

GOODWIN SANDS CARAFE	61mm	7.50	12.00

(Goss Record. 8th Edition: Page 27)
Inscribed: *Model of Ancient Carafe dredged off Goodwin Sands.*
Matching Arms: *BROADSTAIRS, DEAL, MARGATE, RAMSGATE,* OR *WALMER*

GRAVESEND ORIENTAL WATER COOLER	72mm	21.50	47.00

Inscribed: *Model of Ancient Water Cooler found at Gravesend, from the original in Gravesend Public Library. Copyright.*
Matching Arms: *GRAVESEND*

(THE) GREAT PYRAMID	60mm	80.00	100.00

(Goss Record. 8th Edition: Page 42)
Inscribed: *Model of the Great Pyramid at Gizeh, Near Cairo, Egypt. Rd. No. 602907.*
Could be considered as a Monument or Building often found chipped at the corners.
Matching Arms: *EGYPT* OR *ANY EGYPTIAN ARMS*, particularly *SAKKARA*

Model			With any Arms £ p	With Matching Arms £ p

GREEK AMPHORA VASE   138mm   190.00
(Goss Record 9th Edition: Page 40 and Plate A)
Inscribed: *Model of Greek Amphora Vase (circa 350 B.C.)*
which was given f illed with oil as a prize in the
Panathenaic Games. This model is only issued to Members of the
League and cannot be bought.
International league model for 1921.
Correct Arms: *INTERNATIONAL LEAGUE OF*
   GOSS COLLECTORS

GREENWICH VASE   86mm   55.00
Inscribed: *Model of Ancient Vase found in Greenwich Park*
and of a similar one dredged out of the Thames, near Eton.
Rd. No. 539422.
This model, which is uncommon, is exactly the
same as the Eton Vase as stated on the base.
It can only be found with matching arms.
Matching Arms: *GREENWICH* OR *GREENWICH ANCIENT*

GRINLOW TOWER   95mm   160.00   300.00
Inscribed: *Model of Grinlow Tower (known as*
Soloman's Temple) . The building was erected by public
subscription and stands on the site of a prehistoric barrow
explored in 1894. Copyright.
Probably the rarest white glazed Tower.
Matching Arms: *BUXTON*

GUERNSEY FISH BASKET
(Goss Record. 8th Edition: Page 17)   45mm   19.00   38.50
Inscribed: *Guernsey Fish Basket.*   Length 104mm   58mm   30.00   47.00
(With outpressed shield)   Length 116mm 58mm[1]   35.00   85.00
Matching Arms: *GUERNSEY*

GUERNSEY MILK CAN and lid   70mm   25.00
(Goss Record. 9th Edition: Page 11)   108mm   20.00   55.00
Inscribed: *Model of Guernsey Milk Can*   140mm   25.00   65.00
This model is incomplete without its lid,
value £15.00 in all three sizes.
Matching Arms: *GUERNSEY*

GUILDFORD ROMAN VASE   63mm   17.00   28.50
(Goss Record. 8th Edition: Page 34)
Inscribed: *Model of Roman Vase in Surrey Archaeological*
Museum, Guildford. Rd. No. 602904.
Matching Arms: *GUILDFORD* OR *GUILDFORD ANCIENT*

Goodwin Sands Carafe

*Greek Amphora Vase
League Model, 1921*

The Great Pyramid

Greenwich Vase

Grinlow Tower

Guernsey Fish Basket

Guernsey Milk Can and Lid

Guildford Roman Vase

*Guillemot Egg, pointed end
and closed*

*Guy's Porridge Pot;
inscription on base or side*

*Guy's Porridge Pot (identical
to small Irish Bronze Pot*

Haamoga Amaui, Tonga

Model			With any Arms £ p	With Matching Arms £ p

GUILLEMOT EGG (a) Coloured, Open   83mm   115.00
Found closed, or open as (b) Coloured, Closed   93mm   115.00
hanging posy vase either (c) White, unglazed, Closed 96mm   85.00
with or without arms, none of which may be considered
matching. It is however preferable to have the arms of a
coastal town. Found in different speckled colours with
the ground usually of blue, brown, green, beige or pink.
See also BIRD'S EGG, FIRST PERIOD 9C ORNAMENTAL

GUY'S PORRIDGE POT   (a) 50mm   15.00   23.00
(Goss Record. 8th Edition: Page 35)   (b) 50mm   47.00
Inscribed, usually on the side together with the Goshawk:
Model of Guy's Porridge Pot in Warwick Castle Rd. No. 413579.
for version (a), *Model of Guy's Porridge Pot* in Gothic script on
the side of version (b).
Matching Arms: *WARWICK* OR *SEAL OF WARWICK*

GUY'S PORRIDGE POT   40mm   80.00
Better known as a small Irish Bronze Pot but named *Guy's
Porridge Pot* in large Gothic script on side. Only one example has
been seen with the arms of Stratford-on-Avon.

HAAMOGA AMAUI, TONGA   Length 106mm Height 82mm   700.00   2150.00
Inscribed: *Model of Haamoga Amaui Tonga. Copyright.
Made in England.*
This trilithon has a bowl-shaped depression on the top of the lintel
stone to catch the sun's rays. Correctly, it is the locally named
Ha'amonga-'a-Maui, believed to date from 1200 A.D .
The model was made for the Goss agent in Tonga, and only four
examples with the Tonga crest are now known to exist.
An example has been seen with the Blackpool arms and the base
glazed, and shards have been found in the factory spoilheap.
Matching Arms: *TONGA*

HAFOD GREEK VASE and lid   82mm   70.00   80.00
Inscribed: *Model of Greek Vase in Hafod Church near Devil's
Bridge. Copyright.*
The lid has a knob on top which tends to get chipped.
Can be found also with a brown or black transfer of
DEVIL'S BRIDGE - the matching arms value of which
is given here as there are no correct arms.
An undated leaflet gave Goss souvenir china among the list of items
available at "the picturesque little rustic hut" at the exit from the
waterfalls, so that perhaps the proprietor of Devil's Bridge Hotel
held the Goss agency, some time after 1902 when the railway
was built.
Both the lid and the base are worth £35.00 each.

Model		With any Arms £ p	With Matching Arms £ p

HAMBLEDON CRICKET STONE   Grey 80mm†   1250.00
(Goss Record.9th Edition: Page 16)
Inscribed on front: *This Stone marks the site of the Ground
of the Hambledon Cricket Club circ. 1760-1787.*

HAMWORTHY LAMP   Length 100mm   12.00   24.50
(Goss Record. 8th Edition: Page 21)   Width   65mm
Inscribed: *Model of Ancient Lamp found at Lake Clay
Pits, Hamworthy, Poole. Rd. No. 489579.*
Matching Arms: *POOLE*

HARROGATE ANCIENT EWER   62mm   7.50   22.50
(Goss Record. 8th Edition: page 38)
Inscribed: *Model of Ancient Ewer found at Aldborough Park,
Harrogate. Rd. No. 639837.*
Matching Arms: HARROGATE

HASTINGS KETTLE   51mm   7.50   12.50
(Goss Record. 8th Edition: Page 34)
Inscribed: *Model of Ancient Kettle dredged up off
Hastings, 1873. In Hastings Museum.*
Matching Arms: *HASTINGS* OR *SEAL OF HASTINGS*

HAWES ANCIENT BRITISH URN   Dia. 95mm   24.00   38.50
(Goss Record. 8th Edition: Page 38)
Inscribed: *Model of Ancient British Urn found near Aysgill
Force, Hawes, 1897. Rd. No. 517520.*
This model has two pairs of small holes on its underside.
Matching Arms: *HAWES*

each   each
HAWKINS HENLEY SCULL   Length 152mm   65.00   85.00
(Goss Record. 9th Edition: Page 25)
Inscribed: *Hawkins Famous Henley Scull as used in the
Diamonds Henley Royal Regatta. Rd. No. 636992.*
The sculls are usually seen with either of the
two Henley coats of arms. Although
Kingston-upon-thames has also been recorded.
The local agent had presentation boxes made to sell them
individually, or, more commonly, in pairs.
The correct box is worth an additional £50.00.
Matching Arms: *HENLEY-ON-THAMES ANCIENT* OR
HENLEY- ON-THAMES 1624

for HEN CLOUD LEEK URN
see Leek Urn

Model			With any Arms £ p	With Matching Arms £ p

for HENLEY HAWKINS SCULL
see Hawkins Henley Scull

HEREFORD TERRACOTTA KETTLE and lid   70mm   22.50   47.00
(Goss Record. 8th Edition: Page 24 and   121mm[1]   38.50   57.50
advertisement page 66)
Inscribed: *Model of Old Terra Cotta Kettle in Hereford*
Museum.
This model is incomplete without its lid, worth
£10.00 small and £20.00 large of the prices shown
Matching Arms: *HEREFORD*

HERNE BAY RECULVER TOWERS
(Goss Record. 8th Edition: Page 27)
Inscribed: *Model of Reculver Towers.*
Rd. No. 639536.

	(a) White glazed	101mm	82.50	140.00
	(b) Grey†	101mm	240.00	
	(c) Brown†	101mm	275.00	

Matching Arms: *HERNE BAY*

HERNE BAY ANCIENT EWER   78mm   7.50   17.00
(Goss Record. 8th Edition: Page 27)
Inscribed: *Model of Ancient Ewer found in brickfield, Herne Bay.*
Rd. No. 559523.
Matching Arms: *HERNE BAY*

HERTFORD ANCIENT EWER   69mm   17.00   34.00
(Goss Record. 8th Edition: Page 24)
Inscribed: *Model of Ancient Ever in Hertford Museum.*
Rd. No. 617574.
Matching Arms: *ARMS OF HERTFORD*

HEXHAM ABBEY FRID STOL   (a) White unglazed 60mm   38.50   55.00
(Goss Record. 8th Edition: Page 30)   (b) White glazed   60mm   30.00   55.00
     (c) Brown   60mm   40.00   55.00
     (d) Brown, two-   60mm   85.00   120.00
         piece as pin box
         and lid
Inscribed: *Model of Ancient Frid Stol in Hexham Abbey,*
Northumberland.
Each of the three basic versions of this model can be
found both with and without a coat of arms, and
occasionally in the original box in which they were
sold labelled: *Model of Saxon Sanctuary Chair in Hexham Abbey*, and
the Agent's name: *Gibson & Son Hexham.*
Matching Arms: *HEXHAM ABBEY*

Haford Vase and Lid

Hambledon Cricket Stone

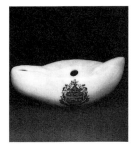

Hamworthy Lamp

Harrogate Ancient Ewer

Hastings Kettle

Hawes Ancient British Urn

*Hawkins Henley Sculls in
Presentation Box*

*Hereford Terracotta Kettle
and Lid*

Herne Bay Reculver Towers

Herne Bay Ancient Ewer

Hertford Ancient Ewer

Hexham Abbey Frid Stol

Model		With any Arms £ p	With Matching Arms £ p

for HIGHLAND CUACH or WHISKEY CUP
see National Highland Cuach or Whiskey Cup

for HIGHLAND MILK CROGAN
see Stornoway Highway Milk Crogan

HITCHIN POSSET CUP   51 mm   16.00   33.00
(Goss Record. 8th Edition: Page 24)
Inscribed: *Model of Ancient Posset Cup found at Hitchin.*
Rd. No. 521971.
Matching Arms: *HITCHIN*

HORNSEA ATWICK ROMAN VASE   51mm   10.50   34.00
(Goss Record. 8th Edition: Page 38)
Inscribed: *Model of Roman Vase found at Atwick near*
Hornsea. Rd. No. 500864.
Matching Arms: *HORNSEA*

(THE OLD) HORSE SHOE   115mm   21.50
(Goss Record. 8th Edition: Page 43)
Inscribed on front: *The Old Horse Shoe*
May the good old shoe bring luck to you!
Good health and sweet content:
And may your path be ever blessed .
With peace from Heaven sent. Jno. Crowther.
And on the reverse:
The Legend. The Horse Shoe has long been regarded
as of great potency against evil . All Europe believes,
in a more or less degree, that the hanging up of a Horse
Shoe in the home is significant of Good Luck.
All the Kings of old up to the 13th Century carried out
the custom of having a Horse Shoe hung on the entrance
of the Palace. When the great St. Dunstan was asked to
shoe the hoof of Evil the One, he bound him up so fast, and
so tortured him, that he had to promise he would never
enter a doorway over which a Horse Shoe was hung.
Lord Nelson, England's greatest Admiral, had a Horse
Shoe nailed to the Victory. Copyright.

This model is classified under the heading Miscellaneous at the end of
the special historical shapes list in the 9th Edition of *The Goss Record.*
If the decoration is large, the descriptive matter is printed on the
reverse. It has no matching arms, but those of *PORTSMOUTH* OR
ADMIRAL LORD NELSON are preferable.

Hitchin Posset Cup

Hornsea Atwick Roman Vase

(The Old) Horse Shoe

Horsham Jug

Hunstanton Ewer

Hythe Cromwellian Mortar

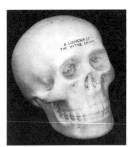

Hythe Crypt Skull

Ilkley Roman Ewer

Ipswich Ancient Ewer

Ipswich Roman Ewer

Irish Bronze Pot

(Ancient) Irish Cruisken League Model, 1929

Model		With any Arms £ p	With Matching Arms £ p

HORSHAM JUG   60mm   7.50   25.00
(Goss Record. 8th Edition: Page 34)
Inscribed: *Model of Mediaeval Jug in Brighton Museum
found at Horsham.*
Matching Arms: *HORSHAM*

HUNSTANTON EWER   65mm   7.50   26.00
(Goss Record. 8th Edition: Page 29)
Inscribed: *Model of Ancient Ewer found on Hunstanton Estate.
Rd. No. 495669.*
Matching Arms: *HUNSTANTON ST EDMUNDS*

HYTHE CROMWELLIAN MORTAR   38mm   9.00   16.50
(Goss Record. 8th Edition: Page 27)
Inscribed: *Model of Cromwellian Mortar found at Hythe.
Rd. No. 590790.*
Matching Arms: *HYTHE* OR *CINQUE PORT OF HYTHE*

HYTHE CRYPT SKULL
(Goss Record. 9th Edition: Page 20)
Inscribed: *A Souvenir of the Hythe Crypt.*
                 (a) Small pale yellow†   38mm   75.00
                 (b) Large white†   72mm   110.00
                 (c) Large pale yellow†   72mm   190.00

ILKLEY ROMAN EWER   60mm   7.50   25.00
(Goss Record. 8th Edition: Page 38)   132mm   27.50   47.00
Inscribed: *Model of Roman Ewer in Ilkley Museum.
Rd. No. 489582.*
Matching Arms: *ILKLEY*

IPSWICH ANCIENT EWER   60mm   25.00   22.50
(Goss Record. 8th Edition: Page 34)
Inscribed: *Model of Ancient Ewer dug up in Ipswich
now in Museum. Rd. No. 553188.*
Matching Arms: *IPSWICH*

IPSWICH ROMAN EWER   98mm   25.00   55.00
(Goss Record. 8th Edition: Page 34)
Inscribed: *Model of Roman Ewer dug up in Ipswich now in
Museum.*
Matching Arms: *IPSWICH*

Model		With any Arms £ p	With Matching Arms £ p
IRISH BRONZE POT	43mm	7.50	21.50
(Goss Record. 8th Edition: Page 40)	72mm	22.50	34.00

Inscribed: *Model of Ancient Irish Bronze Pot.*
Matching Arms: *ARMS OF IRELAND* OR *ANY IRISH ARMS*

(ANCIENT) IRISH CRUISKEN	95mm		235.00

Inscribed: *Model of Ancient Irish Cruisken. Copyright 1929.*
This model is issued to Members of the League and cannot be
bought.
International league Model for 1929
Correct Arms: *INTERNATIONAL LEAGUE OF*
    GOSS COLLECTORS

IRISH MATHER	76mm	12.00	22.00
(Goss Record. 8th Edition: multi crested	152mm	55.00	77.50

Page 40 and advertisement page 61)
Inscribed: *Model of Irish Mather or Wooden Drinking Cup in*
Dorset County Museum.
See also chapter 5 POSTCARDS
The large size is usually multi-crested and often carries a verse.
The original of this model is in Dorset County
Museum, Dorchester and was chosen by the Dorchester
agent as a local model (see *Goss Record*
8th Edition page 61) Dorchester could therefore
possibly be considered being correct arms for this model.
Matching Arms: *ARMS OF IRELAND* OR *ANY IRISH ARMS*

IRISH WOODEN NOGGIN	63mm	12.00	21.50

(Goss Record. 8th Edition: Page 40)
Inscribed: *Model of Ancient Irish Wooden Noggin. Rd . No.*
489580.
Matching Arms: *ARMS OF IRELAND* OR *ANY IRISH ARMS*

for ISLE OF WIGHT ROMAN EVER
see Brading Roman Ewer

ITALIAN KRATER	100mm		140.00

Inscribed: *Model of Italian Krater from the original*
in British Museum. This model is only issued to Members
of the League and cannot be bought.
International league Model for 1922.
Correct Arms: *INTERNATIONAL LEAGUE OF*
    GOSS COLLECTORS

Model		With any Arms £ p	With Matching Arms £ p

ITFORD LEWES URN   66mm   8.50   27.50
(Goss Record. 8th Edition: Page 35)   [l]mm[l]   25.00   55.00
Inscribed: *Model of British Urn found at Itford near*
Lewes. Rd. No. 573577.
Matching Arms: *LEWES*

JAPAN EWER   90mm   14.00   30.00
(Goss Record. 8th Edition: Page 42)   200mm[1]   30.00   55.00
Inscribed: *The Japan Ewer.*
Both sizes are found named and unnamed,
same price
Matching Arms: *JAPAN*
See also FIRST PERIOD 9C ORNAMENTAL

JERSEY FISH BASKET   45mm   17.00   25.00
(Goss Record. 8th Edition: Page 17)   60mm[1]   30.00   55.00
Inscribed: *Jersey Fish Basket*
This model can also be found without a coat of arms and
no flat area to receive a decoration, but this has little or no
bearing on the price.
Matching Arms: *JERSEY*

JERSEY MILK CAN and lid   70mm   25.00
(Goss Record. 9th Editiom Page 11)   108mm   25.00   47.00
Inscribed: *Model of Jersey Milk Can*   150mm   30.00   47.00
This model is incomplete without its lid
which is worth £ 15.00 in all three sizes
Matching Arms: *JERSEY*

for JOHN BARROW'S MONUMENT
see Sir John Barrow's Monument, Ulverston

KENDAL JUG   86mm   12.00   30.00
(Goss Record. 8th Edition: Page 36)   145mm[1]   34.00   60.00
Inscribed: *Model of Jug in Kendal Museum dated 1602.*
Matching Arms: *SEAL OF KENDAL AND ARMS OF KIRKBY-KENDAL 1575*

KETTERING URN   43mm   7.50   25.00
(Goss Record. 8th Edition: Page 30)
Inscribed: *Model of Ancient Urn found at Kettering now in*
Northampton Museum. Rd. No. 543008.
Matching Arms: *KETTERING*

for KING ALFRED'S STATUE
See THIRD PERIOD 11.0 BUILDINGS AND MONUMENTS

Irish Mather 152mm

Irish Wooden Noggin

Italian Krater
League Model, 1922

Itford Lewis Urn

Japan Ewer

Jersey Fish Basket

Jersey Milk Can and Lid

Kendal Jug

Kettering Urn

King Richard's Well Cover

King's Newton Anglo-Saxon
Cinerary Urn. League Model

Kininmonth Moss Ancient Pot

Model		With any Arms £ p	With Matching Arms £ p

KING RICHARD'S WELL COVER   100mm   160.00   245.00
(Goss Record. 9th Edition: Page 21)
Inscribed: *Model of structure covering King Richard's Well on*
Bosworth Field. Copyright.
Translation of inscription: *With water drawn from this well*
Richard 111 King of England, assuaged his thirst (when)
fighting in the most desperate and hostile manner with Henry,
Earl of Richmond, and about to lose before night his life,
together with his sceptre. August 22. (O.S.) A.D. 1485.
Matching Arms: *MARKET BOSWORTH*

KING'S NEWTON ANGLO SAXON
CINERARY URN   (a) 60mm   115.00
(Goss Record. 9th Edition: Pages 22, 41 and   (b) 60mm   140.00
Plate B)
Inscribed: *Model of Anglo-Saxon Urn found at*
King's Newton. Copyright. This is only issued to Members of
more than 6 years standing & cannot be purchased.
This model was first introduced bearing THE LEAGUE
OF GOSS COLLECTORS motif (a), and re-introduced
later bearing the INTERNATIONAL LEAGUE OF GOSS
COLLECTORS motif (b) .

KININMONTH MOSS ANCIENT POT   49mm   21.50   55.00
(Goss Record. 9th Edition: Page 35 and Plate M)
Inscribed: *Model of Ancient Moss Pot dug out of Kininmonth*
Moss near Old Deer in 1855. Copyright
Matching Arms: *OLD DEER*

for KIRKPARK URN
see Musselburgh Urn

LANCASHIRE CLOG   Length 93mm   47.00   77.50
(Goss Record. 9th Edition: Page 21)
Inscribed: *Model of Lancashire Clog. Copyright.*
Matching Arms: *LANCASHIRE* OR ANY *LANCASHIRE ARMS*

LANCASTER JUG   68mm   7.50   34.00
(Goss Record. 8th Edition: Page 27)
Inscribed: *Model of Ancient Jug in Lancaster Museum.*
Rd. No. 500863.
Matching Arms: *LANCASTER* OR *COUNTY PALATINE OF LANCASTER*

for LANDGATE CANNON BALL
see Rye Cannon Ball

Lancashire Clog

Lancaster Jug

Lanlawren Celtic Sepulchral Urn

(Battle of) Largs Memorial Tower

Las Palmas Ancient Covered Jarra and Lid

Las Palmas Ancient Earthen Jar

Las Palmas Ancient Jarra

Laxey Gretch-Veg Urn

Leek Urn

Leicester Tyg

Leiston Abbey Pitcher

Lewes Roman Vase

234

Model			With any Arms £ p	With Matching Arms £ p

for LANDS END, LONGSHIPS LIGHTHOUSE
see Longships lighthouse Lands End.

LANLAWREN CELTIC SEPULCHRAL URN

50mm	7.50	20.00
102mm[1]	22.00	28.50

(Goss Record. 8th Edition: Page 18)
Inscribed: *Model of Celtic Sepulchral Urn, found at
Lanlawren, Cornwall.*
There are no correct arms for this model, but any
Cornish arms would be considered as local. Lanlawren is
near Fowey and this must, therefore, be considered
the correct arms, although *The Goss Record* does not give
any particular agency as being stockists of this model.
Matching Arms: *FOWEY*

(BATTLE OF) LARGS MEMORIAL TOWER
(Goss Record. 8th Edition: Page 40)

(a) White glazed	128mm	35.00	47.50
(b) Grey glazed	128mm	320.00	

Inscribed: *Model of Battle of Largs
Memorial Tower. Rd. No. 610012.*
Matching Arms: *LARGS*

LAS PALMAS ANCIENT COVERED JARRA and lid   58mm   15.00   38.50
(Goss Record. 8th Edition: Page 42)
Inscribed: *Model of Ancient Covered Jarra in Museum
Las Palmas Grand Canary. Rd. No. 572205.*
This model is incomplete without its lid, value £8.00
Matching Arms: *LAS PALMAS, GRAND CANARY*

LAS PALMAS ANCIENT EARTHEN JAR   58mm   14.00   25.00
(Goss Record. 8th Edition: Page 42)
Inscribed: *Model of Ancient Earthen Jar in Museum
Las Palmas Grand Canary. Rd. No. 610010.*
Matching Arms: *LAS PALMAS, GRAND CANARY*

LAS PALMAS ANCIENT JARRA   53mm   14.00   28.50
(Goss Record. 8th Edition: Page 42)
Inscribed: *Model of Ancient Jarra in Museum Las Palmas
Grand Canary. Rd. No. 572204.*
Matching Arms: *LAS PALMAS, GRAND CANARY*

for LAS PALMAS CANARY PORRON
see Canary Porron

Model of Roman Cinerary Urn 120-140 AD in Letchworth Museum. Copyright 83mm Very rare.

Model			With any Arms £ p	With Matching Arms £ p

LAXEY GRETCH-VEG URN   Dia. 55mm   12.00   30.00
(Goss Record. 9th Edition: Page 19)
Inscribed: *Model of Ancient Urn found on Gretch-Veg near*
Laxey 1. O.M. Rd. No. 489581.
This model can be found bearing arms on the base (on
the inside) or in the usual position on the outside.
Matching Arms: *LAXEY, ISLE OF MAN.*

for LEEK
see Welsh Leek

LEEK URN   63mm   12.00   30.00
(Goss Record. 8th Edition: Page 32)
Inscribed: *Model of British Urn found at Hen Cloud Near*
Leek. Rd. No. 500865.
Matching Arms: *LEEK, STAFFS*

LEICESTER TYG   (a) I coat of arms   59mm   12.00   21.50
(Goss Record. 8th Edn: Page28)   (b) 3 coats of arms   59mm   20.00   33.00
Inscribed: *Model of Tyg found in Highcross Street*
1867 now in Leicester Museum. Rd. No. 495670.
Matching Arms: *LEICESTER OR CITY OF LEICESTER*

LEISTON ABBEY PITCHER   61mm   7.50   23.50
(Goss Record. 8th Edition: Page 34)   107mm   28.50   55.00
Inscribed: *Model of Pitcher in Ipswich Museum found at*
Leiston Abbey.
Matching Arms: *LEISTON ABBEY*

LETCHWORTH CELTIC CINERARY URN   97mm   55.00   77.50
(Goss Record. 9th Edition: Page 19 and Plate J)
Inscribed: *Model of late Celtic Cinerary Urn in Letchworth*
Museum found in 1912 Copyright.
Matching Arms: *LETCHWORTH*

LETCHWORTH ROMAN CARINATED VASE   60mm   85.00   200.00
Inscribed: *Model of Roman Carinated Vase 120-140 A.D. in*
Letchworth Museum. Copyright.
Matching Arms: *LETCHWORTH*

LETCHWORTH ROMAN CINERARY URN   83mm   375.00   550.00
Inscribed: *Model of Roman Cinerary Urn 120-140 AD.*
in Letchworth Museum Copyright.
Matching Arms: *LETCHWORTH*

Lincoln Leather Jack. Matt black with multi coloured bells and pale brown rim, base and handle 153mm.

Model		With any Arms £ p	With Matching Arms £ p

LETCHWORTH ROMAN VASE   86mm   375.00   550.00
Inscribed: *Model of Roman Vase, late first century in*
Letchworth Museum Copyright
Matching Arms: *LETCHWORTH*

LEWES ROMAN VASE   35mm[1]   7.50   21.50
(Goss Record. 8th Edition: Page 35)
Inscribed: *Model of Roman Vase in Lewes Castle.*
Matching Arms: *LEWES*

for LEWES URN
see Itford Urn

for LHANNAN SHEE CUP
see Ballafletcher (Cup of)

LICHFIELD JUG   60mm   7.50   21.50
(Goss Record. 8th Edition: Page 32)   121mm[1] 25.00   38.50
Inscribed: *Model of Ancient Jug dug out of the*
foundations of Lichfield Museum.
Matching Arms: *CITY OF LICHFIELD*

for LIMPET SHELL
see SECOND PERIOD 10K5 ORNAMENTAL and
FIRST PERIOD 9C ORNAMENTAL Chapters.

LINCOLN LEATHER JACK
(Goss Record. 8th Edition: Page 28)
Inscribed: *Model of Lincoln Jack. This Jack was the gift of*
Alderman Bullen to the Company of Ringers. (a) and (c), with
the addition of: *1782 City Ringers* on (b), (d) and (e)
   (a) White glazed   56mm   12.00   25.00
   (b) Correct marking-coloured bell and shield, no arms 56mm   77.50
   (c) White glazed   153mm   27.50   47.00
   (d) White glazed, brown trim, blue and red shields
       on white glazed ground   153mm   800.00
   (e) Matt black with multi-coloured bells, no arms 153mm   1100.00
Matching Arms: *CITY OF LINCOLN* OR *ANCIENT ARMS OF LINCOLN*

LINCOLN VASE   67mm   8.50   21.50
(Goss Record. 8th Edition: Page 28)   88mm   17.00   28.50
Inscribed: *The Lincoln Vase, from Original at Cathedral.*
Matching Arms: *CITY OF LINCOLN* OR *ANCIENT ARMS OF LINCOLN*

Letchworth Roman Carinated Vase

Letchworth Celtic Cinerary Urn

Letchworth Roman Vase

Lichfield Jug

Lincoln Leather Jack, small with City Ringers Decoration

Lincoln Vase

Littlehampton Roman Ewer

Llandudno (Little Orme) Roman Vase

Llandudno (Gogarth) Ancient Ewer

Llangollen or Welsh Coracle

Lobster Trap

London Christ's Hospital English Wine Flagon

240

Model		With any Arms £ p	With Matching Arms £ p

LITTLEHAMPTON ROMAN EWER   73mm   10.00   21.50
(Goss Record. 8th Edition: Page 35)
Inscribed: *Model of Roman Ewer found when pulling down houses in Arundel Road, Littlehampton. Rd. No. 521977.*
Matching Arms: *LITTLEHAMPTON*

LLANDUDNO (LITTLE ORME) ROMAN VASE   82mm   17.00   35.00
(Goss Record. 9th Edition: Page 34 and Plate K)
Inscribed: *Model of Roman Vase found on the Little Orme, Llandudno 17/Dec/19. Copyright.*
Matching Arms: *LLANDUDNO*

LLANDUDNO (GOGARTH) ANCIENT VASE   84mm   17.00   30.00
(Goss Record. 9th Edition: Page 34 and Plate K)
Inscribed: *Model of Vase found at Gogarth, Marine Drive Llandudno. Copyright.*
Matching Arms: *LLANDUDNO*

LLANGOLLEN CORACLE   Length 77mm   21.50   37.50
(Goss Record. 8th Edition: Page 39 and advertisement page 101)
Inscribed on base or on seat: *Model of Llangollen Coracle. Survival of Ancient British wicker and hide boats.*
Matching Arms: *LLANGOLLEN*
Up until 1903, the Welsh Coracle was so called and listed in *The Goss Record* as a national model having no particular town or city arms . From 1904 onwards, it was re-named The Llangollen Coracle, with Llangollen given as the matching arms, which explains the confusion of the two descriptions that can be found on the same piece.
See also WELSH CORACLE

LOBSTER TRAP   50mm   17.00   34.00
(Goss Record. 8th Edition: Page 17)   84mm[1]   34.00   47.00
Inscribed: *Model of Lobster Trap.*
Matching Arms: *ANY OF THE CHANNEL ISLANDS (ALDERNEY, GUERNSEY, JERSEY, SARK)* OR *BOGNOR.*
The smaller size and Second Period larger size have a flat background to receive the coat of arms, but earlier First Period examples have the decoration applied directly to the moulded surface.

Model			With any Arms £ p	With Matching Arms £ p

LONDON CHRIST'S HOSPITAL ENGLISH WINE FLAGON   90mm   14.00   30.00

(Goss Record. 8th Edition: Page 29)
Inscribed: *Model of Early English Wine Flagon found under the foundations of Christ's Hospital, London. Rd. No. 539425.*
Matching Arms: *CHRIST'S HOSPITAL* OR *CITY* OF *LONDON*

LONDON STONE   (a) White†   109mm   125.00

(Goss Records, 8th edition: page 73   (b) Brown†   109mm   300.00
advert & War edition page 8).

Inscribed on base: *Model of the London stone near Staines*
Inscribed Side One Top: *To perpetuate and preferve this ancient Monument of the jurisdiction of the Citizens of London The fame was raised on this Pedestal A.D. 1781 S^R Watkin Lewis KN^T Lord Mayor*
Base: *The Conservators of the River Thames 1857 Samuel Wilson ESQ^{RE} Lord Mayor 27th July 1859 John Johnson ESQ^{RE} Lord Mayor 8th August 1846*
Side Two Top: *The ceremony of claiming the jurisdiction of the City of London was repeated at this ftone by the R^T Hon^{BLE} Clau^{DS} Step. Hunter Lord Mayor A.D. 1812.*
Base: *The Right Hon^{BLE} Thomas Quested Finnis Lord Mayor Warren Stormes Hale ESQ^{RE} Alderman John Humphery ESQ^{RE} Alderman Jonathan Thorp ESQ^{RE}*
Side Three Top: *The ancient stone above this infcription is raised upon this pedestal exactly over the spot where it formerly ftood inscribed God preferveye City of London A.D. 1285.*
Base: *Commodore John Shepherd Captain B.J. Sulivan R.N. C.B. Captain John Shepherd Deputy Master of the Trinity House Captain William Pigott.*
Side Four Top: *The Right Honourable William Venables Lord Mayor of the City of London and Conservator of the River of Thames viewed the weftern boundary of the City's Jurisdiction in the said river marked by the ancient stone raised upon this pedestal erected A.D. 1285 on the 29th day of July A.D. 1826 God preferve the City of London*
Base: *Joseph Turner ESQ^{RE} Thomas Henry Fry ESQ^{RE} Thomas Dakin ESQ^{RE} Deputy Captain Horatio Thomas Austin R.N. C.B.*

LONGSHIPS LIGHTHOUSE, LAND'S END   122mm   40.00   80.00
(Goss Record. 8th Edition: Page 18)
Inscribed: *Model of the Longships Lighthouse Land's End.*
Matching Arms: *LAND'S END*

Model		With any Arms £ p	With Matching Arms £ p

LOOE EWER   65mm   7.50   25.00
(Goss Record. 8th Edition: Page 18)
Inscribed: *Model of Ancient Ewer in St. Nicholas Church Looe.*
Rd. No.450629.
Matching Arms: *LOOE* OR *EAST LOOE* OR *WEST LOOE EAST*

for LOTUS VASE
see Egyptian Lotus Vase

LOUTH ANCIENT EWER   43mm   7.50   25.00
(Goss Record. 8th Edition: Page 28)   113mm   30.00   40.00
Inscribed: *Model of Ancient Ewer found at Louth.*
Rd. No. 449119.
Matching Arms: *LOUTH* OR *ANCIENT ARMS OF LOUTH*

LUDLOW SACK BOTTLE (a) with one coat of arms 75mm[1]   17.00   30.00
                                  (b) with three coats of arms   22.00   40.00
(Goss Record. 8th Edition: Page 31)
Inscribed: *Model of Sack Bottle dug up at Castle Mount,*
Ludlow, now in Ludlow Museum.
Matching Arms: *LUDLOW*

LUTON BOTTLE OR COSTREL   Length 65mm   17.00   42.50
(Goss Record. 8th Edition: Page 16)
Inscribed: *Model of "Costrell" or Farm Labourers Water Bottle,*
circa 16th century. Made of local clay at St. Mary's Pottery,
Skimpot. Dug up on the site of the London & County Bank,
Luton, May 1898. Rd. No. 630308.
Matching Arms: *LUTON*

LYME REGIS AMMONITE   73mm   55.00   80.00
(Goss Record. 9th Edition: Page 14)
Inscribed: *Model of Lyme Regis Ammonite. Rd. No. 513063.*
This model is identical to the Whitby Ammonite
Matching Arms: *ARMS OF LYME REGIS OR SEAL OF LYME REGIS*

MADEIRA BULLOCK CAR   58mm   1950.00
Inscribed: *Model of Madeira Bullock Car. Copyright 778.*
One model only has been found, with the delicate trace pole and
the front and rear ring bars all missing. Even in that condition, it
remains an extremely rare and desirable collector's piece.
The model has now been restored with the aid of photographs of
the originals.
Matching Arms: *FUNCHAL, MADEIRA*

London Stone

*Longships Lighthouse.
Land's End*

Looe Ewer

Louth Ancient Ewer

Ludlow Sack Bottle

Luton Bottle or Costrel

Lyme Regis Ammonite

*Madiera Bullock Car
(restored)*

Maidstone Roman Ewer

*Maldon (Essex) German
Incendiary Bomb*

Maltese Carafe

*Maltese Double-mouthed
Vase*

Model		With any Arms £ p	With Matching Arms £ p

MAIDSTONE ROMAN EWER
(Goss Record. 8th Edition: Page 27)
Inscribed: *Roman ewer. From the original in*
Maidstone Museum.
Matching Arms: *MAIDSTONE*

	82mm	10.00	25.00
	130mm	27.50	38.50

MALDON (ESSEX) GERMAN INCENDIARY   75mm   34.00   55.00
BOMB
(Goss Record. 9th Edition: Page 16)
Inscribed: *Model of Incendiary Bomb dropped at Maldon*
16 April 1915 from a German zeppelin. Copyright.
This model has a delicate handle which is frequently
found broken, in which condition it is of little value.
Matching Arms: *MALDON*

**Either MALTA or VALLETTA would be considered
matching on any Maltese Model**

MALTESE CARAFE   105mm   23.50   55.00
(Goss Record. 8th Edition: Page 42)
Inscribed: *Model of Maltese Carafe. Rd. No. 539424.*
Matching Arms: *MALTA*

MALTESE DOUBLE-MOUTHED VASE   60mm   34.00   55.00
(Goss Record. 9th Edition: Page 36 and Plate P)
Inscribed: *Model of Double-mouthed Vase of Bronze Age*
period, from Tarxien Sanctuary.
Matching Arms: *MALTA*

MALTESE FIRE GRATE   53mm   19.50   27.50
(Goss Record. 8th Edition: Page 42)
Inscribed: *Model of Maltese Fire Grate.*
Matching Arms: *MALTA*

MALTESE FUNEREAL URN   61mm   12.00   38.50
(Goss Record. 8th Edition: Page 42)
Inscribed: *Model of Maltese Funereal Urn (circa 600 B. C.)*
found in Rock Tombs, Malta. Rd. No. 559525.
Matching Arms: *MALTA*

MALTESE TWIN VASE   50mm   55.00   80.00
(Goss Record. 9th Edition: Page 36 and Plate P)
Inscribed: *Model of Maltese Twin Vase from Tarxien*
Sanctuary. Bronze Age period.
Matching Arms: *MALTA*

Maltese Fire Grate

Maltese Funereal Urn

Maltese Twin Vase

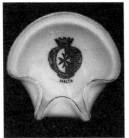

Maltese Two-wick Lamp

Maltese Vase à Canard

Manx Lobster Trap

Manx Peel Pot

Ancient Manx Spirit Measure

The Maple Leaf of Canada 813

Mary, Queen of Scots Nightlight

Melrose Cup

Minster Ancient Ewer

Model			With any Arms £ p	With Matching Arms £ p

MALTESE TWO-WICK LAMP   Length 81mm   17.00   27.50
(Goss Record. 8th Edition: Page 42)
Inscribed: *Model of Maltese Two-wick Lamp*
(circa 600 B. C.) found in Rock Tombs, Malta.
Rd. No. 562738.
Matching Arms: *MALTA*

MALTESE VASE à CANARD   45mm   21.50   34.00
(Goss Record. 9th Edition: Page 36)
Inscribed: *Model of Maltese Vase a Canard of Bronze Age*
period from Tarxien Sanctuay.
Matching Arms: *MALTA*

MANX LOBSTER POT   Dia.67mm Height 51mm   75.00
Inscribed: *Model of Manx Lobster Trap.*
This model is identical to the Lobster Trap, but
specifically named.
Usually found with the matching arms of *ISLE OF MAN*
but any Manx arms could be considered matching.

MANX PEEL POT   49mm   12.00   27.50
(Goss Record. 8th Edition: Page 26)
Inscribed: *Model of old Manx Pot at Peel. Rd. No. 390789.*
This model is identical to The Devon Cooking Pot.
Matching Arms: *CITY OF PEEL, ISLE OF MAN* OR *ANY MANX ARMS*

(ANCIENT) MANX SPIRIT MEASURE   68mm   17.00   38.50
(Goss Record. 8th Edition: Page 26)
Inscribed: *Model of Ancient Manx Spirit Measure. Rd. No. 578695.*
Matching Arms: *ISLE OF MAN* OR *ANY MANX ARMS*

(THE) MAPLE LEAF OF CANADA   118mm   80.00   175.00
Inscribed: *813 The Maple Leaf of Canada Copyright*
Matching Arms: *CANADA* OR *ANY CANADIAN*
COAT OF ARMS OR *B.E.E. WEMBLEY 1924 OR 1925.*

MARY QUEEN OF SCOTS

Face in high relief on				
	(a) two-piece night-light	78mm	150.00	170.00
	(b) two handled mug	80mm	80.00	125.00
	(c) two or three-handled mug	118mm	115.00	160.00

Inscriptions:
(a)   *Mary Queen of Scots Night Light*
      Rd. No. 273298
(b)   *Mary Queen of Scots Cup*
      Rd. No. 273244
Correct Arms: *MARY QUEEN OF SCOTS*

Model		With any Arms £ p	With Matching Arms £ p
MELROSE CUP	128mm	55.00	80.00

(Goss Record. 8th Edition: Page 40 and advertisement
page 101)
Inscribed: *The Melrose Cup*
Not really a model in the true sense of the word, it was
designed by and made, with the arms of Sir Walter Scott,
expressly for William Dick, the Melrose Agent, and first
marketed exclusively by him. The bowl of the cup
incorporates the same leaf design that can be found at
the top of the pillars in Melrose Abbey, which represents
a ladies hand grasping a bunch of foliage.
Matching Arms: *SIR WALTER SCOTT, MELROSE ABBEY* OR *MELROSE*

for MILK CROGAN
see Stornoway Highland Milk Crogan

MINSTER ANCIENT EWER	88mm	21.50	37.50

Inscribed: *Model of Ancient Ewer found at Minster,*
Thanet. Copyright.
Matching Arms: *MINSTER*

MINSTER ANCIENT URN	65mm	19.50	47.00

Inscribed: *Model of Ancient Urn found at Minster,*
(or Thanet), Kent. Copyright.
Matching Arms: *MINSTER*

for MONMOUTH MASK
See FIRST PERIOD 9C ORNAMENTAL Chapter

for MONNOW GATE
see Old Gateway on Monnow Bridge

MONS MEG, EDINBURGH CASTLE	Length 122mm	38.50	65.00

(Goss Record. 8th Edition: Page 40)
Inscribed: *Model of "Mons Meg" Edinburgh*
Castle. Rd. No. 605732.
Matching Arms: *CITY OF EDINBURGH*

MUNICH BEER SEIDEL	52mm	75.00	125.00

Inscribed: *Model of Munich Beer Seidel.*
Matching Arms: *MÜNCHEN*

Model		With any Arms £ p	With Matching Arms £ p
MUSSELBURGH KIRKPARK ANCIENT URN	51mm	7.50	25.00

(Goss Record. 8th Edition: Page 40)
Inscribed: *Model of Ancient Urn found in Kirkpark*
Musselburg N.B. Rd. No. 448431.
N.B. Inscription misspelt Musselburg; the arms correctly
captioned Musselburgh.
Matching Arms: *MUSSELBURGH*

for MYCENAEAN VASE
see Cyprus Mycenaean Vase

NATIONAL HIGHLAND CUACH or WHISKEY CUP
(Goss Record. 8th Edition: Page 40)   Width 94mm   12.00   16.00
Inscribed: *Model of Highland Cuach or Whiskey Cup.*
Any Scottish Highland Arms are considered matching.

for NAUTILUS SHELL
see SECOND PERIOD 10K5 ORNAMENTAL and
    FIRST PERIOD 9C ORNAMENTAL chapters.

NEWBURY LEATHER BOTTLE

			£ p	£ p
(Goss Record. 8th Edition: Page 16	(a)	58mm	7.50	19.00
	(b)	114mm[1]	22.50	30.00
	(c) With Stopper	125mm[1]	40.00	60.00

Inscribed: *Model of Leather Bottle found on Battle-field of Newbury, 1644.*
Now in Museum.
First Period examples of the larger size have a thicker rim to take a
porcelain and cork stopper, whilst Second Period models are
thinner and no stopper was included, nor indeed will fit.
MatchingArms: *BURGUS NEWBERIE*

NEWCASTLE (STAFFORDSHIRE) CUP   70mm[1]   30.00   38.50
(Goss Record. 8th Edition: Page 32)
Inscribed: *Model of an Ancient Black-&-brown Cup dug*
up at the south side of Red Lion Sq., Newcastle, Staffs.
in 1882: now in the possession of Messrs. Chapman &
Snape.
Matching Arms: *NEWCASTLE-UNDER-LYME*

Minster Ancient Urn

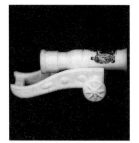

Mons Meg. Edinburgh Castle

Munich Beer Seidel

*Musselburgh Kirkpark
Ancient Urn*

*National Highland Cuach or
Whiskey Cup*

*Newbury Leather Bottle,
small*

*Newbury Leather Bottle
(large) with Stopper*

Newcastle (Staffordshire) Cup

Newcastle Castle

Newcastle Roman Jug

North Foreland Lighthouse

*Northwich Sepulchral Urn
League Model, 1930*

250

Model			With any Arms £ p	With Matching Arms £ p
NEWCASTLE CASTLE	(a) White glazed	88mm	125.00	250.00
	(b) Brown†	88mm	340.00	625.00

Inscribed: *Newcastle on Tyne. Robert Curthose eldest son of the Conqueror, built a fortress here in 1080, which, in contradistinction to the old Roman Castrum of Pons Aelii, was called The New Castle, whence the present name of the town. Copyright.*
Matching Arms: *NEWCASTLE-ON-TYNE* OR *NEWCASTLE-UPON-TYNE*

Model				
NEWCASTLE ROMAN JUG		63mm	7.50	23.00

(Goss Record. 8th Edition: Page 30)
Inscribed: *Model of Roman Jug in the Museum Newcastle on Tyne. Rd. No. 392069.*
Matching Arms: *NEWCASTLE-ON-TYNE* OR *NEWCASTLE-UPON-TYNE*

for NORMAN TOWER, CHRISTCHURCH
see Christchurch Priory Church Norman Tower

Model				
NORTH FORELAND LIGHTHOUSE		108mm	80.00	95.00

(Goss Record.8th Edition: Page 27)
Inscribed: *Model of the North Foreland Lighthouse. Rd. No. 639537.*
Matching Arms: *BROADSTAIRS* OR *WESTGATE-ON-SEA* OR *MARGATE*

Model				
NORTHWICH SEPULCHURAL URN		85mm		360.00

Inscribed: *Model of Britano-Roman Sepulchural Urn found near Northwich (Salinæ) now in Warrington Museum. Copyright 1930. This model is only issued to Members of the League and cannot be bought.*
International League Model for 1930
Correct Arms: *INTERNATIONAL LEAGUE OF GOSS COLLECTORS*

Model				
NORWEGIAN BUCKET		58mm	15.00	65.00

(Goss Record. 8th Edition: Page 42)
Inscribed: *Model of Norwegian Bucket. Rd. No. 599332.*
Can be found with either plain or gilded rim.
Matching Arms: *NORGE*

Norwegian Bucket

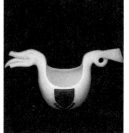

*Norwegian Dragon-shaped
Beer Bowl*

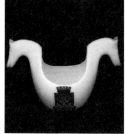

*Norwegian Horse-shaped
Beer Bowl*

Norwegian Wooden Shoe

Norwich Urn

Nottingham Ewer

Nottingham Urn

*Old Gateway on Monnow
Bridge*

Orkney Craisie

Ostend Flemish Bottle

Ostend Flemish Tobacco Jar

Ostend Vase

Model			With any Arms £ p	With Matching Arms £ p

NORWEGIAN DRAGON-SHAPED BEER BOWL

(Goss Record. 8th Edition: Page 42)   (a) Length 155mm   30.00   55.00

Inscribed: *Model of Norwegian Dragon-shaped*   (b) Length 155mm   77.50

Beer Bowl. Rd No. 526382.

Can be rarely found (b) with the following
inscription in Norwegian: *Model of Norsk*
Ølbolle (Kjenge) med Draghoved.
Rd. No. 526382.
Matching Arms: *NORGE*

NORWEGIAN HORSE-SHAPED BEER BOWL

(Goss Record. 8th Edition: Page 42)   (a) Length 115mm   25.00   55.00

Inscribed: *Model of Norwegian Horse-shaped*   (b) Length 115mm   77.50

Beer Bowl. Rd. No. 526383.

Two varieties with joined or separate ears .
Can rarely be found (b) with the following inscription
in Norwegian: *Model of Norsk Ølbolle (Kjenge) med*
Hesthoved Rd. No. 526383.
Matching Arms: *NORGE*

NORWEGIAN WOODEN SHOE

   (a)Length 103mm   25.00   80.00

(Goss Record. 8th Edition: page 42)   (b)Length 103mm   97.50

Inscribed: *Model of Norwegian Shoe.*
Can rarely be found (b) with the
following inscription in
Norwegian: *Model af Norsk Traesko*
Matching Arms: *NORGE*

**The Arms of any Norwegian Town would also be
considered matching on any of the four Norwegian
models. BERGEN is the most common, followed
by Trondheim, spelt in Norwegian, TRONDHJEM**

NORWICH URN

		51mm	7.50	22.00
		62mm	13.00	22.00
		90mm[1]	17.00	30.00

(Goss Record. 8th Edition: page 29)

Inscribed: *Model of the Norwich Urn from the original*
in the Museum.
Matching Arms: *NORWICH* OR *CITY OF NORWICH*

for NOSE OF BRASENOSE

see (The Nose of) Brasenose

NOTTINGHAM EWER

(a) 1 coat of arms   63mm   7.50   22.00

(Goss Record. 8th Edition: (b) 2 coats of arms   63mm   8.50   25.00

Page 30)

Inscribed: *Model of Ancient Ewer found during excavations*
top of Long Stairs High Pavement, now in Castle Museum.
Rd. No. 172576.
Matching Arms: *CITY OF NOTTINGHAM*

Model			With any Arms £ p	With Matching Arms £ p
NOTTINGHAM URN		40mm	7.50	20.00

NOTTINGHAM URN   40mm   7.50   20.00
(Goss Record. 8th Edition: Page 30 and advertisement
page 79)
Inscribed: *Model of Ancient Urn found during excavations in
Nottingham. 1897. Now in Castle Museum. Rd. No. 472577.*
Matching Arms: *CITY OF NOTTINGHAM*

for OLD BRAZIER (ISLES OF SCILLY)
see Tresco Old Brazier

OLD GATEWAY ON MONNOW BRIDGE
(Goss Record. 9th Edition: Page 23
and Plate J)   (a) White glazed   95mm   85.00   225.00
                 (b) Brown†   95mm   215.00
Inscribed: *Model of Monnow Gate Monmouth.*
This model is the MONNOW GATE and not
MONMOW GATE as misspelt in the 9th Edition of
The Goss Record and usually on the model itself. The
side gates are found both open and closed.
Matching Arms: *ARMS OF MONMOUTH* OR *SEAL OF MONMOUTH*

for OLD HORSE SHOE
see Horse Shoe (The Old)

for OLD PILLION STONE, FLOWERGATE, WHITBY
see Whitby Pillion Stone

for OLD SARUM KETTLE
see Salisbury Kettle

ORKNEY CRAISIE   80mm   25.00   55.00
(Goss Record. 9th Edition: Page 35)
Inscribed: *Model of Orkney Craisie. Rd. No. 559522.*
This model of the basket used in the Orkney Islands
has the description and mark on its inside and has a high
thin handle which can frequently be found either cracked
or completely broken off, in which condition it is of
little value.
Matching Arms: *COUNTY OF ORKNEY* OR *KIRKWALL*

OSTEND FLEMISH BOTTLE   65mm   10.00   23.50
(Goss Record.8th Edition: Page 42)
Inscribed: *Model of Flemish Bottle, Ostend Museum.*
Rd. No. 495673. or more rarely *Importe D'Angleterre.*
Model of Flemish Bottle of 1617. Found inside a fishing
smack in the fisherman's dock at Ostend now
in Ostend Museum Rd. No. 495672
Matching Arms: *OSTENDE*

	With any Arms £ p	With Matching Arms £ p
Model		

OSTEND FLEMISH TOBACCO JAR   54mm   7.50   25.00
(Goss Record. 8th Edition: Page 42)
Inscribed: *Model of Flemish Tobacco Jar in Liebaert Museum at Ostend. Rd. No. 495674.*
Matching Arms: *OSTENDE*

OSTEND VASE   57mm   7.50   23.50
(Goss Record. 8th Edition: Page 42)
Inscribed: *Model of Ostend Vase A.D. 1617, found inside a fishing smack in the Fisherman's Dock at Ostend. Now in Ostend Museum. Rd. No. 495672.*
Matching Arms: *OSTENDE*

OXFORD EWER   76mm   9.00   17.00
(Goss Record. 8th Edition: Page 31)   126mm[1]   20.00   30.00
Inscribed: *The Oxford Ewer from the original in the Ashmolean Museum, found at Exeter Coll.*
Matching Arms: *CITY OF OXFORD* with *EXETER* College Oxford perhaps being considered the next appropriate.

OXFORD JUG   173mm [1]   28.50   38.50
(Goss Record. 8th Edition: Page 31)
Inscribed: *The Oxford Jug from the original in the Ashmolean Museum, found at Trinity Coll.*
Matching Arms: *CITY OF OXFORD* with *TRINITY* College Oxford perhaps being considered the next appropriate.

for OYSTER SHELL
see Colchester Native Oyster Shell or
FIRST PERIOD 9C ORNAMENTAL AND DOMESTIC Chapter

PAINSWICK POT   50mm   7.50   28.50
(Goss Record. 8th Edition: Page 22)
Inscribed: *Model of Roman Pot found at Ifold Villa Painswick 1902. Rd. No. 500869.*
Matching Arms: *PAINSWICK*

PANAMA VASE   130mm   35.00
Inscribed: *Panama Vase. Rd. No. 639532.*
Matching Arms: *PANAMA*, but not yet seen on this model.
As there was no agent in Panama, this model was probably sold by Ritchie & Co. the Stoke-Upon-Trent agent.

Oxford Ewer

Oxford Jug

Painswick Pot

Panama Vase

Penmaenmawr Urn

Perth Coronation Chair

Peterborough Tripod

Plymouth Spanish Jug

Pompeian Ewer

Portland Lighthouse

*Portland Vase
League Model*

Preston Old Bushel Measure

Model			With any Arms £ p	With Matching Arms £ p
PENMAENMAWR URN		45mm	7.50	22.50

(Goss Record. 8th Edition: Page 39)
Inscribed: *Model of Ancient Urn found at Penmaenmawr.*
Matching Arms: *PENMAENMAWR*

Model			With any Arms £ p	With Matching Arms £ p
PERTH CORONATION CHAIR	(a) White glazed	85mm	82.50	125.00
(Goss Record. 9th Edition: Page 36)	(b) Stone in brown	85mm	120.00	170.00
	(c) Brown†	85mm	300.00	

Inscribed: *Model of the Coronation Chair in Westminster Abbey. Rd . No. 578694. The chair contains the Ancient Stone on which the Kings and Queens of Scotland were formerly crowned at Scone, Perthshire.*
This model is the same as the Westminster Abbey Coronation Chair except that it carries the longer inscription.
Earlier versions have an open space between the back legs; later versions have a solid back, are 90mm high and have the top of the back-rest gilded .
Matching Arms: *PERTH*

Model			With any Arms £ p	With Matching Arms £ p
PETERBOROUGH TRIPOD	(a) 1 coat of arms	47mm	13.00	22.00
(Goss Record. 8th Edition: Page 30)	(b) 3 coats of arms	47mm	9.50	22.00

Inscribed: *Model of Bronze Roman Tripod in Peterborough Museum found at Whittlesey Mere.*
This model is identical to the Witch's Cauldron
An example has been found named incorrectly as the Scarborough Jug.
Matching Arms: *PETERBOROUGH, CITY OF PETERBOROUGH* AND *CITY AND BOROUGH OF PETERBOROUGH*

for PILGRIM'S BOTTLE
see Ancient Costril

for PINE CONE
see Bournemouth Pine Cone

for PIPES
see German Smoking Pipe and Twickenham Antique Pope's Pipe

Model		With any Arms £ p	With Matching Arms £ p
PLYMOUTH (SPANISH) JUG	55mm	7.50	21.50

(Goss Record. 8th Edition: Page 20)
Inscribed: *Model of Old Spanish Jug dredged up near Eddy stone now in Athenaeum Plymouth.*
Matching Arms: *PLYMOUTH, DEVONPORT* OR *STONEHOUSE*

Model			With any Arms £ p	With Matching Arms £ p
POMPEIAN EWER		91mm	14.00	
(Goss Record. 8th Edition: Page 42)		208mm	38.50	

Inscribed: *Model of Pompeian Ever*
Both sizes are also found unnamed.
Italian Arms have yet to be recorded on this model, but
they would certainly be considered matching were they to exist.
Matching Arms: *NONE*

for POPE'S PIPE, TWICKENHAM
see Twickenham Antique Pope's Pipe

Model			With any Arms £ p	With Matching Arms £ p
PORTLAND LIGHTHOUSE	(a) Plain	120mm	68.00	
(Goss Record. 8th Edition:Page21)	(b) Brown band	120mm	78.00	100.00
	(c) Orange band	120mm	110.00	150.00

Inscribed: *Model of the Portland Lighthouse. Rd. No. 622476.*
A previously reported version with black
band is not now believed to exist.
Matching Arms: *THE ISLAND & ROYAL MANOR*
OF PORTLAND URBAN DISTRICT COUNCIL

Model		With any Arms £ p	With Matching Arms £ p
PORTLAND VASE	(a) 51mm	7.50	30.00
Inscribed: *Model of The Portland Vase in The*	(b) 51mm	28.50	65.00
British Museum.	(c) 51mm	47.50	

This is one of the most interesting models. All have
the above inscription on the base (a), and some
additionally have commemorative wording on the
base, marking the anniversary of the death of Josiah
Wedgwood, viz: *MEMORIAL OF JOSIAH
WEDGWOOD* (b), and are thus much sought after:
collectors picking up every Portland Vase could
easily have a pleasant surprise. Mr. J.J. Jarvis
when starting The League of Goss Collectors, chose
this as the first League model (c).
Collectors can read about the discovery and history
of the original in The Goss Record. 8th Edition:
page 28.
There are no correct town arms for this model as the
Goss original is currently in the British Museum.
As the original was purchased by the Duchess of
Portland, the arms of the Duke of Portland could be
considered matching, or perhaps also those of The
Island & Royal Manor of Portland U.D.C.
Matching Arms: *(a) DUKE OF PORTLAND*
                (b) JOSIAH WEDGWOOD
                (c) THE LEAGUE OF GOSS COLLECTORS

Model		With any Arms £ p	With Matching Arms £ p

PRESTON OLD BUSHEL MEASURE

Dia. 58mm   75.00   170.00

(Goss Record. 9th Edition: Page 21 and Plate M)
Inscribed: *Model of The Old Bushel Measure made for Preston in 1670 and used by the Mayor and Clerk of the Markets under the Old Charters granted to the Town. Copyright.*
This model is the rarest of the small bushels, and is embossed on the side: *For Preston in the County of Lancashire 1670.*
Matching Arms: *PRESTON*

for PRINCESS VICTORIA'S FIRST SLIPPER
see Queen Victoria's First Shoe

for PYRAMID
see Great Pyramid (The)

for QUEEN CHARLOTTE'S KETTLE
see Windsor Kettle

QUEEN ELIZABETH'S RIDING SHOE

Length 105mm   115.00   140.00

(Goss Record. 9th Edition: Page 16 and Plate L)
On page 16 of *The Goss Record* it is referred to as a slipper and under Plate L as a shoe.
Inscribed: *Model of Queen Elizabeth's Riding Shoe originally at Horham Hall, Thaxted. Copyright.*
This model is by far the rarest of the Goss shoe models.
Matching Arms: *THAXTED*

QUEEN PHILLIPA'S RECORD CHEST

(Goss Record. 9th Edition)

Length (a)	80mm	36.00	47.00
(b)	94mm	36 00	65.00

Inscribed: *Model of Queen Phillipa's Record Chest found in Knaresborough Castle. Rd. No. 643868.*
Matching Arms: *KNARESBOROUGH (ABBEY)*

Queen Elizabeth's Riding Shoe

Queen Phillipa's Record Chest

Queen Victoria's First Shoe

Ramsey Cronk Aust Cinerary Urn

Ramsgate Romano-British Ewer 794

Ramsgate Romano-British Jug 795

Ramsgate Urn 787

Rayleigh Ancient Cooking Pot

Reading Jug

Reading (Silchester) Urn

Reading (Silchester) Vase

Rochester Bellarmine Jug

Model				With any Arms £ p	With Matching Arms £ p

QUEEN VICTORIA'S FIRST SHOE

	(a) Without Arms	102mm	47.00†	
(Goss Record .8th Edition:Pagc20)	(b) Pre-1901	102mm	47.00	55.00
	(c) Post- 1901	102mm	30.00	35.00

Inscribed on Pre 1901 examples: *Model, exact size of first shoes worn by Princess Victoria - H.M. The Queen Made at Sidmouth 1819.*
Inscribed on Post 1901 examples: *Model, exact size, off first shoes worn by Princess Victoria - H.M. late Queen (who died Jan. 22nd. 1901) made at Sidmouth in 1819.*
Can sometimes be found with a hole in the back of the shoe for hanging.
A descriptive leaflet was issued with this model and is valued at £ 20.00. (see page 56)
Matching Arms: *H.M. QUEEN VICTORIA* OR *SIDMOUTH*

RAMSEY CRONK AUST CINERARY URN   59mm   14.00   30.00
(Goss Record. 8th Edition: Page 26)
Inscribed: *Model of Cinerary Urn from Cronk Aust, Ramsey. Rd. No. 521976.*
Matching Arms: *RAMSEY, ISLE OF MAN*

RAMSGATE ROMANO-BRITISH EWER   47mm   32.00   50.00
Inscribed: *Model of Romano British Ist Century Ewer found at Ramsgate. 794 Copyright.*
Matching Arms: *RAMSGATE*

RAMSGATE ROMANO-BRITISH JUG   70mm   19.00   55.00
Inscribed: *Model of Romano-British Ist Century Jug found at Ramsgate 795 Copyright.*
Matching Arms: *RAMSGATE*

RAMSGATE URN   75mm   19.00   55.00
Inscribed: *Model of Ancient Urn found at Ramsgate 787 Copyright*
Matching Arms: *RAMSGATE*

An example of each of the three Ramsgate models, all unglazed and unmarked, and without decoration were discovered in rooms above a Ramsgate shop in 1990. The dimensions, and quality of the porcelain render them unmistakably Goss prototypes of the actual models in Ramsgate museum, or travellers samples.

Model		With any Arms £ p	With Matching Arms £ p
RAYLEIGH ANCIENT COOKING POT (Goss Record. 8th Edition: Page 22) Inscribed: *Model of Ancient Cooking Pot found at Rayleigh Castle Essex. Rd. No. 602903.* Matching Arms: *RAYLEIGH (ESSEX)* OR *PARISH OF RAYLEIGH (ESSEX)*	33mm	7.50	55.00
READING JUG (Goss Record. 8th Edition: Page 16) Inscribed: *Model of 15th Cent. Jug dug up in Minster St. Reading. Now in Museum.* Matching Arms: *ARMS OF READING*	82mm 140mm	7.50 20.00	14.00 25.00
READING (SILCHESTER) URN (Goss Record. 8th Edition: Page 16) Inscribed: *Model of Roman Urn from Silchester in Reading Museum. Rd. No. 573577.* Matching Arms: *ARMS OF READING*	50mm	7.50	15.00
READING (SILCHESTER) VASE (Goss Record. 8th Edition: Page 16) Inscribed: *Model of Vase from Silchester in Reading Museum.* Matching Arms: *ARMS OF READING*	50mm	7.50	19.00
for RECULVER TOWERS see Herne Bay Reculver Towers			
ROCHESTER BELLARMINE JUG (Goss Record. 8th Edition: Page 27) Inscribed: *Model of Bellarmine Jug 17th Century found in Rochester. Rd. No. 403421.* The effigy of a bearded man is embossed on the neck of this model, also known as a Greybeard Matching Arms: *ROCHESTER*	65mm	7.50	19.50
for ROMAN EWER see Cirencester Roman Ewer			
ROMAN MORTARIUM (Goss Record.8th Edition: Page 43) Inscribed: *Model of Ancient Roman Mortarium.* This model has no matching arms.	Dia. 95mm (a) Named (b) Unnamed	85.00 30.00	
for ROMAN TETINAE see Wilderspool Roman Tetinae			

Model	With any Arms £ p	With Matching Arms £ p
ROMAN VASE (a) White glazed 160mm	47.50	
Inscribed: *The Roman Vase 783 Copyright* (b) Lustre 160mm	95.00	
It has no matching arms.		

ROMSEY BUSHEL Dia. 68mm 17.00 38.50
(Goss Record. 8th Edition: Page 23)
Inscribed: *Model of Ancient Romsey Bushel in the possession of the Corporation. Rd. No. 489663.*
Inscribed on side: *Winchester Bushel-Romsey Joseph Mortimer Mayor 1792. Corcoran Fecit London*
Matching Arms: *ROMSEY*

ROTHESAY STONE Brown† Length 95mm 1350.00
(Goss Record. 9th Edition: Page 35   Width 25mm
and Plate G) Only two examples of this rare model are
known to exist and only in brown, 6mm thick.

RUFUS STONE 94mm 14.50 22.00
(Goss Record. 8th Edition: Page 23 and advertisement
page 64)
Occasionally appears with no arms 94mm 10.00
This model can also be found with a flat
rather than patterned top. 100mm same price
see also *THIRD PERIOD 110 BUILDINGS
AND MONUMENTS* for a late example.

Inscribed with its history and legend on all three faces of
this triangular-shaped model as follows: *Here stood the
oak tree, on which an arrow shot by Sir Walter Tyrrell at
a Stag, glanced and struck King William the Second,
surnamed Rufus, on the breast, of which he instantly died,
on the second day of August ANNO 1100.
King William the Second surnamed Rufus being slain as
before related was laid in a cart belonging to one Purkis
and drawn from hence to Winchester and buried in the
Cathedral Church of that City.
That the spot where an event so memorable might not
hereafter be forgotten, the enclosed stone was set up by
John, Lord Delaware who had seen the tree growing in this
place. This stone having been much mutilated and the
inscriptions on each of its three sides defaced this more
durable memorial with the original inscriptions was
erected in the year 1844. By am Sturges Bourne Warden.*
The nearest Agency to the Rufus Stone is Lyndhurst and
this may also be considered matching, as is New Forest.
Matching Arms: *KING WILLIAM RUFUS*

Roman Mortarium

Roman Vase 783

Roman Bushel

Rothesay Stone

Rufus Stone

Russian Shrapnel Shell

Rye Cannon Ball with Plinth

Rye Cannon Ball without Plinth

Saffron Walden Covered Urn and Lid

St. Albans Ancient Cooking Pot

St. Mary's Lighthouse Whitley Bay

St. Neots Ancient Urn

Model		With any Arms £ p	With Matching Arms £ p

RUSSIAN SHRAPNEL SHELL   110mm   31.00   65.00
(Goss Record. War Edition: Page 5 [illustrated] and 7)
Inscribed: *Model of Russian Shrapnel Shell. The original was
captured by the Huns & fired by them at the British.* Copyright.
Matching Arms: *RUSSIA* OR *ANY ARTILLERY
REGIMENT* for which £60 should be added

RYE CANNON BALL, Black and brown.
(Goss Record.8th Edition: Page 35)
Inscribed: *Model of Cannon Ball excavated at Landgate, Rye
1907. This ball was probably fired by the French who twice
burnt Rye to the ground (1377 & 91448)*
           (a) On plinth   106mm   77.50   125.00
           (b) Without plinth   68mm   50.00   77.50
Matching Arms: *SEAL OF RYE* OR *CINQUE PORT OF RYE*

SAFFRON WALDEN COVERED URN and lid   70mm   21.00   38.50
(Goss Record. 8th Edition: Page 22)   121mm   34.00   68.00
Inscribed: *Model of Covered Urn found near site of Walden
Abbey in 1878.*
This model, the original of which, according to *The Goss Record* is
undoubtedly of Eygptian manufacture has a lid that looks very
like an Egyptian Mummy's Head without which it is incomplete,
value £10.00 small or £20.00 large.
Matching Arms: *SAFFRON WALDEN* OR *WALDEN ABBEY*
With any Egyptian Arms add £ 15.00

ST. ALBANS ANCIENT COOKING POT   58mm   17.00   38.50
(Goss Record. 8th Edition: Page 24)
Inscribed: *Model of Ancient Cooking Pot in St. Albans
Museum. Rd. No. 633430.*
Matching Arms: *ST. ALBANS* OR *THE CITY OF ST. ALBANS*

ST. MARY'S LIGHTHOUSE, WHITLEY BAY   135mm   550.00   750.00
Inscribed: *Model of St. Mary's Lighthouse Whitley Bay.
Copyright.*
This model is not listed in any edition of The Coss
Record and is the second rarest lighthouse.
Matching Arms: *DUKE OF NORTHUMBERLAND "MANOR OF WHITLEY BAY"*

ST. NEOTS ANCIENT URN   63mm   8.50   27.50
(Goss Record. 8th Edition: Page 24)
Inscribed: *Model of Ancient Urn found 1816 near
St. Neot's, Hunts. Rd. No. 413576.*
Matching Arms. *SAINT NEOTS*

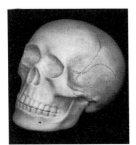

St. Simon of Sudbury's Skull

Salisbury (or Old Sarum) Kettle

Salisbury Leather Jack

Salisbury

Denbigh Brick, red

Salisbury Leather Jack. Large

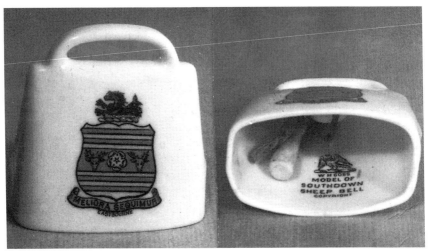

The Southdown Sheep Bell showing inscription and clapper

Model			With any Arms £ p	With Matching Arms £ p
ST. SIMON OF SUDBURY'S SKULL	(a) White†	72mm	190.00	
Inscribed: *Skull of St.Simon of Sudbury*	(b) Brown†	72mm	300.00	
SALISBURY KETTLE		88mm	15.00	30.00
(Goss Record. 8th Edition: Page 36 and		133mm	25.00	35.00
advertisement page 114)				

SALISBURY KETTLE (continued)
Inscribed: *Model of Old Kettle in Salisbury Museum.*
Also known as the Old Sarum Kettle
Matching Arms: *SALISBURY*

SALISBURY LEATHER GILL	75mm	21.50	35.00

(Goss Record. 8th Edition: Page 36)
Inscribed: *The Salisbury Leather Gill from original in
Museum*. This model is always found with RSM 1658
in red and blue letters on the side. It can be found
both crested and uncrested. Same price.
Matching Arms: *SALISBURY*

The Salisbury Jack and Gill are thought to be the
inspiration for the popular nursery rhyme, with the
broken crown being that of Charles I. The initials C R
(Carolus Rex) 1646 on the Salisbury Jack is held to be
a commemoration of the visit by Charles I to the
neighbourhood, and the loyal owner of the Jack
marked it thus. 1658 on the Gill is the year of Oliver
Cromwell's death. R S M stands for Resurgam
meaning: I shall rise again, referring to the rising
hopes of the Loyalists on hearing of the death of
Cromwell. The originals should still be in
Salisbury Museum.

SALISBURY LEATHER JACK	44mm	7.50	20.00
(Goss Record. 8th Edition: Page 36)	80mm		300.00
Inscribed: *Model of the Royal Salisbury Jack from original*	140mm[1]	23.00	38.50

in Museum.
The large size is always, and the small size is
sometimes found with C R 1646 on the side under a
crown. In addition, it appears both crested and
uncrested. Same price.
Matching Arms: *SALISBURY*

for SALTWOOD EWER
see Folkestone Roman Ewer

Sark Fish Basket

Sark Milk Can and Lid

Scarborough Jug

Scarborough Kettle

Seaford Urn

Shakespeare's Jug

*Shrewsbury (Uriconium)
Ewer*

*Shrewesbury
Romano-Salopian Ewer*

*Sir John Barrow's Monument,
Ulverston*

Skegness Clock Tower

Southampton Ancient Pipkin

Southampton Bargate

Model		With any Arms £ p	With Matching Arms £ p

SARK FISH BASKET   45mm   65.00
(Goss Record. 8th Edition: Page 17)   58mm   75.00
Inscribed: *Sark Fish Basket.*
Matching Arms: *SERCQ*

SARK MILK CAN and lid   70mm   65.00
(Goss Record. 9th Edition: Page 11)   108mm   75.00
Inscribed: *Model of Sark Milk Can.*   140mm   80.00
This would be incomplete without its lid,
value £15.00 in all three sizes
Matching Arms: *SERCQ*

for SCALLOP SHELL
see SECOND PERIOD 10K5 ORNAMENTAL Chapter

SCARBOROUGH JUG   51mm   9.00   19.00
(Goss Record. 8th Edition: Page 38)   70mm   19.50   28.00
Inscribed: *Model of Jug about 600 years old found in the*
Ancient Moat of Scarborough.
Matching Arms: *SCARBOROUGH*

SCARBOROUGH KETTLE   65mm   14.50   21.00
(Goss Record. 8th Edition: Page 38)   88mm   22.00   33.00
Inscribed: *Model of the Scarboro Kettle found near Ancient*
Pottery, North Side.
This model can be found labelled as a Scarborough Jug,
same price.
Matching Arms: *SCARBOROUGH*
Up until 1911 - 1916, the two Scarborough models were
both known as Scarborough Jugs. The name of one
was changed, probably to avoid confusion.
Originally one jug was named as follows:
Model of Jug found in Old Moat at the back of Huntress Row 600
years old
and the other:
Model of Jug found near Ancient Pottery.
It was the latter which was re-named a kettle between
1911 and 1916. *The Goss Record* prior to 1911 lists both as
Scarborough Jugs. Both shapes were in production
before 1900.

Model				With any Arms £ p	With Matching Arms £ p
SEAFORD URN	(a) with one coat of arms	48mm		10.00	22.50
	(b) with two coats of arms	48mm		12.50	21.50

(Goss Record. 8th Edition: Page 35)
First Period models inscribed: *Seaford Urn or The Seaford Urn* [1]
Second Period Models inscribed: *Model of Roman Urn found
at Seaford 1825.* [2]
One of the first models to be introduced.
Matching Arms: *SEAFORD (Three versions)*

SHAKESPEARE'S JUG		58mm		14.00	19.00
(Goss Record. 8th Edition: Page 35)		76mm		17.00	25.00
Inscribed: *Model of Shakespeare's Jug, in the Museum,*		88mm		21.50	38.50

Stratford-on-Avon.
Also named on the side: *Model of the Jug of William Shakespeare*; the
title in illuminated Gothic script, and his name as a facsimile
signature.
Matching Arms: *SHAKESPEARE'S ARMS* OR
STRATFORD ON AVON

for SHELLS
see 10K ORNAMENTAL AND SHELLS

for SHEPHERD'S CROWN SEA URCHIN
see Steyning Shepherd's Crown

SHREWSBURY (URICONIUM) EWER					
	(a) with one or two coats of arms	100mm		30.00	55.00
	(b) with three coats of arms	100mm		34.00	65.00

(Goss Record. 8th Edition: Page 31)
First Period models inscribed: *The Uriconium Ewer* [1]
Second Period models inscribed: *Model of Ewer, found in the
Ancient Roman City of Uriconium, Nr. Shrewsbury.* [2]
One of the first models to be introduced.
Matching Arms: *SHREWSBURY*

SHREWSBURY ROMANO-SALOPIAN EWER	68mm	7.50	21.50

(Goss Record. 8th Edition: Page 31)
Inscribed: *Model of Romano-Salopian Ewer found at
Uriconium. Now in Shrewsbury Museum.*
Matching Arms: *SHREWSBURY*

for SILCHESTER URN
see Reading (Silchester) Urn

for SILCHESTER VASE
see Reading (Silchester) Vase

		With any Arms £ p	With Matching Arms £ p

for SIMON OF SUDBURY'S SKULL
see St. Simon of Sudbury's Skull

SIR JOHN BARROW'S MONUMENT

Model		With any Arms £ p	With Matching Arms £ p
ULVERSTON Inscribed: *Model of Sir John Barrow's Monument Ulverston. Copyright. "In Honour of Sir John Barrow Bart. Erected A.D. 1850".* Matching Arms: *ULVERSTON*	120mm	115.00	165.00
SKEGNESS CLOCK TOWER Inscribed: *Model of the Clock Tower Skegness.* Matching Arms: *SKEGNESS*	132mm	100.00	155.00

for SKULLS
see Hythe Crypt Skull, St. Simon of Sudbury's Skull
and Yorick's Skull

for SOLDIER'S WATER BOTTLE
see Waterlooville Soldier's Water Bottle

SOUTHAMPTON ANCIENT PIPKIN (Goss Record. 8th Edition: page 23) Inscribed: *Model of Ancient Pipkin dug up at N.P. Bank Southampton.* Matching Arms: *SOUTHAMPTON*	56mm 76mm 101mm[l]	7.50 25.00 28.50	12.75 38.50 45.00

SOUTHAMPTON BARGATE
(Goss Record. 8th Edition: page 23)
Inscribed: *The Bargate Southampton. Of the seven gates which formerly gave entrance to Southampton only two now remain. Of these the finest is the Bargate which contains Norman work . It was originally defended by a drawbridge over a moat. On the north side are two semicircular towers through which side arches have been cut for the convenience of pedestrians, and between which is a fine projecting front supposed to have been added in the reign of Richard II. Rd. No. 594375*

(a) Small, white glazed	55mm	47.50	100.00
(b) Small, grey†	55mm	87.50	
(c) Large, white, glazed†	87mm	65.00	145.00
(d) Large, white, unglazed†	87mm	87.00	125.00
(e) Large, grey†	87mm	155.00	
(f) Large, brown†	87mm	185.00	

Matching Arms: *SOUTHAMPTON*

Southport Vase

Southwold Ancient Gun

Southwold Jar

*Staffordshire Drinking Cup
League Model, 1926*

*(Staffordshire) One-handled
Tyg*

*(Staffordshire) Two-handled
Tyg*

Southdown Sheep Bell

*Staffordshire Tyg
League Model*

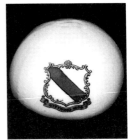

*Steyning Shepard's Crown
Sea Urchin*

Stirling Pint Measure

Stockport Plague Stone

Stockton Ancient Salt Pot

272

	With any Arms £ p	With Matching Arms £ p
Model		

SOUTHDOWN SHEEP BELL 54mm 65.00 125.00
Inscribed: *Model of Southdown Sheep Bell. Copyright.*
This model is identical to the Small Swiss Cow Bell and is
incomplete without the loose porcelain clapper suspended
inside it, worth £10.00 alone.
It has no correct arms - any Sussex Downland arms are to be
considered as matching, Steyning 1685 in particular.

SOUTHPORT VASE 50mm 7.50 20.00
(Goss Record. 8th Edition: Page 27)
Inscribed: *Model of Vase at Botanic Gardens Southport.*
Rd. No. 403423.
Matching Arms: *SOUTHPORT*

SOUTHWOLD ANCIENT GUN Length 94mm 117.50 165.00
(Goss Record. 9th Edition: Page 28)
Inscribed: *Model of Ancient Gun washed out of*
Gun Hill Cliff, Southwold, now in the Town Hall.
Matching Arms: *SOUTHWOLD ANCIENT,*
SOUTHWOLD FIRST COAT
OR *SOUTHWOLD SECOND COAT*

SOUTHWOLD JAR 88mm 7.50 21.50
(Goss Record. 8th Edition: Page 34) 140mm[1] 25.00 38.50
Inscribed: *Model of Ancient Jar washed out of cliff near*
Southwold, now in Town Hall.
Matching Arms: *SOUTHWOLD ANCIENT,*
SOUTHWOLD FIRST COAT
OR *SOUTHWOLD SECOND COAT*

for SPANISH CARAFE
see Gibraltar Alcaraza

for SPANISH (EDDYSTONE) JUG
see Plymouth (Spanish) Jug

STAFFORDSHIRE DRINKING CUP 111mm 190.00
Inscribed: *Model of Staffordshire Drinking Cup circa. 1650.*
Copyright. This model is only issued to Members of the
League and cannot be bought.
International League Model for 1926
Correct Arms: *INTERNATIONAL LEAGUE OF*
    GOSS COLLECTORS

(STAFFORDSHIRE) ONE-HANDLED TYG 65mm 7.50 23.00
(Goss Record.8th Edition: Page 32)
Inscribed: *Model of Ancient Tyg.*
Matching Arms: *STAFFORDSHIRE*

		With any Arms £ p	With Matching Arms £ p
Model			

(STAFFORDSHIRE) TWO-HANDLED TYG   65mm   7.50   30.00
(Goss Record. 8th Edition: Page 32)
Inscribed: *Model of Ancient Tyg.*
Matching Arms: *STAFFORDSHIRE*

STAFFORDSHIRE TYG   (a) 70mm   115.00
(Goss Record. 9th Edition: Pages 22 and 28   (b) 70mm   150.00
and Plate B)
Inscribed: *Model of Ancient Staffordshire Tyg.*
Rd. No. 641312. The model is only issued to Members of
more than 4 Years standing and cannot be purchased.
This model was first introduced bearing THE LEAGUE
OF GOSS COLLECTORS motif (a), and
re-introduced later bearing the INTERNATIONAL
LEAGUE OF GOSS COLLECTORS motif (b) .

STEYNING SHEPHERD'S CROWN SEA URCHIN   50mm   33.00   77.50
(Goss Record. 9th Edition: page 29)
Inscribed: *Model of Fossil Sea Urchin found on The Downs at*
Steyning, locally known as Shepherds Crown. Copyright.
Matching Arms: *STEYNING 1685*

STIRLING PINT MEASURE   61mm   14.00   38.50
(Goss Record. 8th Edition: Page 40)
Inscribed: *Model of the Stirling Pint Measure. One of the*
Ancient Standard Measures of Scotland deposited in Stirling by
Act of Parliament l 457. Rd . No. 543012.
Matching Arms: *STIRLING, BURGH OF STIRLING,*
STERLINI OPPIDVM OR *COUNTY OF STIRLING*

STOCKPORT PLAGUE STONE   Length 75mm   30.00   47.00
(Goss Record. 8th Edition: Page 17)
Inscribed: *Model of Plague Stone found during excavations in*
Stockport Market Place. Original now in Vernon Park Museum,
Stockport. The hollow was filled with vinegar, and when food
etc. was brought into the town, the money was placed in the
vinegar to prevent infection.
Matching Arms: *STOCKPORT*

STOCKTON ANCIENT SALT POT   73mm   13.00   38.50
(Goss Record.8th Edition: Page 21)
Inscribed: *Model of Ancient Salt Pot found in bed of river at*
Stockton-on- Tees. Rd. No . 406301.
Matching Arms: *STOCKTON- ON- TEES*

Model		With any Arms £ p	With Matching Arms £ p

STORNOWAY HIGHLAND MILK CROGAN   56mm   15.00   77.50
(Goss Record. 8th Edition: Page 40)
Inscribed: *Model of Highland Milk Crogan made by Crofters
at Barvas, Isle of Lewis. Rd. No. 617576.*
Matching Arms: *STORNOWAY*
Also found decorated in red overall with black and green drip,
similar in style to C.J. Noke's Sung pattern for Royal Doulton   300.00†
See illustration on jacket rear of *The Price Guide to Arms and
Decorations on Goss China 1991 Ed.*

STRATFORD ON AVON SANCTUARY KNOCKER
in high relief on two-handled mug   Height of detail   62mm   145.00   215.00
(Goss Record. 9th Edition: Page 30)
Inscribed: *Model of the Stratford on Avon Sanctuary
Knocker. Copyright.*
Matching Arms: *STRATFORD ON AVON*

STRATFORD ON AVON TOBY BASIN
Multi-coloured   53mm   105.00†
(Goss Record. 8th Edition: Page 35)
The jug fits into the basin easily and this was often
done causing the base of the latter to crack -
check carefully before buying

STRATFORD-ON-AVON TOBY JUG
Multi-coloured   78mm   80.00†
(Goss Record. 8th Edition: Page 35)
Inscribed: *Model of the Stratford Toby Jug.*
Also, white glazed (Blackpool arms)   78mm   40.00

The above two models are a pair.

During the Goss family ownership of the pottery,
Stratford models could only be obtained from the
Stratford agency. This is why, for example, that
Shakespeare's Font is rarely found without matching arms.

SUNDERLAND BOTTLE   58mm   7.50   19.00
(Goss Record. 8th Edition: Page 21 and advertisement
page 65)
Inscribed: *Model of Ancient Bottle in Sunderland Museum.
Rd. No. 392068.* (One example found with *392089*)
Matching Arms: *SUNDERLAND*

Stornoway Highland Milk
Crogan

Stratford-on-Avon Sanctuary
Knocker

Stratford-on-Avon Toby
Basin

Stratford-on-Avon Toby Jug

Sunderland Bottle

Swindon Vase

Swiss Cow Bell

Swiss Milk Bucket

Swiss Milk Pot and Lid

Swiss Vinegar Bottle

Teignmouth Lighthouse

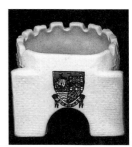

Tenby Gateway

Model		With any Arms £ p	With Matching Arms £ p

SWINDON VASE   55mm   7.50   25.00
(Goss Record. 8th Edition: Page 36)   110mm[1]   17.00   28.00
Inscribed: *Model of Vase dug up near Swindon.*
Matching Arms: *SWINDON* OR *SWINDON, WILTS*

SWISS COW BELL   51mm   15.00   25.00
(Goss Record. 8th Edition: Page 43)   73mm   19.50   34.00
Inscribed: *Model of Old Swiss Cow Bell.*
Only the 73mm size is listed in *The Goss Record.*
The small size is identical to the Southdown Sheep Bell.
This model is incomplete without the loose porcelain
clapper hanging inside it which is worth £10.00.
Matching Arms: Any Arms from *SWITZERLAND*

SWISS MILK BUCKET   56mm   16.50   42.50
(Goss Record. 8th Edition: Page 43)   82mm   21.50   38.50
Inscribed: *Model of Swiss Milk Bucket. Rd. No. 526385.*
Matching Arms: Any Arms from *SWITZERLAND*

SWISS MILK POT and lid   82mm   19.00   55.00
(Goss Record. 8th Edition: Page 43)
Inscribed: *Model of Old Swiss Milk Pot. Rd. No. 500867.*
Often found cracked in the base.
This model is incomplete without its lid which is
valued at £10.00.
Matching Arms: Any Arms from *SWITZERLAND*

SWISS VINEGAR BOTTLE   Length 75mm   15.00   42.50
(Goss Record. 8th Edition: Page 43)
Inscribed: *Model of Old Swiss Vinegar Bottle. Rd. No. 496832.*
Matching Arms: Any Arms from *SWITZERLAND*

for TEAR BOTTLE
see Caerleon Glass Lachrymatory

TEIGNMOUTH LIGHTHOUSE   118mm   77.50   95.00
(Goss Record. 8th Edition: Page 20)
Inscribed: *Model of Teignmouth Lighthouse. Rd. No. 622474.*
Matching Arms: *TEIGNMOUTH*

TENBY GATEWAY   (a) White glazed   65mm   87.50   190.00
                                  (b) Brown   65mm   175.00   320.00
                                  (c) Grey   65mm   300.00†
Inscribed: *Model of South West Gateway (known as Five Arches)*
in the Town Walls of Tenby. The walls date from the reign of
Edward 111 about 1328. Copyright.
Matching Arms: *TENBY*

Tewkesbury Saxon Urn

Tintern Ancient Water Bottle

Tonbridge Eastcheap Roman Ewer

Tresco Old Brazier

Tresvannack Ancient Urn

Tuscan Vase, 785, white

Truro Glen Dorgal Cinerary Urn

Twickenham Antique Pope's Pipe

Walmer Roman Vase

Wareham Bottle

Waterlooville Soldier's Water Bottle

Welsh Crochon

Model		With any Arms £ p	With Matching Arms £ p
TEWKESBURY SAXON URN	45mm	7.50	21.50

TEWKESBURY SAXON URN   45mm   7.50   21.50
(Goss Record. 8th Edition: Page 22)
Inscribed: *Model of Saxon Urn found at the Tolsey,*
Tewkesbury. Rd. No. 411451.
Matching Arms: *TEWKESBURY*

TINTERN ANCIENT WATER BOTTLE   76mm   16.00   33.00
(Goss Record. 8th Edition: Page 29)
Inscribed: *Model of Ancient Water Bottle found during*
excavations for bridge at Brockweir, Tintern. 1907.
Rd. No. 626750.
Matching Arms: *TINTERN ABBEY OR CHEPSTOW*

for TOBY BASIN
see Stratford-on-Avon Toby Basin

for TOBY JUG
see Stratford-on-Avon Toby Jug

TONBRIDGE EASTCHEAP ROMAN EWER   63mm   9.00   25.50
(Goss Record. 8th Edition: Page 27)
Inscribed: *Model of Roman Ewer found in Eastcheap London*
now in Tonbridge Museum. Rd. No. 599334
Matching Arms: *TONBRIDGE*

TRESCO OLD BRAZIER   69mm   21.50   65.00
(Goss Record. 8th Edition: Page 18)
Inscribed: *Model of the Old Brazier at Tresco formerly the*
Beacon Light at St. Agnes, Isles of Scilly. Rd. No. 589292.
Matching Arms: *F ALGERNON DORRIEN-SMITH,*
LORD PROPRIETOR OF THE ISLES OF SCILLY

TRESVANNACK ANCIENT URN   55mm   12.00   22.50
(Goss Record. 8th Edition: Page 18)
Inscribed: *Model of Ancient Urn found at Tresvannack,*
St. Paul, Cornwall. Rd. No. 594378.
Matching Arms: *PENSANS ANNO DOMINI 1614 (PENZANCE)*

TRURO GLEN DORGAL CINERARY URN   54mm   12.50   22.00
(Goss Record. 8th Edition: Page 18)
Inscribed: *Model of Cinerary Urn found at Glen Dorgal, now*
in Truro Museum. Rd. No. 594376.
Matching Arms: *TRURO*

TUSCAN VASE   (a) White glazed   150mm   125.00
           (b) Lustre (orange, purple or yellow) 150mm   235.00
Inscribed: *The Tuscan Vase. 785 Copyright.*
It has no matching arms

Model	With any Arms £ p	With Matching Arms £ p

TWICKENHAM ANTIQUE POPE'S PIPE
(Goss Record. 8th Edition: Page 29)   Length 118mm   38.50   77.50
Inscribed: *Model of Antique Pipe found among the debris*
of Pope's House at Twickenham.
Matching Arms: *TWICKENHAM*

for TYG (ONE HANDLE)
see Staffordshire One-Handled Tyg

for TYG (TWO HANDLES)
see Staffordshire Two-Handled Tyg

for ULVERSTON, SIR JOHN BARROW'S MONUMENT
see Sir John Barrow's Monument, Ulverston

for URICONIUM EWER (First Period models so marked)
see Shrewsbury Ewer

for WALDEN ABBEY COVERED URN
see Saffron Walden Covered Urn

WALMER ROMAN VASE   65mm   7.50   15.00
(Goss Record. 8th Edition: Page 27)
Inscribed: *Model of Roman Vase. Found at Walmer Lodge.*
Rd. No. 382437.
Matching Arms: *WALMER* OR *DEAL*

WAREHAM BOTTLE   67mm   7.50   21.50
(Goss Record. 8th Edition: Page 21)
Inscribed: *Model of Roman Bottle found at Wareham.*
Rd. No. 500866.
Matching Arms: *WAREHAM*

for WARWICK - GUY'S PORRIDGE POT
see Guy's Porridge Pot

WATERLOOVILLE SOLDIER'S WATER BOTTLE   83mm   22.50   34.00
(Goss Record. 8th Edition: Page 24)
Inscribed: *Model of Army Water Bottle used at the Battle of*
Waterloo. Waterlooville. When the troops came back after
"Waterloo" their first camp was at this place which thus
obtained its name. The original water bottle which is of oak,
bound with brass, was left behind by one of the soldiers
Rd. No. 638373.
Matching Arms: *WATERLOOVILLE*

Model	With any Arms £ p	With Matching Arms £ p

Any Welsh arms may be considered matching on Welsh
models

WELSH CORACLE   Length 77mm   24.50   33.00
(Goss Record. 8th Edition: Page 39)
Inscribed: *Model of Welsh Coracle. Survival of Ancient
British wicker and hide boats.*
Matching Arms: *LLANGOLLEN* OR *ANY WELSH ARMS*
First Period version plain with inscription on base.
Second Period version with ribbed sides and
inscription on top of seat.
Up until 1903, the Welsh Coracle was called thus and
is listed in *The Goss Record* as a national model having no
particular town or city arms. From 1904 onwards, it
was re-named The Llangollen Coracle with
Llangollen given as the matching arms, which
explains the confusion of the two descriptions that
can be found on the same piece.

WELSH CROCHON	50mm	14.00	20.00
(Goss Record. 8th Edition: Page 39)	61mm	19.00	28.50
Inscribed: *Model of Ancient Welsh Bronze Crochon,*	76mm[1]	22.00	38.50
about A.D. 400, dug up at Caerhun (Conovium) near	107mm[1]	25.00	65.00
Conway in collection of W.H. Goss.	115mm[1]	30.00	77.50

Also see POSTCARDS Chapter 5.
(**N.B.** The Welsh word for cauldron is correctly spelt Crochan)
Matching Arms: *CONWAY*

WELSH FISH BASKET   58mm   125.00
Inscribed: *Model of Welsh Fish Basket.*
Matching Arms: *ARMS OF WALES* OR *ANY WELSH ARMS*

WELSH HAT	(a) Plain brim Dia. 74mm	17.50	25.00
	(b) Llanfair P.G. on brim	40.00	67.50

Inscribed: *Model of Hat formerly worn by women in Wales.*
Matching Arms: *ARMS OF WALES* OR *ANY WELSH ARMS*

WELSH JACK and lid   120mm   25.00   42.50
(Goss Record. 8th Edition: Page 39)
Inscribed: *Model of Welsh Jack.*
This model is not complete without its lid, value £ 15.00.
Matching Arms: *ARMS OF WALES* OR *ANY WELSH ARMS*

Welsh Fish Basket

Welsh Hat

Welsh Jack and Lid

Welsh Leek

Welsh Milk Can and Lid

Welsh Picyn

Wensleydale Leyburn Leather Jack

Westminster Abbey Coronation Chair, Brown

Weymouth Roman Vase

Whitby Ammonite

Whitby Pillion Stone

Whitstable Roman Patera

Model		With any Arms £ p	With Matching Arms £ p
WELSH LEEK	90mm	19.00	30.00

Inscribed on the base or more commonly, the side: *K. Henry V.*
The Welshmen did goot servace (at Crecy) in a garden where leeks
did grow". Shakespeare.
This model has six leaf tips each coloured green.
Matching Arms: *ARMS OF WALES* OR *ANY WELSH ARMS*

Model			
WELSH MILK CAN and lid	70mm	20.00	30.00
(Goss Record. 8th Edition: Page 39)	108mm	30.00	40.00
Inscribed: *Model of Old Welsh Milk Can.*	130mm	34.00	60.00

The model is incomplete without its lid which is
worth £15.00 of the price shown in all three sizes.
Can also be found incorrectly

named *Welsh Jack and Lid*	120mm	25.00	45.00

Matching Arms: *ARMS OF WALES* OR *ANY WELSH ARMS*

WELSH PICYN	62mm	16.00	30.00

(Goss Record.8th Edition: Page 39)
Inscribed: *Model of Welsh Picyn or Porridge Bowl* .
Rd. No. 543010.
Matching Arms: *ARMS OF WALES* OR *ANY WELSH ARMS*

for WELSH PORRIDGE BOWL
see Welsh Picyn

WENSLEYDALE LEYBURN LEATHER JACK	67mm	14.00	47.00

(Goss Record. 8th Edition: Page 38)
Inscribed: *Model of Wensleydale Jack date about 1500 in*
Hornes Museum Leyburn. Rd. No. 521972.
Matching Arms: *LEYBURN*

WESTMINSTER ABBEY CORONATION CHAIR
(Goss Record. 8th Edition: Page 29)
Inscribed: *Model of The Coronation Chair in Westminster*
Abbey. Rd. No. 578694.
See also Perth Coronation Chair
Two varieties, one with hole in rear of stone

(a) White	85mm	38.50	65.00
(b) Stone in brown	85mm	80.00	115.00
(c) Brown	85mm	250.00†	285.00

A blue version is rumoured to exist, but has not yet
been seen. I doubt that it does exist. The model was
probably inspired by the Coronation of King George V
in 1911. The brown example (c) is described in the
London agent, Henry Jones & Co Ltd. Advertisement
on page 1 of the 8th Edition of *The Goss Record* as 'Old stone'.
Matching Arms: *WESTMINSTER ABBEY*

Model		With any Arms £ p	With Matching Arms £ p

WEYMOUTH ROMAN VASE   56mm   13.00   22.00
(Goss Record. 8th Edition: Page 21   94mm[1]   22.00   38.50
and advertisement page 61)
Inscribed: *Model of Roman Vase found at Jordan Hill,*
Weymouth, now in Dorset Museum.
The original of this model is in the Dorset County Museum,
Dorchester and was selected as a local model by the
Dorchester agent (see Goss Record 8th Edition page 61)
Dorchester could therefore be considered as being correct arms.
Matching Arms: *ARMS OF WEYMOUTH AND*
MELCOMBE REGIS and SEAL OF WEYMOUTH
AND MELCOMBE REGIS

for WHISKEY CUP
see National Highland Cuach or Whiskey Cup

WHITBY AMMONITE   73mm   42.00   77.50
(Goss Record. 7th Edition: Page 52-Illustrated)
Inscribed: *Model of the Whithy Ammonite. Rd. No. 513063.*
Identical to the rarer Lyme Regis Ammonite
Matching Arms: *WHITBY*

WHITBY PILLION STONE   Length 72mm   38.50   77.50
(Goss Record. 9th Edition: Page 33)
Inscribed: *Model of Old Pillion Stone Flowergate,*
Whitby. Rd. No. 641311.
MatchingArms: *WHITBY*

for WHITEHALL, CENOTAPH
see (The) Cenotaph, Whitehall

for WHITLEY BAY, ST. MARY'S LIGHTHOUSE
see St. Mary's Lighthouse, Whitley Bay

WHITSTABLE ROMAN PATERA   Dia. 88mm   25.00   60.00
(Goss Record. 8th Edition: Page 27)
Inscribed: *Model of Roman Patera about 1600 years old*
dredged up off Whitstable.
Matching Arms: *THE SEAL OF THE CORPORATION*
OF THE DREDGERS OF WHITSTABLE, 1793

WILDERSPOOL ROMAN TETINAE   105mm   200.00
Inscribed: *Model of Roman Tetinae or Feeding Bottle*
found at Wilderspool - Copyright l 924. This model is only
issued to Members of the League and cannot be bought.
International League Model for 1924
Correct Arms: *INTERNATIONAL LEAGUE OF*
GOSS COLLECTORS.

GOSS IN WINCHESTER

William Savage opened a shop in Winchester in 1839 selling fancy needlework. He was a most enterprising man, typical of many in the Victorian era. His shop was near the Cathedral and when the tourist trade blossomed with the advent of cheap railway travel in the 1850s he began to sell a whole range of Winchester china. This was decorated with transfer prints of local scenes from photographs taken by himself, crests of the Hospital of St. Cross and William of Wykeham, and The Trusty Servant. This china was 'published' by himself and produced by the great firm of Copeland. In addition to a wide range of domestic china he stocked models of the Winchester Cathedral Font, the Winchester Bushel and the Leathern Jack (from Winchester College). The last item was probably the earliest model, it can be found in Davenport china marked as *The Winchester Flagon*.

It must have been through this business with Copeland that W.H. Goss got to know William Savage. It is probable that William Savage inspired W.H. Goss in the possibilities for the production of souvenir ware. He was one of the first in the country to offer models of 'ancient artefacts' and china with local crests and views to the expanding tourist trade.

Although William Savage continued to do business with Copeland after W.H. Goss started up on his own, it is apparent that Goss was producing items for William Savage from a very early date. Copies of the Copeland Jacks can be found, these are very rare and usually unmarked, but recognisably Goss. This early period also saw the production of the William of Wykeham and St. Cross parian plates, designed by William Savage himself. The W.H. Goss prizewinning entry in the International Exhibition of 1862 shows a William of Wykeham plate and a Winchester Bushel. Gradually over the years the design of the Jacks changed to the one typical of W.H. Goss, and more models were introduced. New models of the Warder's Horn, Cardinal Beaufort's Salt Cellar and Candlestick, the Elizabethan Quart and the magnificent model of the Trusty Servant were introduced.

William Savage died on the 6th April 1887. The contents of his shop were auctioned in July of that year - what an auction to have attended! His niece, Mrs. Fieldwick, took over the Goss agency in July. She only stayed in business for about a year, advertising QUEEN VICTORIA IVORY PORCELAIN as well as the Winchester Memorial China in the local paper.

Although A.L. Henty bought the shop at 58, High Street on the death of William Savage in 1887, he did not become the Goss agent until the middle of 1888 when Mrs. Fieldwick closed. William Savage had catered to the expensive end of the souvenir trade. Henty went more down market. He introduced more (and cheaper) new models - the Winchester College Black Jacks, the Winchester Pot, the small size Bushel and a wide range of domestic and miniature shapes. It seems probable that the Winchester Flagon was dropped out of production during the Henty period accounting for its relative rarity. In 1893 he introduced the second Winchester figure, William of Wykeham, to celebrate the Quingentenary (500th anniversary) of Winchester College. Up until 1903 the Winchester models were only available from Henty; after that time they were available to other agents to order with their own crests.

In 1915 Henty closed and Prouten and Dugen, next door, took over the agency and held it until they, in turn, closed in 1926. They had sold cheap, poorer quality crested china for many years before they started to sell Goss china. They do not appear to have introduced any new models during their time as Goss agent.

The agency then passed to Watson and Sons London Bazaar Stores at the other end of the High Street. This was an old established business that had stocked the better ranges of crested ware (Arcadian, Carlton, etc.) A new Goss model that appears about this time is that of King Alfred's Statue. This model does seem to be from a different pattern to the corresponding Willow and Arcadian models (which Watson and

Wilderspool Roman Tetinae League Model, 1924

Winchester Bushel

Winchester Flagon

Winchester Jack

Winchester Pot

Winchester Quart

Winchester Castle Warden's Horn on Plinth

Winchester Castle Warden's Horn

Windsor Round Tower Two-piece Night Light

Windsor Urn

Windsor Kettle and Lid (Queen Charlotte's)

Windleshaw Chantry

286

	With any Arms	With Matching Arms
Model	£ p	£ p

Sons had been selling for many years). It was probably produced towards the end of the Second Period at their request. The fine Goss Trusty Servant was also available from Watson and Sons up until the end of the Second Period. An Arcadian model marked *Goss England* then replaced it. Watson and Sons were still advertising Goss china in 1939 right up to the closure of the factory.

The story of Goss in Winchester mirrors the Goss story itself. It is very probable that the idea of Winchester Memorial China as William Savage called it, was the inspiration for the models, crests and transfers that made W H Goss famous. Every period is represented in Winchester Goss, from the earliest, relatively crude parian ware, through the very high quality Second Period pieces and on up to the poorer Third Period. Winchester has more varieties of models and more decorations than any other single place, illustrating the rich history of the city.

WINCHESTER BUSHEL
(Goss Record. 8th Edition: Page 24)
Decorated with red and blue lettering
in relief, and various symbols.

		With any Arms	With Matching Arms
100mm across Height 38mm		155.00†	190.00
Height 51 mm		125.00†	265.00
120mm across Height 55mm[1]		600 00†	750.00

Impressed: *Old Winchester Bushel now in the Cathedral, Winchester.*
Inscribed: *Reduced Model of Winchester Bushel.*
The largest size is normally unmarked.
Matching Arms: *CITY OF WINCHESTER*
There is also a rare First Period example, unglazed,
with pale blue legs, brushed gilding, red and blue
lettering in relief. Published by A. L. Henty, and also
a black unglazed version, similarly coloured.

	With any Arms	With Matching Arms
Both 170mm across Height 70mm[1]		750.00

WINCHESTER FLAGON
This model is not listed in any edition of *The Goss
Record*. It is an unnamed historical shape and
traditional to the first Winchester Agent, W Savage,
who stocked this model manufactured by the Copeland
works until Goss set up on his own and was able to
meet his requirements.

	With any Arms	With Matching Arms
105mm[1]	26.00	65.00
130mm[1]	30.00	77.50
152mm[1]	36.00	85.00

Characteristics of Goss examples include typical Goss body,
hatched gilding, hollow base; verse lettering type is specific to
Goss, and the lettering style on the base is typical Goss, i.e. upper
case serif italics.
See also FIRST PERIOD 9C ORNAMENTAL WARE
Matching Arms: *CITY OF WINCHESTER*

WINCHESTER FLAGON

	With any Arms	With Matching Arms
150mm[1]†	500.00	

Overall surface decoration representing crinkled leather.
Row of dots in relief around top, base and handle, turquoise blue
line to rim and base. Gilded rim and handle.

| | With any Arms | With Matching Arms |
Model	£ p	£ p

for WINCHESTER BLACK JACK
see Winchester Jack

WINCHESTER JACK			
(Goss Record. 8th Edition: Page 23)	32mm	17.50	28.50
Inscribed: *Model of the Black Jack at Winchester*	44mm	10.00	19.00
College.	83mm	19.00	30.00
Matching Arms: *CITY OF WINCHESTER*	121mm[1]	25.00	40.00

WINCHESTER POT   74mm   25.00   38.50
(Goss Record. 8th Edition: Page 24)
Inscribed: *Model of Pot dug up at George Hotel, Winchester.*
Matching Arms: *CITY OF WINCHESTER*

WINCHESTER QUART   92mm†[1]   850.00
(Goss Record. 8th Edition: Page 24)
Inscribed: *Model of The Winchester Quart Temp. Q. Elizabeth.*
This model is not known bearing a coat of arms, but carries
an embossed crown and 1601 E.R. on its side. It is a
most impressive piece - rare and desirable.
see also 9C FIRST PERIOD 9C ORNAMENTAL AND DOMESTIC

WINCHESTER CASTLE WARDER'S HORN   Length
(Goss Record. 8th Edition: Page 24)   (a) on plinth†   152mm[1]   510.00
                                       (b) without plinth†   152mm[1]   340.00
Inscribed: *Warder's Horn, Winchester Castle, A.D. 1300.*
Found named as Warder's or Warden's Horn
A magnificent model in either form which carries no arms.

WINDLESHAW CHANTRY   128mm   85.00   170.00
Inscribed in Gothic script around the four edges on the
base:
A Present From Lowe House New Church Bazaar 1920.
surrounding the further inscription:
*Model of Windleshaw Chantry, in St. Helens Catholic Burial
Ground. Founded by Sir Thomas Gerard of Bryn, after the Battle
of Agincourt (A.D. 1415), for a Priest to celebrate Mass there for
the souls of his ancestors for ever. The last Priest was Richard
Frodsham, of Wyndle (A.D. 1548)*
Matching Arms: *EN DIEU EST MON ESPERANCE*
(Sir Thomas Gerard of Kingsley & Bryn)

WINDSOR KETTLE and lid   170mm   125.00   170.00
(Goss Record. 8th Edition: Page 17)
Inscribed: *Model of Queen Charlotte's Windsor Favourite now
in William H. Goss's Collection.*
This model should have a circular lid with a flat top
surmounted by a round knob. Value £50.00
Matching Arms: *WINDSOR* OR *FLOREAT ETONA (ETON).*

Model				With any Arms £ p	With Matching Arms £ p

WINDSOR ROUND TOWER   (a) white†   145mm   500.00
Two-piece, unglazed night-light   (b) brown†   145mm   650.00
       (c) grey†   145mm   525.00
(This model is illustrated in the
Goss Record. 9th Edition: Page 40, Plate I)
Inscribed: *Round Tower Windsor Rd. No. 209991.*

WINDSOR URN   45mm   7.50   11.50
(Goss Record. 8th Edition: Page 16)   82mm   17.00   30.00
Inscribed: *Urn found at Old Windsor, from original in
Museum.*
Matching Arms: *WINDSOR* OR *ETON (FLOREAT
ETONA)*

WINSFORD SALT LUMP   (a) 80mm   80.00
Inscribed: *Model of Salt Lump as made at Winsford,*   (b) 80mm   100.00
Cheshire.
This is identical to the Cheshire Salt Block, and
appears with the Arms of Winsford either glazed or
unglazed (a) . A rare variety (b) has been seen with
holes for pouring in the top and SALT in Gothic script
on the front.
Matching Arms: *WINSFORD*

WISBECH JUG   82mm[1]   27.50   60.0
(Goss Record. 8th Edition: Page 17)
Inscribed: *Model of Ancient Jug found at Wisbech River,
1848, in Museum.*
Matching Arms: *WISBECH* OR *SEAL OF WISBECH*

WITCH'S CAULDRON   47mm   21.00   35.00
(Goss Record. 9th Edition: Page 30)
This model is identical to the Peterborough Tripod
and carries the following quotation in Gothic
Script, with illuminated initial letter D:
*Double double toyle and trouble
Fyre burne and caldrone bubble, Macbeth.*
Matching with Scottish, *SHAKESPEARE'S ARMS* OR
STRATFORD ON AVON

WORCESTER JUG   64mm   14.00   17.00
(Goss Record. 8th Edition: Page 38)   101mm[1]   17.00   26.00
Inscribed: *The Worcester Jug from the original in the Museum,
found at Castle Hill.*
Matching Arms: *CITY OF WORCESTER*

Wisbech Jug

Winsford Salt Lump

Witch's Cauldron

Worcester Jug

Wymondham Ancient Jar

Yarmouth Ewer

Yarmouth Jug

York Roman Ewer

York Roman Urn

York Roman Vessel

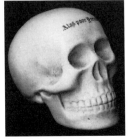

Yorick's Skull (small)

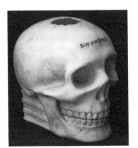

Yorick's Skull (large)
Two-piece Night Light

290

		With any Arms £ p	With Matching Arms £ p
Model			

WYMONDHAM ANCIENT JAR — 61mm — 16.00 — 34.00
(Goss Record. 8th Edition: Page 29)
Inscribed: *Model of Ancient Jar found in the Abbey ruins Wymondham. Rd. No. 617572.*
Matching Arms: *WYMONDHAM*

YARMOUTH EWER — 62mm — 7.50 — 21.50
(Goss Record. 8th Edition: Page 29 and advertisement page 77)
Inscribed: *Model of Early English Ewer dredged up in River Yare now in Yarmouth Museum. Rd. No. 495671.*
Matching Arms: *GREAT YARMOUTH*

YARMOUTH JUG — 132mm — 65.00 — 85.00
(Goss Record. 8th Edition: Page 29 and advertisement page 77)
Inscribed: *Model of Ancient Jug dredged from the sea off Great Yarmouth, now in the Museum. Rd. No. 500870.*
Matching Arms: *GREAT YARMOUTH*

YORICK'S SKULL
(Goss Record. 8th Edition: Page 35)
Usually inscribed: *Alas poor Yorick*

(a)	Pale yellow†	38mm	77.50	
(b)	White unglazed†	75mm	100.00	
(c)	Pale yellow†	75mm	170.00	
(d)	White unglazed†	102mm	130.00	
(e)	Pale yellow†	102mm	175.00	
(f)	White glazed†	102mm	160.00	

The 102mm version is in two pieces and is designed for use as a night-light, the base modelled as three books.

YORK ROMAN EWER — 63mm — 7.50 — 21.50
(Goss Record. 8th Edition: Page 38) — 127mm[1] — 30.00 — 38.50
Inscribed: *From original in Hospitium. Found at York.*
see also POSTCARDS Chapter 5
Matching Arms: *CITY OF YORK*

YORK ROMAN URN — 51mm — 7.50 — 17.00
(Goss Record. 8th Edition: Page 38) — 101mm[1] — 22.00 — 30.00
Inscribed: *Roman Urn, from original in Hospitium. Found at York.*
Matching Arms: *CITY OF YORK*

YORK ROMAN VESSEL — 73mm[1] — 23.00 — 38.50
(Goss Record. 8th Edition: Page 38)
Inscribed: *Roman Vessel, from original in Hospitium. Found at York.*
Matching Arms: *CITY OF YORK*

The Goss China stall at the British Empire Exhibition, Wemberly 1925. The shelf of lustre wares shows the factory moving with the times.

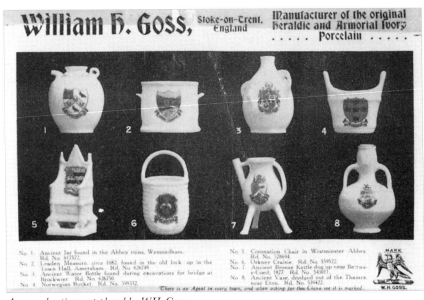

A rare advertisement placed by W.H. Goss

F Cottages and Coloured Buildings

In 1893 Adolphus introduced a new range that was to prove highly successful. These were reproductions in miniature of historic buildings, famous cottages and churches of an exact likeness and colouring. The first seven models were night-lights and those surviving today can often be found with candlewax still inside or with heat cracks as they were sold to be used at bedtime. The smoke came out of hollow chimneys and the light shone out through extra thin porcelain windows and half-open doors when a candle was placed inside. Initially, the three most popular were the famous Shakespeare's Birthplace and Ann Hathaway's Cottage, both at Stratford-on-Avon, and Burns' Cottage, Ayrshire.

Heavy demand for these coloured houses led to the range being gradually extended to 42 buildings with a variety of sizes, some half-size versions and night-light burners. In the latter half of the firm's life, some cottages were glazed and this intensifies the colouring. £20.00 should be added to values for glazed varieties.

Other changes in the moulds occurred when the original buildings that the models were produced from were altered in any significant way. For example, the extensions to The First and Last House at Land's End and Lloyd George's Home, both of which appear in the original and extended forms.

Charles Dickens' House at Gads Hill in Rochester was originally moulded with no porch windows due to ivy completely covering the walls. When the Goss artists discovered that there was a small window either side of the front door after the ivy had been cut away, future models incorporated these windows. Keen collectors of cottages would probably like to have an example of each variation. The coloured houses were not normally crested, but The First and Last House in England can be found with a glass or enamel badge containing the Arms of Cornwall affixed to one end wall. Plain white cottages are rare, and were possibly examples taken home by employees.

There were slight differences in the colours used over the years: hardly surprising with some models like the two Stratford cottages which were in production for over 40 years, and having regard to a succession of different paintresses, new batches of enamels being mixed every week, and differences in firing temperatures. Generally, however, the sizes, colours and moulds were consistent. Most of the cottages were made up from sketches by Adolphus Goss, then later his son, Clarence Richard (Dick), Noel and John Goss (Dick's cousins), and a few of the pottery's best workmen.

The Cat and Fiddle Inn at Buxton was measured up by Noel Goss and a workman Alfred Mollart in 1925, modelled by John Goss and in production all in the same year. John also modelled Isaac Walton's cottage, Shallowford, between 1925 and 1928 using photographs, the original building having burned down completely long before. During the 1920's Noel and Alfred measured up several buildings including the pretty John Knox's House in Edinburgh in 1929.

Massachusetts Hall and Holden Chapel, both in the grounds of Harvard University, Boston, Mass. are large Nightlights and were ordered by the Boston agents, Jones, McDuffie & Stratton Co. who also ordered large Robert Burns Nightlight cottages. Only white glazed and Blackpool crested examples of Massachusetts Hall have been found and only coloured versions of Holden Chapel, the former only in the UK. So either the order was cancelled or there were quality control problems, for examples seen are sub standard and were not exported. Holden Chapels were indeed sold by the Boston agent and the majority of the few examples of this rare and desirable cottage have come to light in New England.

Several new models were in preparation towards the end, such as the An Clachan in 1938, and the later smaller sizes of Shakespeare's and Hathaway's cottages, which are all Third Period Goss and can be found listed in that section. Designs have been found for Plas Newydd, Llangollen, and Atlantic View Hotel, Lands End, but these have never been seen and it is not now thought that even one example of each exists.

Some of the white glazed buildings, for example, Massachusetts Hall, the Abbot's Kitchen, and the Newquay Huers's House with the Blackpool arms are seconds, although no other variation of the latter piece has been found to date. It has been established that Massachusetts Hall did not go into production in coloured form, but small fragments of it have been unearthed at the site of the factory. Perhaps this model and the Atlantic View Hotel, or maybe even Plas Newydd, will appear in colour in the future, but it is now thought to be doubtful.

Cottages and Buildings in this section have been listed alphabetically by person, town or title. Buildings that are not recorded in this section will appear under SECOND PERIOD 10E or THIRD PERIOD 11.O Chapters.

It can be stated with certainty that 99.99% of all pieces of Goss China carry the factory's mark in one form or another. However in the case of the Gretna Green Old Toll Bar, some 50% of the examples seen by me are unmarked. These were definitely produced by the Goss Factory and one can only surmise that one batch of these cottages left the factory unmarked either at the request of the agent or due to an error in the transfer department. Exceptionally for such a rare Second Period model, values are the same whether marked or unmarked.

Exceptionally, all sizes in this chapter are given by length unless otherwise stated.

*John Bunyan's Cottage,
Elstow*

*Robert Burns' Cottage
Ayrshire, small*

*Robert Burns' Cottage
Ayrshire, Night-light*

Buxton, Cat and Fiddle Inn

*Christchurch, Old Court
House*

*Charles Dickens' House,
Rochester, no Porch Windows*

*First and Last House in
England with Annexe*

*First and Last House, Land's
End*

*Charles Dickens' House,
Rochester, with Porch Windows*

*First and Last Post Office, in
England, Sennen*

*Glastonbury, Church of Joseph
of Arimathoea*

Goss Oven, Stoke-on-Trent

£   p

Exceptionally, all dimensions given in this chapter are the length

for ABBOT'S KITCHEN, GLASTONBURY ABBEY
see Glastonbury Abbey, Abbot's Kitchen

for AN CLACHAN COTTAGE
see THIRD PERIOD 11.O BUILDINGS AND MONUMENTS

for ANN HATHAWAY'S COTTAGE, SHOTTERY
see Hathaway's Cottage, Shottery

for ARIMATHŒA, JOSEPH OF
see Glastonbury, Church of

for ATLANTIC VIEW HOTEL, LAND'S END
see Land's End, Atlantic View Hotel

for BEDDGELERT, PRINCE LLEWELYN'S HOUSE
see Prince Llewelyn's House, Beddgelert

for BOURNEMOUTH, PORTMAN LODGE
see Portman Lodge, Bournemouth

(JOHN) BUNYAN'S COTTAGE, ELSTOW   60mm   925.00
Inscribed: *John Bunyan 's Cottage, Elstow, Bedfordshire. John Bunyan was born in this Parish in 1628, not far from this spot and lived in this cottage after his marriage in 1649. Copyright.*
Unglazed

(ROBERT) BURNS' COTTAGE, AYRSHIRE
(Goss Record. 8th Edition: Page 40) glazed or unglazed
Inscribed: *Model of Burns' Cottage. Robert Burns the Ayrshire Poet was born on the 25th January A.D. 1759 died 21st July A.D. 1796 aged 37^1/$_2$ years. Rd. No. 211037.*
    (a) Small   62mm   105.00
    (b) Night-light, blue windows with brown glazing bars   145mm   170.00
    (c) as (b) but with open windows, unglazed only   145mm   310.00
    (d) Night-light, white, unglazed   150mm   170.00

BUXTON, CAT AND FIDDLE INN   68mm   200.00
Inscribed: *Model of the Cat-and-Fiddle Inn. Nr. Buxton, 1690 feet above sea level, the highest Licensed House in England Copyright.*
Unglazed

for CHARLES DICKENS' HOUSE, GADS HILL PLACE
see (Charles) Dickens' House, Gads Hill, Rochester

£   p

CHRISTCHURCH, OLD COURT HOUSE   76mm   300.00
(Not listed in any edition of The Goss Record, but advertised by
Ritchie & Co. on the back cover of the Eighth Edition.)
Inscribed: *Model of the Old House built 1511 Castle
Street Christchurch, Hants. Copyright.*
Unglazed.

for COCKERMOUTH, WORDSWORTH'S HOUSE
see Wordsworth's Birthplace, Cockermouth

for COURT HOUSE, CHRISTCHURCH
see Christchurch Old Court House

**(CHARLES) DICKENS' HOUSE, GADS HILL,
ROCHESTER**   (a)65mm   160.00
(Goss Record. 8th Edition: Page 27)   (b)65mm   235.00
Inscribed: *Model of Charles Dickens' House Gad 's Hill,
Rochester. Rd. No. 630367.*
There are two varieties of this model -
(a) with and (b) without small windows on
either side of the front door. Unglazed.

for DR SAMUEL JOHNSON'S HOUSE
see Johnson's House, Lichfield.

for DOVE COTTAGE, GRASMERE
see (William) Wordsworth's Home, Dove Cottage, Grasmere

for ELLEN TERRY'S FARM, TENTERDEN, KENT
see (Miss Ellen) Terry's Farm, Tenterden, Kent.

for FEATHERS HOTEL
see Ledbury, The Feathers Hotel

FIRST AND LAST HOUSE IN ENGLAND
(Goss Record. 8th Edition: Page 18)
Inscribed: *First and Last House in England. Rd. No. 521645.*
Can be found with the badge of Cornwall on one end for which
£20.00 should be added. The small model can be found with either a
green or black door.
This model can be found glazed or unglazed and sometimes
bears the Penzance agent's name, Stevens and Sons, Western
Esplanade, on the base. A box of these cottages was sold from this
shop for 7/6d in the 1960s!

(a) Small, cream or brown roof, green door	64mm	105.00
(b) Small, grey roof, black or green door	64mm	115.00
(c) Small, all white, unglazed	64mm	105.00
(d) Night-light, cream roof, green door	117mm	300.00
(e) Night-light, grey roof, black door	117mm	275.00
(f) Night-light, white roof, green door, brown chimney	117mm	325.00

Glastonbury Abbey, The
Abbot's Kitchen

Gullane, The Old Smithy

Thomas Hardy's Birthplace,
Dorchester

Ann Hathaway's Cottage,
Shottery, small

Ann Hathaway's Cottage,
Shottery Night-light

Holden Chapel, Harvard
University Cambridge, USA

Hop Kiln, Headcorn, Kent

Dr. Samuel Johnson's House,
Lichfield

Ledbury, The Feathers Hotel

Ledbury, Old Market House

(Rt. Hon.) Lloyd George's
Early Home without Annexe

(Rt. Hon.) Lloyd George's
Early Home with Annexe

£   p

FIRST AND LAST HOUSE IN ENGLAND - WITH ANNEXE
Inscribed: *First and Last House in England Rd. No. 521645.*
Unglazed   140mm   850.00
Can be found with the matching arms of *LAND'S END* on
roof for which £50.00 should be added.

FIRST AND LAST POST OFFICE IN ENGLAND, SENNEN
(Goss Record. 8th Edition: Page 18)   73mm   170.00
Inscribed: *Model of the First and Last Post Office in England at*
Sennen, Cornwall. Rd. No. 618950.
Unglazed or glazed for which £30.00 should be added
Sometimes has the badge of Cornwall on one end for which
£30.00 should be added.

GLASTONBURY ABBEY - THE ABBOT'S KITCHEN
(Goss Record. 9th Edition: Page 26 & 27)
                        Height 88mm Length   70mm
Inscribed: *Model of Abbot's Kitchen Glastonbury Abbey.*   (a) Brown   650.00
Copyright.   (b) WhiteGlazed   170.00
Can be found with either black or brown doors
Unglazed. The white glazed version has been found with
Blackpool coat of arms applied. See 3 NOTES FOR
THE COLLECTOR. THE BLACKPOOL COAT OF ARMS

GLASTONBURY - CHURCH OF JOSEPH OF
ARIMATHŒA   70mm   635.00
Inscribed: *Model of Church built by Joseph of Arimathoea A .D .*
63 at Glastonbury. The first Christian Church in England. Built
of willows and thatched with rushes, it stood on the site now
occupied by St. Joseph's Chapel, Glastonbury Abbey. From a
drawing in the British Museum. Copyright.
Unglazed

GOSS OVEN
(Goss Record. 9th Edition: Page 27 & 28) (Plate G).
There are two varieties: (a) Orange chimney unglazed   75mm   300.00
                             (b) Brown chimney part-glazed 75mm   300.00
Inscribed: *Model of Oven in which Goss porcelain is fired.*
Copyright.
A descriptive leaflet entitled "The Potter's Oven" was issued
with this model and is valued at £45.00 (see page 60).
The ovens were situated in Sturgess Street, Stoke, Stoke-on-Trent
and one is still standing today. W H Goss produced this model
of this, his newly built Glost oven, to commemorate the
completion of major new factory extentions in 1905.

GRETNA GREEN, OLD TOLL BAR   125mm   2200.00
Inscribed in script: *Old Toll Bar, Gretna Green, Over 10,000*
Marriages Performed in the Marriage Room. E^{ST} 1830.
Copyright.
Unglazed, sometimes found not marked W.H. Goss,
a factor which does not affect the price.

£   p

GULLANE, THE OLD SMITHY   75mm   600.00
(Goss Record. 9th Edition: Page 35 and advertisement
in the 8th Edition: Page 98)
Inscribed: *Model of The Old Smithy, Gullane, N.B. Copyright.*
Unglazed

(THOMAS) HARDY'S BIRTHPLACE, DORCHESTER
(Goss Record. 9th Edition: Page 14)   100mm   360.00
Inscribed: *Model of Birthplace of Thomas Hardy*
"The Wessex Poet" Dorchester. Copyright.
Unglazed

(ANN) HATHAWAY'S COTTAGE, SHOTTERY
(Goss Record. 8th Edition: Page 35)
Inscribed: *Model of Ann Hathaway's Cottage Shottery Near*
Stratford-on-Avon. Rd. No. 208047.
Glazed or unglazed
                  (a) Small   64mm   85.00
                  (b) Night-light   148mm   170.00
                  (c) Night-light white unglazed only   148mm   265.00
This model was in constant production from the mid-1890s and
minor variations occurred as moulds were replaced.
Such variations do not affect values. The above are the only models
produced from Goss moulds.
For later examples see THIRD PERIOD 11.O BUILDINGS
AND MONUMENTS.

for HEADCORN HOP KILN
see Hop Kiln, Headcorn, Kent

HOLDEN CHAPEL, HARVARD UNIVERSITY,
CAMBRIDGE, MASSACHUSETTS, USA
(Goss Record. 8th Edition: Page 43)   137mm   2500.00
Inscribed: *Model of Holden Chapel, Built 1744,*
Harvard University. Cambridge, Mass. Rd. No. 643867.
Jones, McDuffee & Stratton Co. 33, Franklin St., Boston, Mass.
Unglazed Night-light.

HOP KILN, HEADCORN, KENT   Height   89mm   1100.00
(Goss Record. 9th Edition: Page 20)
Inscribed: *Model of Hop Kiln, Headcorn, Kent. Copyright.*
Unglazed matt or gloss brown walls.

for HUER'S HOUSE
see Newquay Huer's House

£ p

**for ISAAC WALTON'S COTTAGE or BIRTHPLACE,
SHALLOWFORD**
see Walton's Cottage, (Birthplace), Shallowford

for JOHN BUNYAN'S COTTAGE, ELSTOW
see Bunyan's Cottage, Elstow

(DR. SAMUEL) JOHNSON'S HOUSE, LICHFIELD   Height   75mm   200.00
(Goss Record. 8th Edition: Page 32)   Length   47mm
Inscribed: *Model of the House at Lichfield in which Dr.*
Samuel Johnson was born. Born 1709 died 1784. Educated at
Lichfield Grammar School Buried in Westminster Abbey.
Rd. No. 605733.
Glazed or unglazed

for JOHN KNOX'S HOUSE, EDINBURGH
see THIRD PERIOD I 1 .O. BUILDINGS AND MONUMENTS

for JOSEPH OF ARIMATHŒA'S CHURCH
see Glastonbury - Church of

LAND'S END, ATLANTIC VIEW HOTEL   Unpriced
(Goss Record. 8th Edition: Page 18)
Although this model was listed as being in the course of
preparation in the Eighth Edition, it was apparently never
produced, and was omitted from the Ninth Edition of The Goss
Record

LEDBURY, THE FEATHERS HOTEL   114mm   850.00
Inscribed: *Model of Feathers Hotel, Ledbury, Copyright.*
Unglazed.
Rumour has it that the Hotel owner purchased the entire
remaining output of this model when the Ledbury agency closed,
and presented them to couples honeymooning at the Hotel.

LEDBURY, OLD MARKET HOUSE   68mm   300.00
(Goss Record. 9th Edition: Page 18. Plate H)
Inscribed: *Model of Ye Old Market House, Ledbury. Copyright.*
Unglazed.

for LLANGOLLEN, PLAS NEWYDD
see Plas Newydd, Llangollen

for LLEWELYN'S HOUSE, BEDDGELERT
see Prince Llewelyn's House, Beddgelert

Manx Cottage

Newquay, Huer's House

Newquay, Look-out House

Old Maids' Cottage, Lee, Devon

Old Thatched Cottage, Poole

Gretna Green, Old Toll Bar

Portman Lodge, Bournemouth

Priest's House, Prestbury

Prince Llewellyn's House, Beddgelert

St. Catherine's Chapel, Abbotsbury

St. Nicholas Chapel, Lantern Hill, Ilfracombe

St. Nicholas Chapel, St. Ives.

£   p

(RT. HON.) LLOYD GEORGE'S EARLY HOME   62mm   160.00
Llanystymdwy, Criccieth
(Goss Record. 8th Edition: Page 39)
Inscribed: *Rt. Hon. D. Lloyd George's Early Home*
Llanystymdwy, Criccieth. Rd. No. 617573.
Glazed or unglazed

(RT. HON.) LLOYD GEORGE'S EARLY HOME   102mm   140.00
- WITH ANNEXE, Llanystymdwy, Criccieth
Inscribed: *Rt. Hon. D. Lloyd George's Early Home*
Llanystymdwy, Criccieth. Rd. No. 617573.
Unglazed

for LOOK OUT HOUSE
see Newquay Look Out House

MANX COTTAGE   (a) Small   62mm   125.00
(Goss Record. 8th Edition: Page 26)   (b) Night-light   122mm   190 00
Inscribed: *Model of Manx Cottage. Rd. No. 273243.*
Glazed or unglazed

MASSACHUSETT'S HALL, HARVARD UNIVERSITY,
CAMBRIDGE, USA   175mm   3500.00
(Goss Record. 8th Edition: Page 43)
Inscribed: *Massachusetts Hall 1718-1720. Harvard University*
Cambridge, Mass. Rd. No. 647235.
Jones, McDuffee & Stratton Co. 33, Franklin St.,
Boston, Mass.
The only varieties known to exist are sub standard white glazed
night-lights and bear the Blackpool arms. Exceptionally, these factors
have been taken into account in the price shown above. Shards of a
coloured variety have been found on the factory spoil heap,
but to date a perfect coloured example has not come to light.
Found with the Goshawk mark and inscription in blue.

NEWQUAY, HUER'S HOUSE
(Goss Record. 8th Edition: Page 18)   (a) Grey   70mm   170.00
                                    (b) White   70mm   190 00
Inscribed: *Model of Huer's House*
Newquay Cornwall . Rd . No . 610011.
Glazed and unglazed.

NEWQUAY, LOOK OUT HOUSE   (a) 4 portholes   Height   65mm   125.00
(Goss Record. 8th Edition: Page 18)   (b) 5 portholes   Height   65mm   125.00
Inscribed: *Model of Look Out House Newquay, Cornwall.*
Rd. No. 605735.
Glazed only

for OLD COURTHOUSE, CHRISTCHURCH
see Christchurch, Old Courthouse

£ p

OLD MAIDS' COTTAGE, LEE, DEVON   73mm   145.00
(Goss Record. 8th Edition: Page 20)
Inscribed: *Model of Old Maid's Cottage at Lee, Devon.*
Rd. No. 622406.
Glazed or unglazed

for OLD MARKET HOUSE, LEDBURY
see Ledbury - Old Market House

for OLD SMITHY, GULLANE
see Gullane, The Old Smithy

OLD THATCHED COTTAGE, POOLE   68mm   465.00
(Goss Record. 9th Edition: Page 14)
Inscribed: *Model of The Old Thatched Cottage Poole. Copyright.*
Unglazed

for OLD TOLL BAR, GRETNA GREEN
see Gretna Green, Old Toll Bar

PLAS NEWYDD, LLANGOLLEN
(Goss Record. 8th Edition: Page 39)   Unpriced
It has been reported that seven of these models were produced,
and sold by the local agent. Apparently no more were made,
and none have as yet been discovered.

for POOLE, OLD THATCHED COTTAGE
see Old Thatched Cottage, Poole

PORTMAN LODGE, BOURNEMOUTH   (a)84mm x   72mm   350.00
Inscribed: *Portman Lodge the Second House built in*   (b)84mm x   72mm   425.00
Bournemouth. Copyright. Built by Squire Tregonwell about
1810 & called "Tregonwell House". Name altered to "Portman
Lodge" when it was occupied by Lord Portman.
Appears either with an aperture for a door (a)
or more rarely with a closed door (b).
Unglazed.

PRIEST'S HOUSE, PRESTBURY   Height   71mm   1000.00
Inscribed: *786 Model of the Priests House Prestbury,*   Length   90mm
Cheshire. Copyright.
Unglazed

PRINCE LLEWELYN'S HOUSE, BEDDGELERT   63mm   150.00
(Goss Record. 8th Edition: Page 38)
Inscribed: *Model of Prince Llewelyn's house Beddgelert.*
Rd. No. 594374.
Glazed or unglazed

£   p

ST. CATHERINE'S CHAPEL, ABBOTSBURY   87mm   475.00
(Goss Record. 9th Edition: Page 14)
Inscribed: *Model of St. Catherine's Chapel, Abbotsbury.*
Dorset. Copyright.
Brown unglazed

for ST. IVES, ANCIENT CHAPEL OF ST. NICHOLAS
see St. Nicholas Chapel, St. Ives

ST. NICHOLAS CHAPEL, LANTERN HILL,
ILFRACOMBE
(Goss Record. 8th Edition: Page 20)   (a) Grey roof   74mm   170.00
Inscribed: *Model of St. Nicholas Chapel, Lantern*   (b) White roof   74mm   250.00
Hill, Ilfracombe, which up to the time of Henry VIII was used
as a Place of Worship for Sailors. Rd. No. 613770.
Glazed or unglazed

ST. NICHOLAS CHAPEL, ST. IVES
(Goss Record. 8th Edition: Page 18)
Inscribed on gable end: *Model of the Ancient Chapel of*
St. Nicholas, St. Ives, Cornwall. Partially destroyed by Order
of the War Office, 1904. Rebuilt & restored by Sir Edward
Hain 1911. Rd. No: 602905.
                     (a) White, glazed   55mm   170.00
                     (b) Coloured, glazed or unglazed   55mm   220.00

SHAKESPEARE'S HOUSE, STRATFORD-ON-AVON
(Goss Record. 8th Edition: Page 35)
Inscribed: *Model of Shakespeare's House. Rd . No. 225833.*
Many variations in size may be found, both glazed and
unglazed. These are the only models made from Goss moulds: for
all other sizes see THIRD PERIOD I 1 .O BUILDINGS AND
MONUMENTS
(a) Small. Full-length   Height 32mm   68mm   85.00
(b) Small. Full-length   78mm   85.00
(c) Medium. Full-length   110mm   95.00
(d) Medium. Full-length   140mm   105.00
(e) Night-light. Full-length. Coloured   185mm   170.00
(f) Night-light. Full length. White unglazed   185mm   210.00
(g) Small. Half-length open door.   70mm   115.00
(h) Small. Half-length closed door.   70mm   140.00
(i) Large. Half-length open or closed door   83mm   140.00
(j) Night-light. Half-length. Separate base. Coloured glazed   105mm   150.00
(k) Night-light, Half-length. Separate base. White unglazed   105mm   135.00
(l) Night-light, two piece, First Period impressed mark only
     so obviously a trial piece [1]   115mm   170.00
(m) Night-light, half length, separate base, coloured (no
     threshold at base of door opening)   122mm   220.00

Shakespeare's House,
Stratford-on-Avon, small

Shakespeare's House,
Half-length

Shakespeare's House, Two-
piece Nightlight

Southampton Tudor House

Sulgrave Manor,
Northamptonshire

Miss Ellen Terry's Farm,
Tenterden, Kent

Isaac Walton's Cottage
(Birthplace), Shallowford

A Window in Thrums small

A Window in Thrums
Nightlight

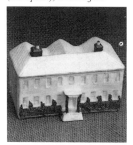

William Wordsworth's
Birthplace, Cockermouth

William Wordsworth's Home,
Dove Cottage, Grasmere

Massachusetts Hall, Harvard
University Cambridge, USA

£ p

SOUTHAMPTON TUDOR HOUSE   83mm   350.00
(Goss Record. 8th Edition: Page 23)
Inscribed: *Tudor House, Southampton, Built 1535. Its Royal Visitors.*
If only the old house itself could speak what stories it could tell of the doings
of the dozen generations who have dwelt within its walls or have passed
athwart the Square beneath its windows. Tradition associates it doubtfully
with two Royal visits. Henry VIII is said to have brought Anne Boleyn
beneath its roof. Philip of Spain is supposed to have made it his lodging
during his three days sojourn in Southampton (20th to 23rd July, 1554)
prior to his marriage with Queen Mary at Winchester. It is impossible at
this late day either to confirm or disprove these legends. There is nothing
impossible or even improbable in either of them. Copyright.
Unglazed
The House, in Bugle Street, Southampton, is now a museum
and a Goss model of itself is on view inside.

SULGRAVE MANOR, NORTHAMPTONSHIRE
(Goss Record. 8th Edition: Page 30) Overall length   125mm   1250.00
Inscribed: *Model of Sulgrave Manor, Co. Northampton, England.*
Rd . No. 638372. Lawrence Washington had A Grant of Sulgrave 30 Hen.
VIII. His great-grandson John Washington went to America about 1657
and was the great-grandfather of George Washington.
There are many restored and few perfect examples of this model,
which means that sub-standard models are worth less than half of
the perfect price.
Unglazed.

(MISS ELLEN) TERRY'S FARM, TENTERDEN, KENT.
(Goss Record. 8th Edition: Page 27)   70mm   325.00
Inscribed: *Model of Miss Ellen Terry's Farm near Tenterden,*
Kent. Rd. No. 641313.
This cottage is unglazed and unusually has a glazed, brown roof.

for THOMAS HARDY'S HOUSE
see Hardy's Birthplace

(ISAAC) WALTON'S COTTAGE (BIRTHPLACE),
SHALLOWFORD
Inscribed: *Model of Isaac Walton's Birthplace, Shallowford.*
There are two sizes of this model, but the variations   (a)   86mm   400 00
in size are minimal. The larger size is numbered 834.   (b)   95mm   700.00
Unglazed

A WINDOW IN THRUMS   (a) Small   60mm   150.00
(Goss Record. 8th Edition: Page 40) (b) Night-light, grey roof   130mm   300.00
Inscribed: *"A Window in Thrums".*   (c) Night-light, white roof 130mm   300.00
Rd. No. 322142.
Both varieties found glazed and unglazed.
This cottage in Kirriemuir was the subject of a novel by
author J.M. Barrie

£   p

(WILLIAM) WORDSWORTH'S BIRTHPLACE, COCKERMOUTH

(Goss Record. 8th Edition: Page 18)   81 mm   235.00

Inscribed: *Model of Wordsworth's Birthplace Cockermouth.*
Rd. No. 639535.
Unglazed

(WILLIAM) WORDSWORTH'S HOME, DOVE COTTAGE, GRASMERE

(Goss Record. 9th Edition: Page 31) Overall length   102mm   425.00

Inscribed: *Model of Dove Cottage, Grasmere. The Home of*
Wordsworth 1799 to 1808. Now the Wordsworth Memorial
Copyright
Unglazed

The base of Holden Chapel , Harvard University. A Large Nightlight made for the American Market.

G Crosses

The unglazed brown crosses are nearly all pre-1900. Possibly the first cross was the Sandbach model, which was made in three parts, the two crosses being held to the base with large corks. William Henry Goss himself was very fond of the Sandbach crosses as one of his homes was nearby and often paid them a visit. The chosen originals were usually in the country and well off the beaten track often in the Western Isles of Scotland. This inaccessability to the potential customer may account for their rarity, although they could be obtained at the Stoke Agency of Ritchie and Co as well as agencies local to the site of the original. They were somewhat expensive at up to 4/-, when small crested models sold for between 1/- and 1/ 6d. each. No brown crosses bore arms, and their colouring was as natural as the artists could make them, with green tinges of moss and brown shading.

The Richmond Market Cross was introduced much later, in 1916, with the St Buryan, St Columb Major and Buxton, being introduced after the Great War. The white glazed and unglazed varieties are also post 1900, all brown examples are unglazed. Another of Mr Goss's favourite crosses was the St Martin's Cross, Iona, a large stone replica of which was used as his memorial in Hartshill Cemetery, Stoke-upon-Trent.

All crosses are uncrested with the exception of the Richmond Market Place Cross and all are unglazed unless stated otherwise.

Models which bear no arms are included in the first column and are marked thus †. The only cross which carries arms is the Richmond Market Place Cross.

All dimensions refer to the height unless otherwise stated.

Where no price is given, no piece exists in that category.

Bakewell Ancient Cross

Buxton Old Market Cross

Campbeltown Ancient Cross

Carew Ancient Cross

Eyam Ancient Cross

Llandaff Ancient Cross

St. Martins Cross, Iona

Kirk Braddan Cross

Inverary Ancient Cross of the Nobles

Richmond Market Place Cross

St. Buryan Ancient Cross

St. Columb Major Ancient Cross

Model	With any Arms £ p	With Matching Arms £ p

BAKEWELL ANCIENT CROSS   (a) White glazed   145mm   190.00
(Goss Record. 8th Edition: Page 18)   (b) Brown   145mm   255.00
Impressed on front: *Bakewell*.

for BANBURY CROSS
See THIRD PERIOD 11.O - BUILDINGS AND MONUMENTS

BUXTON, OLD MARKET CROSS   Grey 88mm   1500.00
Inscribed: Old Market Cross, Buxton

CAMPBELTOWN ANCIENT CROSS   Brown 152mm   650.00
(Goss Record. 8th Edition: Page 40)
Inscribed: *Model of The Campbeltown Cross*

CAREW ANCIENT CROSS
(Goss Record. 9th Edition: Page 34)
Impressed on front: Carew Near Pembroke. Inscribed on
front step: *Model of Ancient Cross at Carew, Near Pembroke,
with inscription in unknown Literature Restored.*
                          (a) White   150mm   95.00
                          (b) Brown   150mm   125.00
                          (c) White   216mm   135.00
                          (d) White glazed   216mm   250.00
                          (e) Brown   216mm   250.00

EYAM ANCIENT CROSS
(Goss Record. 8th Edition: Page 18)
Impressed on front: *Eyam*
                          (a) White glazed   168mm   170.00
                          (b) White   168mm   185.00
                          (c) Brown   168mm   340.00

INVERARY - ANCIENT CROSS OF THE NOBLES
(Goss Record. 8th Edition: Page 40)   Brown 145mm   1150.00
Impressed on front: Inverary Cross. Inscribed on back:
*This is the Cross of the Nobles, viz:- Duncan, McComyn,
Patrick his son and Ludovick the son of Patrick who caused
the Cross to be erected.*

for IONA CROSS
see St. Martin's Cross, Iona

Bakewell Cross Brown 145mm

Llandaff Ancient Cross Brown 147mm

Agents Ordering Card shows four white unglazed crosses
Left to right: Bakewell, Eyam, St. Martins Iona and Campbeltown.

	With any Arms	With Matching Arms
Model	£ p	£ p

KIRK BRADDAN CROSS
(Goss Record. 8th Edition: Page 26)
Inscribed on back: *Model of Cross at Kirk Bradden I. of Man probably more than 1000 years old.*

(a) Brown	84mm	125.00
(b) White	84mm	185.00
(c) White glazed (Blackpool arms)	84mm	60.00

LLANDAFF ANCIENT CROSS
(Goss Record. 8th Edition: Page 39)
Impressed on front: *Llandaff.*

(a) White	147mm	340.00
(b) Brown	147mm	725.00

RICHMOND MARKET PLACE CROSS
(Goss Record. 8th Edition: Page 38)
Inscribed: *Model of the Cross in the Market Place, Richmond, Yorkshire. Rebuilt 1771.*

(a) White glazed	130mm	65.00	105.00
(b) Brown	130mm	325.00	

Matching Arms: *RICHMOND*

ST. BURYAN ANCIENT CROSS
Inscribed: *Model of Ancient Cross in St. Buryan Churchyard near Lands End Cornwall.*

(a) White glazed	43mm	125.00
(b) White	43mm	155.00
(c) Brown	43mm	215.00

ST. COLUMB MAJOR ANCIENT CROSS
(Goss Record. 8th Edition: Page 18)
Impressed on back: *Model of Ancient Cross in St. Columb Major Churchyard.*

(a) White glazed	90mm	55.00
(b) White	90mm	75.00
(c) Brown	90mm	190.00

Versions (a) and (b) can be found with the Blackpool arms which would halve their values.

The Magnificent Sandbach Crosses. This model comes in three parts, both crosses are secured to the base by means of large cork plugs.

Model	With any Arms £ p	With Matching Arms £ p

ST. IVES ANCIENT CROSS
(Goss Record. 8th Edition: Page 18)
Impressed, bottom front:
St. Ives Cornwall.

(a)	White glazed	140mm	190.00
(b)	White	140mm	190.00
(c)	Brown	140mm	300.00
(d)	White	204mm	220.00
(e)	Brown	204mm	300.00

ST. MARTIN'S CROSS, IONA
(Goss Record. 8th Edition: Page 40) Impressed, bottom front:
St. Martin Iona.

(a)	White, detailed reverse	142mm	150.00
(b)	White glazed, flat reverse	142mm	100.00
(c)	Brown, detailed reverse	142mm	170.00
(d)	White glazed, flat reverse	216mm	165.00
(e)	White	216mm	180.00
(f)	Brown, detailed reverse	216mm	220.00
(g)	Brown, flat reverse	216mm	275.00

SANDBACH CROSSES
(Goss Record. 8th Edition: Page 17)
Impressed on plinth front and back: *Sandbach*
Inscribed underneath: *The Sandbach Crosses*
or, more rarely, in addition *The Great Cross shows the chief truths of Christianity. The small cross is supposed to depict the return of Peada (son of Penda King of Mercia 626 - 656) from Northumbria with his bride Alchfleda, after having embraced Christianity.*
This model is made in three sections, the two crosses being held in place by cork plugs and each section bearing the W H Goss impressed mark.

(a)	White	260mm	1300.00
(b)	Brown	260mm	1500.00

Sandbach Crosses

St. Ives Ancient Cross

Model of font in the Cathedral in Winchester, black. This model was made in two sizes, 115mm and 135mm

H Fonts

Twelve fonts were produced, none in great numbers, and are highly prized by collectors. Like crosses, the bulk of the fonts were made before 1900 in brown unglazed form. After 1900 other varieties were introduced including white glazed and glazed crested. Between 1904 and 1916 the Avebury, St Iltyd's and St Ives were produced, with the Buckland Monachorum following later in the 1920s.

Shakespeare's Font could only be obtained from the Stratford agency up until 1929 which explains why that particular model is almost always found with matching arms.

Those fonts which were also produced during the First Period are denoted thus: [1], and those from the Third Period: [3].

Models which bear no arms are indicated in the first column and are marked thus †.
All dimensions refer to the height unless otherwise stated.
All fonts are unglazed unless otherwise stated.
Where no price is given, no piece exists in that particular category.

St. Ives Church Font, Llantwit Major, brown 88mm

Model	With any Arms £ p	With Matching Arms £ p

AVEBURY ANCIENT SAXON FONT (CALNE)

(Goss Record. 8th Edition: Page 36 and Page 91
photograph and advertisement)
Inscribed: *Model of Ancient Saxon Font in Avebury Church
Near Calne, Wilts. Rd No. 617575.*

(a) White glazed	86mm	135.00	250.00
(b) Brown†	86mm	350.00	

Matching Arms: *CALNE*

for BARMOUTH, ST. JOHN'S CHURCH FONT

see FIRST PERIOD 9B FIGURES, Angel, kneeling

BUCKLAND MONACHORUM FONT

Inscribed: *Model of Ancient Saxon Font about 1000 years old
discovered in foundations of Buckland Monachorum Church in
1857 after being buried 400 years now in St. Paul's Church.
Yelverton. Copyright.*

(a) White glazed	75mm		525.00
(b) White glazed(Blackpool arms)	75mm	300.00	

Matching Arms: *BUCKLAND ABBEY,
NR. YELVERTON FOUNDED 1278.*

for CALNE FONT

see Avebury Ancient Saxon Font

for CANTERBURY FONT

see St Martin's Church Font, Canterbury

HADDON HALL NORMAN FONT [1]

(Goss Record. 8th Edition: Page 18)
Inscribed: *Model of Norman Font found at Haddon Hall.*

(a) White glazed	92mm	95.00	130.00
(b) White†	92mm	300.00	
(c) Brown†	92mm	325.00	

On the white version, the inscription is in Gothic script on
the side, whilst on the brown coloured variety it is
printed on the base.
Matching Arms: *BAKEWELL OR DUKE* OF *RUTLAND*,who once
owned the Hall, or *DOROTHY VERNON*(77966 Design) might be
considered appropriate, she having inherited Haddon Hall from
her father in 1567

Avebury Ancient Saxon Font (Calne)

Buckland Monachorum Font

Haddon Hall Norman Font

Hereford Cathedral Font

St.Iltyd's Church Font, Llantwit Major

St. Ives Church Ancient Font

St. Martin's Church Font, Canterbury, lidded

St. Martin's Church Font, Canterbury, Dished

St. Martin's Church Font, Canterbury, Open

St. Tudno's Church Font, Llandudno

Southwell Cathedral Font

Stratford-on-Avon Church Font

Model	With any Arms £ p	With Matching Arms £ p

HEREFORD CATHEDRAL FONT
(Goss Record. 8th Edition: Page 24 and Page 66 photograph)
Inscribed: *Model of Font in Hereford Cathedral. The figures of 12 Apostles were partly erased by the Puritans.*

(a) White glazed	96mm	130 00	190.00
(b) White†	96mm	280.00	
(c) Brown	96mm	300.00	320.00

Matching Arms: *SEE OF HEREFORD A.D.1275,*
SEE OF HEREFORD ANCIENT **or** *SEE OF HEREFORD MODERN*

for LLANTWIT MAJOR NORMAN FONT IN ST. ILTYD'S CHURCH
see St. Iltyd's Church Font (Llantwit Major)

for MONMOUTH FONT
see Warwick Font, Troy House, Monmouth

ST. ILTYD'S CHURCH FONT (LLANTWIT MAJOR)
(Goss Record. 8th Edition: Page 39)
Inscribed: *Model of Norman Font in St. Iltyd's Church, Llantwit Major. Rd. No. 599335*

(a) Brown†	88mm	360.00	
(b) White†	88mm	700.00	
(c) White glazed, Blackpool Arms	88mm	170.00	
(d) White glazed with Matching Arms of	88mm		800.00
LLANTWIT MAJOR			

ST. IVES CHURCH ANCIENT FONT
(Goss Record. 8th Edition: page 18)
Inscribed: *Model of Ancient Font in St. Ives Church, Cornwall. Rd. No. 594379*

(a) White glazed	88mm	47.50	75.00
(b) White†	88mm	115.00	
(c) Brown†	88mm	170.00	

Matching Arms: *ST. I VES*

for ST. JOHN'S CHURCH FONT, BARMOUTH
see FIRST PERIOD 9B FIGURES, Angel ,kneeling

Model	With any Arms £ p	With Matching Arms £ p

ST. MARTIN'S CHURCH FONT, CANTERBURY [1]

(Goss Record. 8th Edition: Page 26)
Inscribed: *Model of Font (Restored) in which King Ethelbert was Baptized by St. Augustine in St. Martin's Church Canterbury.*
The quotation of the inscription can be found to vary from model to model. There are three varieties of this font: Lidded, dished, and open.
Often found inscribed as follows rarely with the year added:
Pub. by J Abrahams, 4 high St, Canterbury 1889

(a) lidded, white glazed†	75mm	77.50	
(b) lidded, white†	75mm	85.00	
(c) lidded, brown†	75mm	175.00	
(d) dished, white glazed	69mm	42.50	77.50
(e) open, white glazed†	74mm	80.00	
(f) open, brown†	74mm	175.00	

Matching Arms: *CITY* OR *SEE OF CANTERBURY*

ST. TUDNO'S CHURCH FONT, LLANDUDNO

(Goss Record. 8th Edition: Page 91 photograph and advertisement)
Inscribed: *Model of Ancient Font in St. Tudno's Church Llandudno. Rd. No. 546713.*

(a) White glazed	95mm	42.50	60.00
(b) White†	95mm	77.50	
(c) Brown†	95mm	245.00	

Matching Arms: *LLANDUDNO*

for SHAKESPEARE'S FONT

see Stratford-on-Avon Church Font

SOUTHWELL CATHEDRAL FONT

(Goss Record. 8th Edition: Page 30)
Inscribed: *Model of Font in Southwell Cathedral.*

(a) White glazed†	95mm	115.00	
(b) White†	95mm	125.00	
(c) Brown	95mm	350.00	350.00

Matching Arms: *SEE OF SOUTHWELL*

STRATFORD-ON-AVON CHURCH FONT

(Goss Record. 8th Edition: Page 35)

(a) White	54mm	30.00	38.50
(b) White glazed and gilded (Blackpool)	54mm	21.50	
(c) Brown†	54mm	380.00	

Model	With any Arms £ p	With Matching Arms £ p

The following inscription appears inside bowl in
Gothic lettering surrounding arms:
Model of Font in which Shakespeare was Baptized
Matching Arms: *STRATFORD ON AVON,*
SHAKESPEARE'S ARMS OR *SHAKESPEARE'S CHURCH*
During the Goss family ownership of the pottery, the Stratford
models could only be obtained from the Stratford agency. This is
why Shakespeare's Font is rarely found without matching
arms .

for TROY HOUSE FONT
see Warwick Font, Troy House, Monmouth

WARWICK FONT, TROY HOUSE, MONMOUTH [1]
(Goss Record. 8th Edition: Page 36)
Inscribed: *Model of Ancient Font at Troy House, Monmouth.*

(a)	White glazed†	55mm	80.00
(b)	White†	55mm	140.00
(c)	White glazed but with coloured shields†	55mm	115.00
(d)	Brown†	55mm	300.00

WINCHESTER CATHEDRAL FONT [1]

(a)	White glazed†	115mm	300.00
(b)	White†	115mm	300.00
(c)	Black†	115mm	350.00
(d)	White glazed	135mm	350.00
(e)	White	135mm	350.00
(f)	Black†	135mm	400.00

Impressed around three sides: *Model of Font in the
Cathedral at Winchester.*
This model was made in two sizes: Height 115mm and 135mm
It was produced from a mould originally used by Copeland.

*Winchester Cathedral Font
large, white, 135mm*

*Winchester Font, Black,
small, 115mm*

*Warwick Font, Troy House,
Monmouth*

I   Animals and Birds

The majority of animals were produced during the latter half of the Second Period, mainly in the 1920s. John Goss, youngest son of Huntley, designed most of these, including the lion, rhino, hippo, and a dog lying on a plinth. They were exhibited and sold at the British Empire Exhibition held at Wembley, Middlesex in 1924 and 1925. Of particular interest would have been the Wembley Lion, produced especially for the exhibition and sold bearing the 1925 B.E.E. Motif. Matching Arms are given where known, in the absence of which B.E.E. Wembley are considered correct.

With only four exceptions, Goss animals are not inscribed or named. First Period animals and birds include the Bear and Ragged Staff, Bird on tree stump, Bullock and two sheep group, Cockatoo, Dolphin inkwell, Elephant with howdah, Falcon inkwell, Fox and its prey, House Martins on wall vase nest, Humming Bird wall vase, Lion and Mouse group, Sheep, Squirrel, Swan, and Wren resting on nest. These will be found listed in the FIRST PERIOD 9C ORNAMENTAL AND DOMESTIC Chapter.

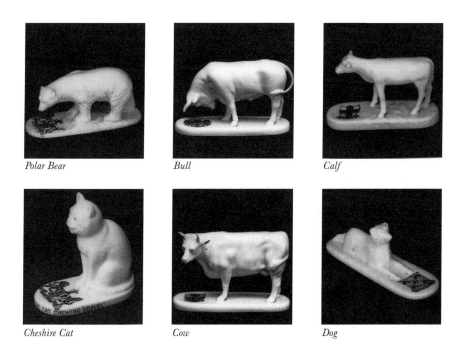

Polar Bear   *Bull*   *Calf*

Cheshire Cat   *Cow*   *Dog*

After the sale of the Goss pottery in 1929, animals continued to be manufactured during the Third Period until 1934, but not in great numbers. These include Budgerigar, Cats (Black, Cheshire and others), Chicken, Crow (Royston), Dogs (Scottie and others), Fish (plaice), Frog, Hippopotamus, Lion, Monkeys, Owl, Pig, Penguin, Ponies (New Forest and Shetland), Rabbit, Racehorse, Rhinoceros, Swan and Toucan, all of which will be found listed in the THIRD PERIOD 11R FIGURES AND ANIMALS Chapter.

Models which bear no arms are included in the first column and are marked thus †.
Models from the First Period are marked thus [1].
Models from the Third Period are marked thus [3].
Where no price is given, no piece exists in that particular category.
Most animals are not named or inscribed.

Model	With any Arms £ p	With Matching Arms £ p

AYLESBURY DUCK Length 100mm 200.00 285.00
Inscribed: *Model of the Aylesbury Duck. Copyright.*
Matching Arms: *AYLESBURY*

BEAR, POLAR (a) Glazed Length 125mm 425.00
(b) Unglazed 425.00
Matching Arms: *B.E.E. WEMBLEY*

for BEAR AND RAGGED STAFF
see FIRST PERIOD 9C ORNAMENTAL Chapter

for BIRD ON TREE STUMP
see FIRST PERIOD 9C ORNAMENTAL Chapter

BULL Length 135mm 400.00 465.00
Matching Arms: *B.E.E. WEMBLEY* OR ANY *SPANISH ARMS*

for BULLOCK AND TWO SHEEP GROUP
see FIRST PERIOD 9C ORNAMENTAL Chapter

CALF Length 117mm 285.00 400.00
Matching Arms: *B.E.E. WEMBLEY* OR *COWES*
as this was one of the prominent towns
in which this animal was sold.

CHESHIRE CAT
(Goss Record. 9th Edition: Page I, Plate M)
(a) Glazed Length 83mm 190.00 215.00
(b) Unglazed 200.00
(c) Unglazed on glazed base 210.00

Inscribed *He grins like a Cheshire Cat Chewing Gravel.*
Sometimes marked *Copyright.*
Can be found with red and green colour to eyes and
mouth, for which £20.00 should be added or
with a blue bow to neck for which £20.00
should also be added. This cat often has a
firing flaw in one or both ears, which
reduces the price by around one-third.
Matching Arms: *CHESHIRE*

for COCKATOO
see FIRST PERIOD 9C ORNAMENTAL Chapter

COW Length 135mm 350.00 400.00
Matching Arms: *B.E.E. WEMBLEY OR COWES*
as this was one of the prominent towns
in which this animal was sold.

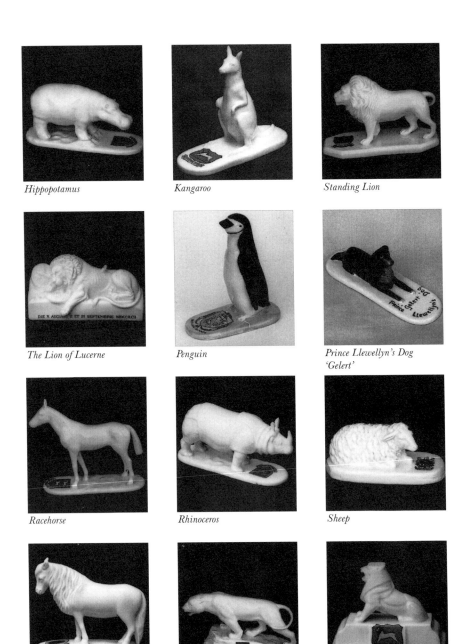

Hippopotamus

Kangaroo

Standing Lion

The Lion of Lucerne

Penguin

Prince Llewellyn's Dog 'Gelert'

Racehorse

Rhinoceros

Sheep

Shetland Pony

Tiger on Rocky Base

Wembley Exhibition Lion

Model		With any Arms £ p	With Matching Arms £ p

DOG   Length 133mm   425.00   510.00
See also Prince Llewellyn's Dog
Matching Arms: *B.E.E. WEMBLEY*

for DOLPHIN INKWELL
see FIRST PERIOD 9C ORNAMENTAL AND DOMESTIC Chapter

for ELEPHANT with Howdah
see FIRST PERIOD 9C ORNAMENTAL Chapter

for FALCON INKWELL
see FIRST PERIOD 9C ORNAMENTAL AND DOMESTIC Chapter

for FOX AND ITS PREY
see FIRST PERIOD 9C ORNAMENTAL Chapter

HIPPOPOTAMUS   Length 127mm   375.00   425.00
Matching Arms: *B.E.E. WEMBLEY*

for HOUSE MARTINS ON WALL VASE NEST
see FIRST PERIOD 9C ORNAMENTAL Chapter

for HUMMING BIRD WALL VASE
see FIRST PERIOD 9C ORNAMENTAL Chapter

KANGAROO   Height 94mm   700.00   925.00
Matching Arms: *B.E.E. WEMBLEY* or any
Australian arms. This model has been found
with the Sydney coat of arms and also with an
Australian transfer.

for LION AND MOUSE GROUP
see FIRST PERIOD 9C ORNAMENTAL Chapter

LION, STANDING   Length 135mm   350.00   400.00
Matching Arms:B.E.E. WEMBLEY

LION, LUCERNE
(Goss Record. 9th Edition: Page 38)
Inscribed: The Lion of Lucerne. Rd. No. 589059.   Length
   (a) White glazed and crested (at front   114mm   42.50   160.00
     or rear, usually Blackpool)
   (b) White glazed with Latin wording   114mm†   135.00
   (c) White unglazed with Latin wording   114mm   125.00   175.00
   (d) Brown unglazed with Latin wording   114mm†   285.00
   (e) Pale yellow unglazed   114mm   325.00

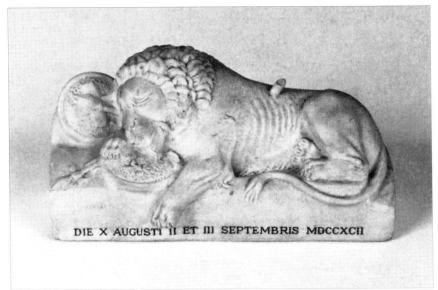

The Lion of Lucerne, brown unglazed with Latin wording and 7mm protuding spear

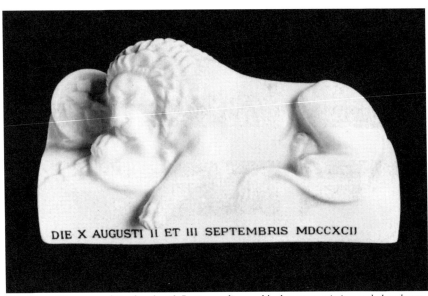

The Lion of Lucerne, white glazed with Latin wording and broken spear missing and glazed over

Model	With any Arms £ p	With Matching Arms £ p

This model should have a spear protruding 7mm out of
the centre of the back. Often the spear is broken off
level with the lion's back in manufacture and is sometimes
glazed over. Beasts without the 7mm spear are worth some
50% less than the varieties priced here.
Latin inscription: *Die X Augusti II et III Septembris MDCCXCII*
And on back: *Helvetiorum Fidei Ac Virtuti. Haec sunt nomina eorum
qui ne sacramenti fidem fallerent fortissime pugnantes
ceciderunt soerti amicorum cura cladi superfuerunt.*
(For the origin of the model, and the English translation
of the inscription, see *The Price Guide to Arms and Decorations
on Goss China*, section K2) (Milestone Publications)
Matching Arms: *LUZERN*

for LION (SCOTTISH)
see THIRD PERIOD 11R FIGURES AND ANIMALS Chapter

for LION (WEMBLEY)
see Wembley Lion

for LUCERNE LION
see Lion, Lucerne

PENGUIN
Inscribed: *Made in England.* (Sometimes omitted).
Length 83mm Height 92mm

	With any Arms	With Matching Arms
(a) Black trim around base, grey feet, coloured beak, black coat	375.00	550.00
(b) Sandy base, no trim, white feet black beak, black coat	375.00	635.00
(c) White base, no trim, grey feet, black coat	340.00	475.00
(d) All white glazed	275.00	385.00

The strong Goss family connection with the Falkland
Islands probably prompted the appearance of this model.
Matching Arms: *FALKLAND ISLANDS*

PRINCE LLEWELLYN'S DOG - GELERT
Inscribed on plinth in manuscript:
Prince Llewellyn's Dog "Gelert".
This is an identical model to the DOG   Length 133mm† 800.00
listed above, but coloured.

RACEHORSE   Length 120mm 325.00   425.00
Inscribed: Model of Racehorse (sometimes missing).
Matching Arms: *NEWMARKET* OR *ASCOT.*

Model	With any Arms £ p	With Matching Arms £ p

RHINOCEROS   Length 129mm   575.00   625.00
Matching Arms: *B.E.E. WEMBLEY*

SHEEP On Plinth   Length 147mm   190.00   235.00
Possible correct arms would be those of any sheep
farming areas, e.g. Tavistock. A First Period
variation of the sheep not on a plinth will be found
in 9C ORNAMENTAL AND DOMESTIC Chapter

SHETLAND PONY   Length 103mm   190.00   235.00
(Goss Record. 9th Edition: Page 36)
The model also appears with arms of places on
Dartmoor and Exmoor and was obviously sold in
these areas as a model of a local pony.
Matching Arms: *LERWICK*

for SQUIRREL
see FIRST PERIOD 9C ORNAMENTAL AND DOMESTIC Chapter

SWAN
Posy holder on ashtray base. This is the First Period
example used again in the later part of the Second Period.
                    Length109mm Height 74mm   300.00

for SWAN
see FIRST PERIOD 9C ORNAMENTAL AND DOMESTIC Chapter

TIGER on rocky base
  (a) White   Length 180mm   Height 100mm   850.00
  (b) Naturally Coloured† Length 180mm   Height 100mm   1500.00

WEMBLEY LION
Made for the British Empire Exhibition 1924/25
Matching Arms: *BRITISH EMPIRE*   Length 100mm   130.00   250.00
EXHIBITION 1924 OR 1925

for WREN RESTING ON NEST
see FIRST PERIOD 9C ORNAMENTAL AND DOMESTIC Chapter

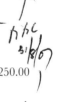

J Miniatures

The range of Goss miniatures was the result of experiments in the 1860s with eggshell porcelain which was chiefly made by Thomas Boden, a highly skilled craftsman. This range of tiny shapes included a variety of delicate jugs and matching bowls, and tea sets with tiny blue and gold butterfly handles on the cups, less than half an inch high! Yet they were so very strong that even now it is unusual to find a broken miniature.

Llewelynn Jewitt waxed lyrical over his friend's best eggshell porcelain in his *Ceramic Art of Great Britain*, hailing it as:

Yet another achievement in the plastic art in which W H Goss stood preeminent. The pieces produced in this almost ethereal and very difficult ware are so light as to be devoid of gravity, and yet the body is of such extreme hardness and firmness to be as strong as thicker and more massive wares, of a finer and purer body than the Sevres, thinner and far more translucent than Belleek, more delicate in tone than Worcester and more dainty to the touch than any other, the eggshell produced by Mr. Goss is an achievement in ceramics of which he may be justly proud. Lighter and more delicate than even the shell itself, and of perfect form down to the minutest detail, nature has in this instance been outdone by imitative art. The specimens of Mr. Goss's egg shell porcelain are worthy of a place in the choicest cabinets!

Most of the miniatures are First and Second Period and embrace a choice variety of decorations, the best known perhaps being forget-me-nots. Others include a jug decorated with blue and gold dots which pairs with a plain bowl, thistles, and The Trusty Servant. A later decoration was the Good Luck Shamrock with a horseshoe. Crested miniatures were Third Period and rather thicker and cruder in quality. The Second Period tea sets are particularly sought after. The lid of the tea pot, being so small, is never found factory marked, it being too small to carry the Goshawk.

KEY TO DECORATIONS

A   Forget-Me-Nots with a ring of blue and gold dots on Jugs and Tea Pots.
B   Blackpool or other Coat of Arms
C   No decoration (except blue and gold dots on Jugs and Tea Pots only)
D   Shamrock, Horseshoe and GOOD LUCK
E   Trusty Servant
F   Thistles
G   Shamrocks

Miniature Tea Service on oval tray
Comprising Oval Crinkle Tray, 165mm long, two or four cups and saucers, tea pot with lid, sugar basin and milk jug. Four 38mm Dia. plates can also be found, but are rare, as is the 60mm cake plate.

*Miniature Tea Service on
Oval Tray, Forget-me-Nots*

Oval Tray, Forget-me-Nots

*Miniature Beaker, Trusty
Servant*

*Miniature Tea Service on
square Tray, Trusty Servant*

*Miniature Tea Plate, Forget-
me-Nots 38mm*

*Niniature Vase two handles,
Shamrock, Horseshoe and Good Luck*

Miniature Jug, Thistles

Miniature Bowl, plain

*Cup and Saucer,
Forget-me-Nots*

*Milk Jug and Sugar Basin,
Forget-me-Nots*

*Jug and Basin, Blue and Gold
dots on jug only*

*Tea Pot and Lid, Trusty
Servant*

Miniature Tea Service on square tray
Comprising 70mm square tray, cup and saucer 35mm Dia.,
tea pot with lid, sugar basin and milk jug.
A Tea Pot lid, always unmarked is worth £ 25.00

Prices for each piece:

Decoration	*Tea Pot and Lid Height 35mm*	*Cup and Saucer Height 16mm*	*Milk Jug Height 20mm*	*Sugar Basin Dia. 28mm*	*Tea Plate Dia. 38mm*	*Cake Plate Dia. 60mm*	*Square Tray Width 70mm*	*Oval Tray Length 165mm*	*Addition for Complete Set*
A	55.00	45.00	34.00	34.00	85.00	120.00	30.00	40.00	40.00
B					30.00		10.00		
C	42.50	34.00	25.00	21.50	50.00				
D	50.00	40.00	30.00	30.00	65.00		25.00		30.00
E	100.00	75.00	55.00	50.00	110.00		38.50	60.00	38.50
F	65.00	60.00	40.00	35.00	100.00[1]		40.00	40.00	40.00

When the Trusty Servant decoration is found on a First Period tray, which is of heavier material, the Trusty Servant verse will be found on the base, but never on a Second Period tray.

Jug and Bowl Set
All sizes are the same price with the exception of the 20mm jug bearing decoration A.
Height of Jug 20mm   Diameter of Bowl 35mm
              25mm   40mm
              30mm   45mm

Each item priced separately. No premium is to be added for a matched pair. The 20mm Jug doubles as the milk jug in tea services.

The large size Bowl can also be found produced from patterns in the Third Period. Such pieces are marked GOSS ENGLAND (See THIRD PERIOD 11S ORNAMENTAL ARTICALS AND DOMESTIC AND UTILITY WARE Chapter).

Two very early First Period jugs have been seen. One 25mm, the other 30mm. Both are unglazed and have a floral decoration not previously seen by the author.

Decoration	*Bowl* £ p	*20mm Jug only* £ p	*25mm & 30mm Jug only* £ p
A	30.00	35.00	35.00
B	13.00[3]	17.00	
C	21.50	25.00	21.50
D	25.00	25.00	25.00
E	55.00	55.00	55.00
F	35.00	37.50	37.50
G	25.00	25.00	25.00

Vase, Two handled All same price regardless of size   £   p
         20mm
         25mm
         30mm

A	Forget-Me-Nots	40.00
B	Blackpool or other Coat of Arms	17.50[3]
C	No decoration (except blue and gold dots)	25.00
D	Shamrock, Horseshoe and GOOD LUCK	30.00
E	Trusty Servant	75.00
F	Thistles	35.00
G	Shamrocks	30.00

Miniature Beaker

A	19mm	47.50
B	19mm	35.00
E	19mm	85.00

Bottle and Four-beaker set on 70mm square tray
E   450.00

A miniature is not known to have a particular decoration where no letter or price is given.

for Miniature Winchester Jack see
10E HISTORIC MODELS AND SPECIAL SHAPES

Miniature tea plate,
thistles 38mm

Miniature Winchester Jack
Trusty Servant

Miniature Vase, two handles,
Forget-me-nots

Miniature tea service on oval
tray, thistles

K Ornamental Articles

Many of the pieces in this section were made during both First and Second
Periods. They most naturally fall in the Second Period and to avoid double
listing are all shown here. Pieces also produced during the First Period are
suffixed thus [1] .

Oviform Vase Numbered 849, 225mm

Bag Vase 45mm

Frilled Shallow Bowl 28mm

Cylinder Vase, Three Tiny Feet 40mm

Early Squat Vase 40mm

Cheese Dish and Cover, Miniature

Bagware Vase 70mm

Bowl, narrow base, 35mm

Taper Beaker 40mm

Club Vase 55mm

Cone Vase 56mm

Wide Taper Vase, vertical rim, narrow neck 50mm

Taper Vase, rounded base, wide neck 45mm

£ p

1 FAIRY SHAPES UP TO 55mm HIGH:

Bag Vase,Crinkle top		45mm	9.00
Ball or Globe Vase, Crinkle top		36mm[3]	7.50
		46mm	7.50
		55mm	8.50
Beaker, taper		40mm	7.50

Bowl, narrow base (identical to Holy Water Bowl
page 351   Dia. 55mm Height   35mm   10.00

Bowl. Shallow frilled   28mm   7.50

Club Vase   55mm   7.50
Earlier varieties have slightly crinkled rims.

Cylinder Vase, three small feet   40mm   7.50

for **Mugs, one two or three handled**
see 10L 20 LOVING CUPS AND MUGS

Squat Vase, angular sides [1]   40mm   13.00

Squat Vase, angular sides [1]   Dia. 74mm Height   48mm   16.00

Taper Vase Rounded Base, wide neck   45mm   10.00

Taper Vase Rounded Base, small vertical rim   50mm   10.00

2 VASES AND URNS 55mm TO 75mm HIGH:

Bag Vase with white or coloured cord	(a) White	70mm	15.50
	(b) Blue	70mm	30.00
	(c) Green	70mm	34.00

Ball Vase, crinkle top   76mm   8.50

Ball Vase, crinkle top. With 2 handles   62mm   17.00

Ball Vase, crinkle top. With 3 handles   60mm   21.50
                                                   67mm   25.00

Barrel Vase   74mm   22.00

Cone Vase   56mm   7.50

*Conical Crinkle Vase, Flat
Base 71mm*

*Conical Crinkle Vase,
Rounded Base 70mm*

Ball Vase, Crinkle Top 55mm

High Lipped Ewer 72mm

*Jar with Decoration in Relief
or Ali Baba Vase, 57mm*

*Narrow Taper Vase with
Everted Rim 75mm*

*Thistle Vase, Two Handles
64mm*

*Trumpet Top Vase, Two
Handles 75mm*

Urn with Handle 70mm

*Wide Taper Vase with Everted
Rim 65mm*

*Ball Vase Three Handles
76mm*

*Ball Vase Two Handles
62mm*

		£ p
Conical Vase, top. Flat base	71 mm	8.50
Conical Vase, top. Rounded base	70mm	8.50
High-Lipped Ewer	72mm	7.50
Jar, with decoration in relief Sometimes called **Ali Baba** Vase	57mm	8.00
Taper Vase, Squat	64mm	10.00
Taper Vase, Wide, everted rim, wide neck	65mm	10.00
	74mm	10.00
Taper Vase, Narrow with everted rim	75mm	9.00
Thistle Vase. Two Handles	75mm	8.50
Trumpet-top Vase, Crinkle top, Two Handles	75mm	8.00
Tub, wooden, same model as Welsh Picyn but without the upright handle Dia 60mm	57mm	20.00
Urn with inner rim, two blue butterfly handles	80mm	60.00
Urn without handle	70mm	20.00
Urn with one handle [1]	70mm	25.00
3 VASES AND URNS 76mm TO 100mm HIGH:		
Amphora Vase	80mm	21.50
Amphora Vase mounted on three Blue Balls and Plinth	93mm	42.50
Amphora Vase on blue, orange or red coral legs	85mm	34.00
Amphora Vase, with 3 butterfly handles, on 3 coral legs	85mm	80.00
Bag Vase, Narrow body with blue cord [1] Dia. (mouth) 50mm (body) 60mm Height	95mm	30.00
Bag Vase. Circular, wide mouth, with blue cord Dia. (top) 70mm (body) 95mm Height	100mm	30.00
Ball Vase. Crinkle top with two handles	76mm	21.50
Ball Vase. Crinkle top, with three handles	76mm	30.00

Amphora Vase with Three Butterfly Handles 85mm

Amphora Vase on three Blue Balls and Plinth 93mm

Amphora Vase on Three Coral Feet 85mm

Amphora Vase, two Butterfly Handles 110mm

Urn with Two Butterfly Handles 85mm

Amphora Vase, two Butterfly Handles, flat base 120mm

Diamond Mouth Vase, with foot 80mm [1]

Diamond Mouthed Vase 80mm

Egg-shaped Vase, Crinkle 80mm

Bulbous, Crinkle Top, Violet Vase curved base 76mm

Egg-shaped Vase, Crinkle Top, Narrow Neck 80mm

Egg-shaped Vase 80mm

£   p

Bulbous vase, curved base, medium width crinkle top.
Known as a **Violet Vase** by the factory.   76mm   17.00

Diamond-mouthed Vase [1]   80mm   10.50

Diamond Vase. Old pattern, with foot [1]   80mm   13.00

Egg-shaped Vase   80mm   9.00

Egg-shaped Vase, crinkle top, narrow 20mm neck   80mm   10.00

Egg-shaped Vase, with crinkle top, 27mm neck,
can be found with Egg-shaped stopper. add £10.00   80mm   10.00

**Egg-shaped Vase. With crinkle top and two blue cord
handles surmounted by butterflies**   88mm   55.00

**Egg-shaped Vase. With plain rim and two handles
surmounted by butterflies**   90mm   50.00

Jar, Flat base, wide top   86mm   10.50

**Lozenge-shaped Vase. With moulded bows at neck.
Oval top** [1] decorated in relief, or flat   86mm   60.00

Taper Vase, wide   (a) vertical rim, narrow neck [1]   80mm   10.50
                   (b) everted rim, narrow neck [1]   80mm   10.50

Taper Vase, rounded base   83mm   10.50

Thistle Vase with pineapple moulding in relief   80mm   11.00
Add £4.00 for Scottish arms

Urn with two butterfly handles [1]   85mm   40.00

Urn   96mm   10.00

Urn with inner rim, two blue butterfly handles   78mm   70.00

4 VASES OVER 100mm HIGH:

Amphora or egg shaped Vase. crinkle edge, taper body, flatbase

     (a)   No butterfly handles   100mm   30.00

     (b)   Two butterfly handles   110mm   120mm   77.50
     (c)   Three butterfly handles,   110mm   120mm   80.00
The first height shown is to the top of the vase and
the second is to the top of the handles.

Urn 70mm

Early Lozenge-shaped Vase,
Oval Top 86mm

Taper Vase Rounded Base
83mm

Thistle Vase, Pineapple
moulding in relief 80mm

Cone Specimen Vase 117mm

Jar 86mm

Crinkle Top Ball Vase 55mm

Ball Vase Four Handles,
Crinkle Top 125mm

Club Specimen Vase 114mm

Bag Vase Narrow 93mm

Bag Vase, Blue Cord [1]
93mm

Bag Vase, Circular, Wide
Mouth 100mm

£   p

Vase, crinkle top, three blue butterfly handles, blue cord
to base   110mm   47.50

Bag Vase, crinkle top, angular body,   103mm   40.00
blue cord [1] everted base

Ball Vase, crinkle top (No handles)   105mm   47.00
                                                               114mm   47.00

Ball Vase, crinkle top, two handles   115mm   65.00

Ball Vase, crinkle top, four diamond shaped handles   125mm   80.00

Circular sided Vase with oval top, blue wreath,
   and pink dot decoration to sides   (a)   118mm   85.00
                                          White (b)   118mm   47.50

Club Specimen Vase   114mm   9.00

Cone Specimen Vase   117mm   9.00

Cylindrical Vase, with everted rim   Dia. 80mm Height   135mm   40.00

Ten Amphora Vase Group, crinkle tops, on flat circular base with
beading, and acanthus leaf pattern in relief around the lower base [1] 200mm 400.00

Classical shaped vase in orange lustre numbered 850.
   Dia. 32mm (neck) 90mm (shoulder) 45mm (base)   Height   160mm   80.00

Egg-shaped Vase, crinkle top, wide mouth,
narrow base tied with blue cord   105mm[1] 60.00

Egg-shaped Vase, pedestal base, blue coral handles
surmounted by butterflies
                      (a) With 2 handles   115mm   65.00
                      (b) With 3 handles   115mm   75.00

Globe Vase, narrow neck   196mm   30.00

Globe Vase. With two small knurled handles,
narrow neck   196mm   45.00

Globe Vase. With three small knurled handles,
narrow neck   196mm   47.50

Goblet with central stem   168mm   75.00

Jar, curved base, narrow top   109mm   17.00

*Quadruple Amphora Vase
Group on Plinth 150mm*

Bagware Sack Vase 110mm

*Quadruple Ball Vase Group
114mm*

Triple Amphora Vases 110mm

*Triple Bag Vase and Shell
Centrepiece*

*Vase, Bell-shaped on Socle
Base 203mm*

*Bulbous Vase with Cup Top
and Strap Handle [1] 176mm*

*Bulbous Vase, Cup Top and 2
Strap Handles [1] 176mm*

*Globular Vase, Two High
Curved Handles 200mm*

*Taper Vase, 2 High Handles
172mm*

*Vase, Pear shaped, Balmoral
transfer, green grapevine 132mm*

*Ball Vase, Crinkle Top
114mm*

£ p

Jar, flat base, wide top	105mm	17.00
Jar, flat base	115mm	17.00
Lozenge-shaped Vase. Upright with diamond top [1]	139mm	80.00
May be found with bud stopper and cork	160mm	120.00

Pear Shaped Vase. Flat with rectangular top and black trim [1]

	106mm	30.00
	122mm	30.00
	130mm	40.00

Pear Shaped Vase as above, with:
(a) Green grapevine decoration overall with brown
    transfer of BALMORAL CASTLE [1]   132mm   325.00
(b) Orange grapevine decoration overall with brown
    transfer of WINDSOR CASTLE [1]   132mm   325.00

Pompeian Centrepiece On Plinth   (a)125mm   67.50
(Illustrated Goss Record. 8th Edition Pages 4 and 75)   (b)340mm[1]   275.00
This magnificent group of three amphora vases   (c)340mm[1]   375.00
surrounding a trumpet vase was produced in the
First Period in the larger size (b) and, rarely, covered in blue dots(c)
and in the smaller size in the Second Period(a)
see illustration on page 389

Pompeian Centrepiece. No plinth.	111 mm	70.00

**Quadruple Amphora Vase Group. On plinth with
intertwined blue trim decorated around trefoil base**   150mm   200.00

Quadruple Ball Vase Group	114mm	100.00
	146mm	125.00

**Quadruple Centrepiece with four oval bag vases,
  central one elongated**   200mm   275.00
(Goss Record. 8th Edition: Page 4)

Sack. Bagware. Blue cord	110mm	95.00

Scent bottle-shaped Vase   115mm   15.00
(See also Scent Bottle Domestic 10. L. 1 9 Miscellaneous)

Taper Vase	110mm	17.00
Taper Vase. Crinkle top (no handles) blue cord	107mm	40.00

**Taper Vase. Crinkle top. With two blue (a)
angular handles and blue cord around neck
(b) with white handles**   (a)115mm   50.00
                                         (b)115mm   35.00

*Taper Vase wide base. Two long knurled handles and eight wide crinkles to everted rim. 170mm
The same Vase was also used to make an unique jewelled vase.*

An example of one of Adolphus Goss's travellers photographs with his own notes.

Another of Adolphus Goss's Travellers photographs.

Vase, cylindrical, everted rim
135mm

Taper Vase, Crinkle Top, 2
Blue Handles 115mm

Globe Vase 2 Small Knurled
Handles, Narrow Neck

Goblet 168mm

Jar, Curved Base, Narrow Top
109mm

Early Lozenge-shaped Vase.
Upright, Diamond Top 139mm

Pear shaped Vase 106mm [1]

Pompeian Centre Piece 340mm

Pompeian Centre Piece 125mm

Bass Basket small 64mm Blue
Handles

Bass Basket Medium 80mm
Blue Handles

Early, 94mm Bass Bucket

£   p

**Taper Vase, wide base, two long knurled handles
and eight wide crinkles to everted rim**   170mm   60.00

**Taper Vase. With two high angular handles, each
incorporating a small circular finger grip, fluted,
everted rim and base**   172mm   65.00

Triple Amphora. Three joined vases   110mm   80.00

Triple Bag Vase and Shell Centrepiece. Having three glazed 159mm 275.00
**66mm bag vases fixed together with a cone-shaped
shell held centrally**

Trumpet Vase, white everted rim and flat foot.   approx   200mm 150.00
A pair of these vases, decorated in apricot lustre,
were known as the Ashfield vases after
William Henry Goss's home where they
were kept for some time.
see illustration page 354

Vase   Dia. (base) 45mm (shoulder) 95mm Height   160mm   40.00

Vase. Bell-shaped on socle base. Rare. May also be 203mm   100.00
found with two handles
can also be found in lustre[3]

Vase. Bulbous. With cup top and strap handle [1]   176mm   75.00
                                                        218mm   80.00

Vase. Bulbous with cup top and two strap handles [1] 176mm   65.00
                                                          218mm   75.00

**Vase, globular with two high handles and
circular mouth**   two handles(a) 200mm   85.00
sometimes found in lustre.   with handles (b) 200mm   85.00

Vase, Oviform. numbered 849   Dia. 100mm Height   225mm 110.00

5 MINIATURE, DOMESTIC AND MISCELLANEOUS ITEMS:

Bass Basket.
(a) Turquoise blue handles sides pinched in at centre
     of top edges. With or without arms   64mm   17.50
(b) Orange handles and without arms   64mm[1] 20.00
(c) Turquoise blue handles   80mm   21.50
(d) Red handles and no arms   88mm[1] 30.00
(e) Turquoise or white handles   94mm[1] 34.00
(f) with yellow handles   94mm   34.00

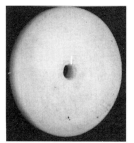

Circular Unglazed Button

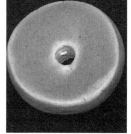

Circular Button. One side Blue Glazed

Oval Cameo

Circular Disc

Limpet Shell. Orange Coral Legs

Nautilus Shell, large 150mm

Scallop Shell on Coral Ring 76mm

Scallop Shell on Three Short Legs 76mm

Pot-pourri Bowl, small 40mm

Pot-pourri Bowl, large, curved top 80mm

Pot-pourri Bowl, large, flat top, gilded rim 80mm

Scarborough Flags Plate 105mm wide

£   p

Buttons Circular with central hole
All found unmarked   (a)Unglazed   Dia.   15mm   20.00
                            (b)Blue glazed one side   Dia.   15mm   30.00
Cameo Oval with bust of a lady in bas-relief
All found unmarked   White glazed   20mm   40.00

Cheese dish and cover   Length 80mm Height   50mm   30.00
CHEDDAR could be considered matching for which add £10.00

Cigarette Holder not marked, but several have
been discovered in the factory spoil heap (See page 39)   Length   75mm   35.00

Cup and saucer Taper. Miniature   38mm   15.00

Disc, circular, probably originally mounted in a silver ring. Dia.   50mm   12.00
see also M - METALWARE

Holy Water Bowl, used in a travelling communion
    set, with **IHS** in red Gothic lettering on
    the side   (a) Dia. 52mm Height[3]   35mm   35.00
        Also found without lettering   (b) Dia 52mm Height   35mm   25.00
An example of this bowl (a) has been recorded at the
base of a large wooden crucifix to which a white
composition figure of christ is affixed.
The whole is affixed to a wooden base with a
pair of chrome plated candlesticks either side
of the cross. The bowl is marked *GOSS ENGLAND.*
                  Overall Length of crucifix   280mm   50.00

Picture Frame, rectangular, Containing sepia transfer
of Romsey Abbey Crucifix, made all in one piece
                    Height 170mm Width   137mm
    (a) Wall hanging, with two pierced holes for Cord hanging   215.00
    (b) Free standing, the stand being 86mm in depth at base   215.00

Pot-pourri Bowl. Small, six holes   Dia. 98mm Height   40mm
        (a)   No rim, no decoration   21.50
        (b)   No rim, with central colourful star   42.50
        (c)   Curved as depicted on page 350   47.50
              with curved top, 5 holes and gilded rim.

Pot-pourri Bowl or Rose Bowl. Large. With central
   hole and 15 smaller holes.
    (a)   With rim gilded around circumference and flat top, star
         decoration around centre hole   80mm   42.50
    (b)   As above but with no central star decoration   80mm   25.00
    (c)   Without rim with curved top and star decoration on top   80mm   40.00

Amphora or Egg-shaped Vase,
flat-base 120mm

Wall Pocket, 75mm

Flower Holder or Hair Tidy
Wall Pocket 122mm

Toilet Salt Mortar 95mm

Largest Wall Pocket 176mm

Holy Water Stoup

Salt Vase and Pestle 55mm

Bagware Tea Pot, Miniature

Flower Holder, profile of
Shakespeare in bas-relief 122mm

Salt Vase and Pestle 55mm

Toilet Salt Mortar

Slipper Wall Pocket 96mm

£   p

Travelling Font, white glazed, with **IHS** in gold Gothic lettering
on the side The piece is similar in style to the Haddon Hall font,
and is found in a leather carrying case lined in blue silk, marked
as sold by *A.R. Mowbray & C.o. Ltd. Oxford & London*, inside the
case lid.   Dia. 90mm Height   70mm 150.00

Salt Vase & Pestle so named in Gothic script on a
club vase.   Height   55mm   85.00

Teapot and lid bagware, miniature (or fairy size) white cord   60mm   35.00

Toilet Salt Mortar so named in Gothic script on a circular dish;
an unnamed Roman Mortarium with inscription on base in
handwriting of W . H . Goss extolling the virtues of cleaning the
teeth with ground salt, as follows: Dia.   95mm   55.00
The very best tooth-powder is table-salt, finely pounded to
prevent bleeding of the gums. It cleanses without scratching,
helps to check decay, and aids sweetness of breath. William H. Goss
                     Above two items priced as a pair   200.00

Lion of Flanders plate. Decorated with 8 flags
of the allies surrounding a central lion motif
and the inscription: *L'Union Fait La Force*
and *Eendracht Maakt Macht.*
See *The Price Guide to Arms and Decorations on*
Goss China page 159 for full description.   250mm 125.00

The Peace Plate crinkle edge plate with a
multicoloured design issued to
commemorate peace in 1919   Approx Dia   200mm 350.00
See *The Price Guide to Arms and Decorations on Goss China*
G3 for full details and illustration.

Scarborough Flags Plate. A three-quarter shaped plate,
specially commissioned by J.G. Nairn of Southport.
Having six flags (Japan, France, Russia, Belgium,
Serbia and Montenegro) around the perimeter, and the
Union Jack central. It bears two inscriptions :
Up, Ye Sons of England, And Wreak Vengeance on the Baby
Killers of Scarborough around the edge, and *We follow*
You In Our Daily Thoughts On Your Certain Road To Victory.
George R.I. Dec. 5th 1914 around the Union Jack.   Width   105mm 450.00
On reverse. Imprinted with The Royal Arms
and inscribed under:
                     No. 22794 - A .D. 1913
                          Patentee
                     John Gordon Nairn
                     "Morland" 84, Promenade
                          Southport
                     _____

The Ashfield Vases in Apricot Lustre

*The "Swabs" Plate with cartoon of Major Embleton and Major Vernon Goss.
Designed by Margaret Goss around 1920*

£   p

Manufacturer
W. H. Goss
Stoke-on-Trent
Rd. Nos. 646416-7

The plate has been found with a special fitting metal stand which
appears to have been made for the special shape of the plate.
Curiously, the Nairn Patent No. is dated one year prior to the
outbreak of war. It is assumed that the special shape was on sale as
a display plate or plaque, with other than flags decorations, and
complete with the metal stand, which is probably the subject of the
patent. For the metal stand add £50.00 to the value of the flags
plate.

"SWABS" Plate, Specially Decorated, one of only twelve
produced in bagware, with coloured cartoon of army Medical
Officers, Major Embleton and Major Vernon Goss,
designed by Margaret Goss around 1920, and most of them
unmarked   Dia.   150mm   300.00
(See *The Price Guide to Arms and Decorations on Goss China*,
Section N. 1 Margaret Goss Decorations, for detailed
explanation and description)

6 SHELLS

see also FIRST PERIOD 9C ORNAMENTAL AND DOMESTIC
for First Period shells

Limpet Shell, coral legs   Dia. 74mm Height   36mm   20.00
see also FIRST PERIOD 9C. ORNAMENTAL Chapter
   for the eggshell variety

Nautilus Shell
Glazed and crested with orange or dull yellow coral legs on white
glazed rocky base   150mm   175.00
See also FIRST PERIOD 9C. ORNAMENTAL Chapter for the
   smaller eggshell variety.

Scallop Shell.				
	(a) 3 short legs	Length	76mm	15.00
	(b) on coral legs	Length	76mm	25.00
	(c) on coral ring	Length	76mm	26.00
	(d) on yellow coral ring base	Length	76mm	35.00
	(e) 3 short legs	Length	101mm	21.50
	(f) 3 short legs	Length	110mm	25.00
	(g) 3 short legs	Length	110mm	25.00
	(h) no legs	Length	140mm	16.50
	(i) 3 short legs	Length	140mm	19.50

See also Third Period for W H Goss
England for same model as (a) above

£   p

7 WALL POCKETS

Shield-shaped

Usually inscribed: HAIR TIDY	(a)	60mm	16.00
With arms other than those fully	(b)	75mm	19.00
covering piece (see below)	(c)	80mm	21.50
	(d)	92mm	25.00
	(e)	100mm	27.50
Can be found Inscribed *FLOWER HOLDER*	(f)	122mm	30.00
	(g)	176mm	77.50

Size (f) is square shield-shaped and inscribed *FLOWER
HOLDER* on the back and Rd. No. 201914 which refers to
the piece.
Size (g) bearing the crest E PLURIBUS UNUM (USA) has been
found marked EMBLEMATIC T ENGLAND, in addition to the
Goshawk mark.

Shield-shaped Wall-pockets or Posy-holders. With arms of
(a) Cambridge University, Eton College (with motto: *FLOREAT ETONA*),
Harrow School (with motto: *STET FORTUNA DOMUS*), Oxford University
(with moto: *DOMIMINA NUSTIO ILLUMEA)* or Harvard University, Boston,
Mass. USA. (Motto: *VERITAS*), fully covering piece
(Goss Record 8th Edition: Page 4 includes
the Cambridge University and Eton College examples)   173mm   150.00
(b) With three coats of arms   173mm   50.00

Slipper. To hang on wall as posy vase   Length   96mm   17.00

Flower Holder with profile of Shakespeare in bas-relief.
Glazed   122mm   175.00

See also 10E HISTORIC MODELS AND SPECIAL SHAPES
for Durham Sanctuary Knocker Flowerholder

See also FIRST PERIOD 9C ORNAMENTAL for Humming Bird
and House Martins nest Wall Vases

8 HOLY WATER STOUPS

			Height	*With any arms*	*With I.H.S*
				£ p	£ p
These are found in five sizes, normally carrying					
the letters I.H.S. in red at the centre of the cross.					
This is the familiar monogram of the first three					
letters of the Greek word for Jesus IHΣOYΣ or	(a)	124mm		45.00	65.00
the Latin, *Iesus Hominum Salvador*. Some examples	(b)	142mm		50.00	70.00
carry normal coats of arms. The design comprises	(c)	190mm		55.00	75.00
a shell-type water container surmounted by a	(d)	219mm		65.00	90.00
cross pierced for wallmounting.	(e)	256mm		90.00	95.00

L Domestic and Utility Wares

This section has been arranged into the various headings listed below. Ornamental ware will be found in Chapter K. The majority of these pieces date from both the First and Second Periods, but the First or Third Periods should be checked when an item cannot be found. Pieces definitely known to have also been produced during different periods are denoted thus: [1] or [3].

Whenever possible, given names for shapes have been taken from The Goss Record. Its compiler J J Jarvis, obtained information from the Goss factory between 1900 and 1921, so that in the absence of any official catalogues, these publications provide the only source of correct terminology. However, reference to the photographs and papers formerly belonging to Adolphus Goss have provided further information. Mugs and loving cups were known at the time of manufacture as 1/2 pint, pint, quart mugs etc. Domestic vases too small for daily use have been catalogued in the 10K ORNAMENTAL SECTION as Fairy Shapes, which is how the factory originally termed them. Other fairy size items are listed in 10K5 MINIATURE DOMESTIC AND MISCELLANEOUS ITEMS.

In previous editions of this book a particular type of vase was refered to as oviform. The description has been changed to egg shaped in this edition as J.J. Jarvis described the shape thus in *The Goss Record.*

All measurements refer to height unless otherwise stated. Height of cups and saucers are of the two items together, not of the cup seperately which will be 5 - 10mm less than the overall height given.

High Melon Cup and Saucer
Height 115mm

Bagware Cup and Saucer
Height 60mm

Low Melon Cup and Saucer
Height 44mm

Taper Cup and Saucer 69mm

Straight Sided cup and saucer
70mm [1]

Coffee Can and Saucer 50mm

Individual Morning Set Cup
on Platter

Octagonal Coffee Cup and
saucer 62mm

Octagonal Sugar basin 46mm

Octagonal Coffee Pot and Lid
192mm

Octagonal Milk Jug 77mm

Cup, to square gilded handles,
68mm [1]

Table Ware

1 BAGWARE TEA SERVICE
£   p

This was the factory's longest running range, and was produced from 1881 to 1925 through all three periods. The ware is in the form of a tied bag, gathered in by a blue cord with gilded tassels and having a matching blue cord handle. Some items have words in illuminated Gothic script emblazoned on the side or lid. Alternatively some cord and handles are coloured green, orange or yellow; other cord can rarely be found uncoloured, or red.

Biscuit barrel and lid				135mm	120.00
not seen by the author.					
Cup and Saucer				50mm	25.00
				60mm	25.00
Cream Jug				65mm	35.00
With red cord Add £10.00				75mm	35.00
Milk Jug				105mm	42.50
				114mm	42.50

Sugar Basin

	(a) Dia.	70mm	Height	45mm	30.00
	(b) Dia.	88mm	Height	40mm	34.00
	(c) Dia.	97mm	Height	55mm	34.00
	(d) Dia.	103mm	Height	47mm	34.00

Bowl

	(a) Dia.	110mm	Height	55mm	25.00
	(b) Dia.	125mm	Height	70mm	34.00
	(c) Dia.	135mm	Height	65mm	34.00

Preserve Dish and Lid circular   Dia. 105mm   Height   86mm   45.00
with MARMALADE, JAM OR CHEESE coloured illuminated lettering and bagware knop.

Preserve Jar and Lid   With word HONEY,

JAM or MARMALADE	(a)	95mm	30.00
(b)		105mm	30.00
With Green Cord	(c)	105mm	40.00

Tea Pot and lid	115mm	80.00
	140mm	85.00
	155mm	95.00

for **Tea Pot and Lid Miniature** see ORNAMENTAL ARTICLES K.5 MINIATURE DOMESTIC AND MISCELLANEOUS ITEMS

Tankard Cream Jug Early,
Angular Handle 67mm

Fluted Milk Jug 86mm

Welsh Lady Cream Jug 94mm

Large Frilled Cream Jug
57mm

Manx Legs Cream Jug 67mm

Big-lipped Cream Jug 67mm

Urn-shaped Cream Jug, Early,
Butterfly Handle 65mm

Ball Cream Jug 47mm

Shaped Low Melon Cream
Jug 53mm

Shaped High Melon Milk Jug
100mm

Bagware Cream Jug 60mm

Bagware Milk Jug 114mm

360

			£ p
Tea Plate	Dia.	100mm	8.50
	Dia.	115mm	8.50
	Dia.	125mm	8.50
	Dia.	130mm	10.50
	Dia.	135mm	10.50
	Dia.	150mm	11.50

The 150mm size also appears with a 5mm blue band
around the edge with the gilding inset.

Cake Plate	Dia.	250mm	26.00

Add around £5.00 for each additional crest.

Empire Plate with 9 crests around United Kingdom
and Colonies   Dia   250mm   75.00

For Bagware Vases
see 10K ORNAMENTAL ARTICLES Chapter

2 TAPER TEA SERVICE

Cup and Saucer	69mm	8.50
	82mm	8.50

For Cup and Saucer Miniature
see 10 K.5 MINIATURE DOMESTIC AND MISCELLANEOUS ITEMS Chapter
All items in this section have a narrower rim than base unless otherwise stated

Cream Jug	80mm	7.50
	87mm	8.50
	95mm	10.00

Milk Jug	108mm	8.50
	124mm	10.00

Jug	145mm	25.00
	159mm	30.00
	176mm	37.50

Hot Water Jug	(a) with pewter flip lid and lip	155mm	45.00
	(b) with lip and lid	165mm	50.00
	(c)	180mm	50.00

Sugar basin narrower base	(a) Dia. 80mm Height	42mm	7.50
and everted rim	(b) Dia. 85mm Height	48mm	8.50

Slop Bowl narrower base	(a)	Dia. 95mm Height	42mm	8.00
with periwinkles in relief	(b)	Dia. 97mm Height	46mm	30.00
	(c)	Dia. 93mm Height	60mm	8.50
	(d)	Dia. 97mm Height	54mm	17.50
	(e)	Dia.125mm Height	60mm	17.50
	(f)	Dia.105mm Height	75mm	17.50
	(g)	Dia.145mm Height	85mm	17.50

Tea Pot and lid	112mm	30.00

Taper Milk Jug 124mm

Giant 176mm Taper Jug

Upright Cream Jug 100mm

Taper Sugar Basin 48mm

*Taper Sugar Basin, everted
rim 42mm*

Fluted Sugar Basin 58mm

*Ball Sugar Basin
Dia 88mm Height 55mm*

*Bagware Sugar Basin
Dia 88mm Height 40mm*

*Bagware Sugar Basin
Dia 70mm Height 45mm*

*Ball Sugar Basin
Dia 72mm Height 55mm*

Taper Sugar Basin 48mm

*Bagware Bowl
Dia 140mm Height 65mm*

			£	p
Coffee Pot, often named *Taper Coffee Pot and lid*		118mm	50.00
		170mm	65.00

3 MELON TEA SERVICE

The Melon saucer can be found with four flutes (rare)
instead of the normal nine

Low Melon Cup and Saucer		44mm	9.00
		52mm	10.50
Medium Melon cup and Saucer		55mm	10.50
		75mm	10.50
High Melon Cup and Saucer		70mm	12.00
		95mm	12.00
		115mm	12.00
Low Melon Cream Jug		55mm	7.50
		60mm	8.50
		72mm	9.00
High Melon Milk Jug		87mm	9.50
		100mm	11.00
		118mm	14.50
Hot Water Jug		155mm	50.00
Hot Water Jug with thumb lip and lid		165mm	55.00
Slop Bowl	Dia. 78mm [1]	38mm	8.50
	Dia. 94mm	48mm	8.50
Sugar Basin		42mm	7.50
		54mm	8.00
Tea Pot and lid		93mm	37.50
		114mm	40.00
		140mm	50.00
		150mm	55.00
Tea Plate	Dia.	100mm	8.50
	Dia.	108mm	8.50
	Dia.	130mm	8.50
	Dia.	150mm	8.50
	Dia.	155mm	8.50
	Dia.	160mm	10.00
Cake Plate	Dia.	250mm	20.00

Add around £5.00 for each additional coat of arms.

Empire Plate with 9 arms of The United
Kingdom and Colonies   Dia.   250mm   75.00

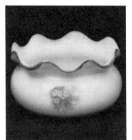

Large Frilled Sugar Basin 35mm

Melon Sugar Basin 42mm

Sugar Basin, Kneeling Manx Legs 67mm

Frilled Sugar Basin 35mm

Bagware Marmalade Dish and Lid 86mm

Circular Tea Pot Stand 102mm

Tea Pot Globular Three Small Feet 116mm [1]

Bagware Teapot 140mm

Taper Coffee Pot 160mm

Tea Pot Kneeling, Manx Legs and lid 110mm

Melon Teapot and Lid 114mm

Taper Tea Pot and Lid 112mm

£   p

4 OCTAGONAL COFFEE SERVICE
With heavily gilded everted rims and handles   45.00

Cup and Saucer	62mm	45.00

(See also Royal Buff version, Third Period T3)

Milk Jug   77mm   45.00

Sugar Basin   46mm   45.00

Coffee Pot and lid   192mm   95.00
(See also Royal Buff version, Third Period T3)

5 OTHER CUPS AND SAUCERS
See also 11 S THIRD PERIOD for late examples.

Coffee Can and Saucer   50mm   9.00
                                60mm   9.00

Straight-sided Cup and Saucer, square handle [1]   70mm   10.00

Curved Cup and Saucer   70mm   14.00
A fluted spiral design part tea service has been seen
decorated with the arms of Royal Leamington Spa.
Namely a cup and uncrested saucer and a teaplate   Trio   45.00

Two-handled Straight-sided Cup and Saucer   68mm   70.00
    with two blue or gold square handles [1]

Individual Morning Set
cup on elongated platter[1]   Length 208mm   Height   64mm   35.00

Moustache Cup and Saucer
98mm   65.00

6 CREAM AND MILK JUGS
See also 11 S THIRD PERIOD for late examples.

Ball   1/3 pint   45mm   7.50
                           1/4 pint   55mm   8.50
                           1/2 pint   70mm   9.50

Ball on three small feet [1]   60mm   12.50

Ball Big-lipped   67mm   8.50
                           75mm   9.50

Upright   3/4 pint (a)   100mm   16.00
      with Adolphus Goss verse and coat of arms (b)   100mm   24.50

Fluted angular handle. Sometimes found with blue,
orange, pink or yellow handle[1] for which add £20.00   1/2 pint   86mm   17.00

Tea Plate 125mm [3]

Bagware Teaplate
Dia 115mm

Melon Teaplate
Dia 100mm

Teaplate Side View 125mm
[3]

Bagware Teaplate Side View
115mm

Melon Teaplate Side View
100mm

Coupe Plate 230mm

Scallop Edge plate 112mm

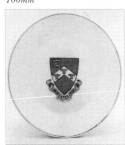

Taper plate 125mm

Coupe Plate Above 250mm
Side View

Empire Bagware Cake plate
250mm

Child's Feeding Bowl Dia
130mm

			£	p
Frilled	(a) small frills	57mm	11.00	
	(b) large frills	57mm	11.00	

Kneeling-Manx legs and handle   (a) blue or yellow [1]   70mm   45.00
(Rd. No. 149157)   (b) White   70mm   30.00
with Isle of Man arms add £30.00

Tankard with everted rim, angular handle[1]   1/5 pint   67mm   12.50

Urn-shaped with blue handle surmounted by a butterfly[1]   75mm   40.00

Welsh Lady (Coloured) Black Hat. Plain or Plaid Red Bodice   94mm   50.00
   Impressed on base rim: *Ychydig O Laeth*

7 SUGAR BASINS

Ball		48mm	7.50
	Dia. 72mm Height 55mm	7.50	
	Dia. 88mm Height 55mm	8.50	

Curved sided   48mm   8.50

Fluted   58mm   8.50

Frilled   (a) small frills Dia. 80mm Height   35mm   11.00
                 (b) large frills Dia. 75mm Height   35mm   11.00
                 (c)   Dia. 78mm Height   45mm   11.00

Kneeling-Manx legs (Rd. No. 149157) in yellow   75mm   45.00
with Isle of Man arms add £30.00

8   TEA POTS and lids

Kneeling Manx Legs in yellow, with a Manx leg as a handle to lid 110mm   85.00
   Add 40.00 for Manx Coat of Arms

Globular, having straight spout, curved handle,
   and 3 small feet [1]   116mm   70.00

9 JUG STANDS
circular   Dia.   82mm   7.50
                                                  Dia.   99mm   9.00
                                                  Dia. 102mm   9.00
                                                  Dia. 110mm   9.00
                                                  Dia. 120mm 12.00
                                                  Dia. 144mm 14.00
                                                  Dia. 160mm 14.00

TEA POT STANDS square
   With one coat of Arms   144mm sq   20.00
   With up to four Arms and verse   144mm sq   34.00

*Bagware Preserve Jar and lid
105mm*

*Preserve Jar and lid, plain,
crested 110mm*

*Taper Hot Water Jug with lip
and hinged lid*

*Small Preserve Jar and lid.
Strawberry knop 100mm*

*Jar and lid, Bees and Clover
110mm*

*Preserve Pot and lid as
Timbered Cottage 115mm*

*Cheese Dish and Cover with
Dolphin handle 90mm*

*Butter Dish, Four Fern Leaves
Dia 143mm*

*Butter Dish, Waste Not
Dia 143mm*

*Invalid Feeding Cup
76mm*

*Jam Dish or Nut Tray
145mm*

*Toast Rack, Four section
Length 170mm*

368

£   p

10   PRESERVE JARS AND LIDS

As well as the normal crested or simple coloured
varieties, these can be found decorated with colour
transfers of the following fruits, etc. and have either
circular white or appropriately coloured fruit shaped
knops on the lids.
Spoon cut outs are to be found on either the lid or
the base.

Cylindrical crested	Dia. 57mm	Height	100mm	25.00
	Dia. 72mm	Height	110mm	30.00
For examples in a single colour, normally blue, green or lilac				45.00

Price for either size decorated with:

Apples on a branch, circular white knop	75.00
Blackberries, blackberry knop	75.00
Californian Poppies (a) purple (b) yellow	110.00
Country Cottage Garden Scene, circular white knop	100.00
Cherries on a branch, cherry knop	75 00
Grapefruit, grapefruit knop	100.00
Grapes red and white bunches	90.00
Honey bees and clover, clover knop	65.00
Lemons, lemon knop	90.00
Life Plant, Bermuda	100.00
Plums, plum knop	100.00
Strawberries, strawberry knop	80.00
Thistles, thistle knop	80.00

For plain knop: Deduct £20.00 from the price
of a piece priced with a fruit shaped knop

Appropriately decorated base plates may be found for
the above.   Dia.   110mm   35.00

for Orange-shaped Preserve Jar and lid
See 11 S THIRD PERIOD.

for Bagware Preserve Jar and Lid
See 10L 1 DOMESTIC AND UTILITY WARES

Preserve Jar and lid, green trim, acorn Dia. 75mm Height   120mm   115.00
knop in green cup, four flat green oak leaves spaced on lid,
four outpressed green oak leaves spaced around body.

Preserve Jar and lid in the shape of a timbered
cottage with thatched, or tiled roof   115mm   75.00

Honey Pot and lid bee hive shaped on small
green hexagon base, with two coloured bees
moulded on side, and bee on lid as handle.
Coloured in natural tones with spoon cut out.   103mm   90.00

Napkin Ring 40mm

Egg-shaped Cruet in stand 100mm

Beaker 80mm

Taper Beaker with handle 95mm

Mustard Pot and lid, one handle 60mm

Shaped Sugar Castor 115mm

Porcelain Spoon 150mm

Tea Infuser and lid 35mm

Shaped Salt Castor 90mm

Trinket Tray small 230mm

Trinket Tray large 310mm

Shaped Pepper Castor 87mm

£   p

**Honey Section Dish - Square, decorated with bees and clover
with bee as knop on lid, square** [3].   145mm x   145mm   56.50

11 OTHER ITEMS OF TABLEWARE

Beakers (or Tumblers) (For 44mm Fairy size		(a)	80mm	10.00
see 10K1 ORNAMENTAL		(b)	95mm	12.00
Note: (a) (b) and (c) varieties are occasionally		(c)	100mm	13.00
found with handles, for which: Add £5.00		(d)	115mm	14.50
		(e)	145mm	20.00
	Barrel-shaped	(f)	75mm	20.00
	Lincoln Imp in high relief	(g)	80mm	65.00
	Lincoln Imp in high relief	(h)	114mm	75.00

Bowl, octagonal (sometimes in lustre)   Width   128mm   22.50

Bowl, soup or dessert   Dia.   185mm   13.00

Child's Feeding Bowl   Dia.   130mm   20.00

Comport, curved on flared foot   Dia. 193mm Height   100mm   65.00

Dish, Butter WASTE NOT and ears of corn in relief   Dia.   143mm   25.00
on white unglazed rim; the centre dished and glazed.

Dish, Butter four fern leaves in relief,   Dia.   143mm   27.50
centre dished

Dish, Butter in carved wooden surround with   Dia.   150mm   18.00
BUTTER carved around rim surround. Also with
BOURNEMOUTH OR SALISBURY

Dish, Butter circular lid and dolphin   Height 85mm Dia.
handle with BUTTER **in illuminated lettering**

(a) with dolphin handle	140mm	47.50
(b) with bagware knop	140mm	70.00

Dish, Cheese circular lid and dolphin   Height 90mm Dia.   152mm   45.00
handle, with CHEESE **in illuminated lettering**

Dish, preserve circular lid and bagware knop
with JAM or MARMALADE **in coloured**
illuminated lettering   Height 85mm Dia.   140mm   70.00

Dish, Cheese in carved wooden surround with
CHEESE carved around rim of surround   Dia.   150mm   20.00

Egg Cup Cylindrical 60mm

Egg Cup Goblet 50mm

Egg Cup on Plate 62mm

Egg Cup, Goblet 58mm [3]

Menu Holder 69mm

*Square Tea Pot Stand
144mm square*

*Oval Crinkle Tray large frills
Length 158mm*

*Elongated Tray with small
frills*

*Square Pin Tray with Tassels
70mm [1]*

*Crinkle Edge Dish
Dia 70mm*

*Round Dish with Turned
Under Rim Dia 82mm*

*Square Pin Tray Plain
70mm*

£   p

Dinner Service:
Two 62-piece dinner services were made for the Goss agent in
Malta. Upon his death they passed to his two daughters living
in England. In 1997, one service was in Australia. Made from
earthenware, each piece carries the arms of Malta and comprises:
One soup tureen and cover with base plate
Two vegetable dishes and covers with base plates
One meat platter
One gravy boat and stand
One cheese dish and cover
Twelve dinner plates
Twelve side plates
Twelve soup dishes
Twelve dessert bowls

Total value of set		400.00

		£ p
Dish Oval, fluted.	200mm	40.00
When decorated with strawberries: Add £50.00	250mm	40.00
add £25.00 if decorated with red poppies	344mm	60.00
Egg Cup, Cylindrical	60mm	20.00
Egg Cup, Goblet	50mm	21.50
Several patterns, one scalloped	58mm[3]	21.50

Egg Cup, Mounted on curved tea plate   Dia. 100mm   62mm   30.00

Egg-shaped Mustard Pot and lid   60mm   17.00

Egg-shaped Pepper Castor   60mm   15.00

Egg-shaped Salt Castor   60mm   15.00
The above three items are found also in a stand
    with tall central handle   Price Complete: 100mm   95.00

for Fruit Basket.
see FIRST PERIOD 9C ORNAMENTAL

Invalid Feeding Cup   110mm   37.50

Jam Dish, twelve sided and crinkle edged	Dia.	110mm	19.00
		125mm	19.00
		145mm	20.00

**Mustard pot with square handle and domed lid with spoon
cut out.** The base doubles as a coffee can   60mm   22.00

Napkin Ring   40mm   23.00

for Nut Tray - see Jam Dish

Sugar Castor electro-plated nickled silver top 108mm

			£ p
Plate, crinkle edge	Dia.	205mm	25.00
	Dia.	230mm	25.00
Plate, cake, fluted octagonal	236mm x	263mm	25.00
Plate, Dinner, curved or coupe shape [1]	Dia.	117mm	8.50
	Dia.	240mm	21.00
	Dia.	255mm	23.00
Plate, plain rim	Dia.	200mm	25.00
Plate, scallop edge	Dia.	112mm	30.00

Plate, with violet pattern in relief around rim; in the centre the arms of *Sir William Wallace*.
Inscribed: *Pub. by W. Middleton Wallace Memorial Stirling* [1]   Dia.   130mm   35.00

Pepper Castor, Shaped- *PEPPER* moulded in blue   87mm   19.00

Salt Castor, Shaped - *SALT* moulded in blue   90mm   19.00
Can be found with either one or several holes in top.   100mm   19.00

Sugar Castor, Shaped - *SUGAR* moulded in blue   115mm   25.00

Sugar Castor, taper, with EPNS, pierced, domed top   60mm   40.00

Sugar Castor, taper, EPNS, rim with removable top.   105mm   40.00

Spoon, Coat of Arms in bowl   Length   150mm   150.00

for EPNS spoon
see M METALWARE

for Tankard Mugs
see L.20 LOVING CUPS AND MUGS

Tea Infuser and lid   Dia. 82mm   Height   35mm   37.50
Inscribed on the outside of the bowl: *Tea Infuser Rd. No. 678890*
Can be found with either small or large holes in base.

Toast Rack
(a) Four section on fluted edge, oval base, with   Length   170mm   40.00
        central circular handle
(b) Five section   Length   183mm   45.00

Tray elongated and heavy fluted   Length   345mm   40.00

Puff Box and lid 40mm　　*Pomade Box and lid 50mm*　　*Hairpin Box, length 98mm*

Candlestick Column 153mm　　*Candlestick Column 89mm*　　*Candle Bracket 175mm*

Tankard Mug, angular handle, everted rim 73mm　　*Tankard Mug, taper, square handle 85mm [1]*　　*Tankard Mug, angular handle 75mm*

Picture Frame one piece Romsey Abbey Crucifix sepia transfer 170mm　　*Hair Tidy, taper and lid 93mm [1]*　　*Hair Tidy and lid 93mm*

12 TRINKET AND PIN TRAYS   £   p

Trinket Tray	(a)	One crest	Length	230mm	22.50
	(b)	Multi-crested			40.00
	(c)	One crest	Length	270mm	30.00
	(d)	One crest	Length	310mm	30.00
	(e)	Multi-crested			60.00

Oval Crinkle Tray	(a)	With large frills	Length	165mm	13.00
	(b)	With small frills	Length	165mm	13.00

Elongated tray with small frills   Length   180mm   18.00

Round Crinkle Dish	Dia. 70mm	7.50
Sometimes found with coral or blue legs	75mm	8.50
when £ 25.00 should be added	85mm	9.00
	95mm	9.00
	105mm	10.00

Round Dish. Plain rim [1]   Dia. 80mm   10.50

Round Dish. Heavy, with turned-under rim [1]   Dia. 80mm   14.00

Round Dish, very flat, shallow   Dia. 95mm   10.50

Round Dish, 6 floral patterns in relief   Dia. 155mm   6.50
   and scallop edged rim.

Square Tray. Plain   70mm sq   13.00
See also 10J MINIATURES

Square Tray. Heavy, with gilded tassel corners [1]   70mm sq   22.50

Square Tray. Heavy with gilded tassel corners, and
hollow base [1]   (Overall depth 17mm) 75mm sq   30.00

13 BOWLS AND BOXES WITH LIDS

Cylindrical pot [1]   Dia. 90mm   17.50

Lip Salve Box, Ball   Dia. 43mm Height   33mm   13.00

Lip Salve Pot, Cylinder   Dia. 43mm Height   35mm   13.00

Stamp Box, Rectangular
          Length 52mmWidth 40mm   Height   18mm   18.00

Puff Box, domed lid   Dia. 82mm Height   40mm   14.00

Pomade Box with small knop on lid   Dia. 62mm Height   50mm   11.50

*Crinkle Edge Dish on three
Coral legs Dia. 75mm*

Ring Tree 62mm

*Pin Cushion
Dia. 78mm*

*Scent Bottle with stopper
130mm*

*Vase. Identical to Scent Bottle
115mm*

Shaving Mug 99mm

*Lip Salve Pot and lid
Cylinder 35mm*

*Lip Salve Pot and lid Ball
33mm*

*Rectangular Stamp Box and
lid Length 52mm*

*CylindricalPot and lid
Dia.90mm*

*Hat Pin Holder shaped as
Candlstick Column 92mm*

*Night-Light. Frilled base and
Globe*

378

£   p

Rectangular Boxes with forget-me-not decoration
in relief around rim of lids
       Length 98mm Width 52mm Height 35mm

(a) Glazed, with Forget-me-nots	18.00
(b) Unglazed [1]	21.50
(c) Word HAIR-PINS in illuminated gothic script	65.00
(d) Illustrated hairpins (one or two)	75.00
(e) Word MATCHES in illuminated gothic script	65.00
(f) Illustrated matches	75.00

Powder Bowl. Large with shaped knop on lid.
Often found in lustre   Dia. 130mm Height   100mm   40.00

14 CANDLE HOLDERS AND NIGHT-LIGHTS

Candlestick Column	(a) Plain	90mm	19.00
	(b) Coloured band	127mm	30.00
	(c) Coloured band	153mm	34.00

Candlestick Column with tapered base and
splayed sconce over central oval decoration   180mm   75.00

Candle Holder, flat, round, low frilled, with handle Length   110mm   21.50

Candle Holder, flat, round, high frilled, with   Length   110mm
handle as above and standing Lincoln Imp   Height   45mm   75.00
on sconce.

Candle Holder, flat, oval, high frilled with handle Length   120mm   21.50

Candle Holder, flat, oval, high frilled, with handle Length   120mm
as above and standing Lincoln Imp on sconce   Height   45mm   75.00

Candle Holder. Flat, oval, frilled, with handle
and Snuffer   Length   170mm   65.00

Candle Bracket. Shield shaped (to hang on wall)   Height   175mm   60.00

Night-light. Base with handle and ovoid
   Globe (in two parts)   Length 105mm Height   80mm   125.00

Night-light, Ovoid, fluted base and Globe   Height   100mm   125.00

For Durham Abbey Knocker, Mary Queen of Scots,
   Windsor Round Tower and Yorick's Skull Night-lights
   see 10 E HISTORIC MODELS AND SPECIAL SHAPES

for Cottage Night-lights
see 10 F COTTAGES AND COLOURED BUILDINGS

Candle Holder, round, frilled with handle 110mm

Large Candle Holder and Snuffer 170mm

Candle Holder with Lincoln Imp 120mm

Candle Holder, oval, frilled with handle 120mm

Extinguisher Holder & Snuffer round frilled with handle

Extinguisher Holder and Cone Candlesnuffer

Mitre Candlesnuffer 60mm

Monk Candlesnuffer 82mm

Nun Candlesnuffer 94mm

Mr. Punch Candlesnuffer 92mm

Conical Shell Candlesnuffer 81mm

Welsh Lady Candlesnuffer white 95mm

£   p

15 CANDLESNUFFERS AND STANDS

These are all white glazed and without arms with the exception of The Conical
Shell and Mr Punch which are found both with and without arms and The Welsh
Lady which was produced both white glazed and multi-coloured.

Cone (round or waved edge)			53mm	13.00
Mitre			60mm†	200.00
Monk			82mm†	185.00
Nun			94mm†	210.00
Mr. Punch			92mm	225.00
Conical Shell			81mm	105.00
Welsh Lady	(a) White glazed		95mm	75.00
	(b) Multi-coloured blue/grey		95mm†	105.00
	(c) Multi-coloured green/red		95mm†	135.00
Extinguisher Holder, on plain white round crinkle dish with crested cone candle snuffer		Dia.	70mm	65.00
Extinguisher Holder, flat, round, frilled with handle and cone candle snuffer		Length	110mm	65.00

16 INKWELLS

Inkwell, safety, tapered sides		57mm	25.00
Inkwell, crinkle top, glazed		80mm	25.00

17 MATCH HOLDERS AND TOBACCO JARS

Match Holder, ball-shaped, unglazed exterior			57mm	12.50
glazed interior			67mm	13.00
			76mm	16.00
Match Holder, ball shaped with hallmarked silver rim, unglazed			68mm	60.00
Match-box Holder	Height 46mm Length		66mm	80.00
Tobacco Jar with word *TOBACCO* on lid or side		(a)	80mm	30.00
		(b)	115mm	45.00
Tobacco Jar and lid bagware, with *TOBACCO* in illuminated red/yellow/blue script			160mm	80.00

Safety Inkwell 57mm

Crinkle Top Inkwell 80mm

Match Box Holder 66mm

Match Holder 76mm

Circular Ashtray Dia. 115mm

Pipetray Length 112mm

Scallop-Edge Fern Pot 92mm (Jardiniére)

Taper Fern Pot on base 78mm

Double Fern Pot. Two-piece 90mm

Barrel Shaped Mug 74mm [1]

Mug One Square Handle 68mm

Ashtray with Map of Isle of Wight [3] 70mm

£ p

18 ASHTRAYS AND PIPE TRAYS

**Ashtray with coloured map of the Isle of Wight standing
on rear edge of the ribbed dish** [3]   70mm   125.00
Only found with Isle of Wight arms.

Ashtray. Circular, ribbed edge   Dia.   115mm   21.50

Ashtray. Oval with rests at each end
    (a) four thistle sprays in relief   Length   100mm   26.00
    (b) four fern sprays in relief   Length   110mm   30.00

Pipe Tray   Length   112mm   19.00

19 MISCELLANEOUS

Fern Pots
(a) Double Flower pot in circular base to hold water (2-piece)   90mm   30.00
(b) Scallop-edge (Jardinière)   92mm   21.50
(c) Taper, on flat, circular 95mm Dia. base,
    with hole in pot base **(2 piece)**   Height 78mm Dia. (top)   80mm   30.00

Flower Pot, taper   Height 78mm Dia. (top)   80mm   21.50

Flower Pot, taper, indented dots at the top,
no hole in pot base, circular base plate Height: Pot 76mm Overall   79mm   30.00

Hair Tidy Inscribed: *HAIR TIDY* in blue, with either
forget-me-nots, pink roses, primroses, thistles, or leeks and shamrocks on lid
     Straight Dia.70mm Height   93mm   21.50
     Taper Dia. 80mm Height   93mm[1]   24.50

Hat-pin, top 50mm diameter (as ball lip salve pot lid),
with short 6mm china stem and 200mm metal pin.
One of a pair with Falkland Islands arms.   Each   100.00

Hat-pin, with porcelain end 45mm diameter and
255mm wire spike.
One of a pair with the St Helena arms   Each   100.00

Hat-Pin Holder in shape of candlestick column   92mm   30.00

Menu Holder [1] in shape of square tray with gilded corner
tassels, supported by a moulded back-stand   69mm   30.00

Pin Cushion. Small, squat, wide vase with circular hole in
centre to receive sawdust filling and velvet cover   Dia.   78mm   30.00
See also FIRST PERIOD 9C ORNAMENTAL

Ring Tree   62mm   30.00

Loving Cup Three handles
85mm

Loving Cup Two handles
110mm

Loving Cup Three handles
95mm

Loving Cup Three handles
133mm

Loving Cup Three handles
121mm

W.H. Goss Profile in High
Relief on Loving Cup 110mm

One handle Mug 68mm

Mug Two square handles
76mm

Loving Cup Three handles
95mm

Loving Cup Three square
handles 38mm

Mug Two handles 57mm

Beaker, Barrel shaped
74mm [1]

			£	p
Scent Bottle with porcelain and cork stopper which is worth half the price shown.		130mm		25.00
Shaving Mug		99mm		47.50

20   LOVING CUPS AND MUGS

See also POSTCARDS Chapter 5 and ADVERTISING WARE AND LEAFLETS Chapter 8 for details of the origins of the loving cup.

Loving Cups-Three Handled			£	p
	Fairy (a)	38mm		13.00
	(b)	43mm		14.00
	Toy(c)	50mm		16.00
	(d)	57mm		23.00
	1/3 Pint(e)	70mm		25.00
	(f)	78mm		30.00
	1/2 Pint(g)	83mm		34.00
	(h)	95mm		40.00
	Pint(i)	121mm		60.00
	Quart(j)	133mm		77.50
Covered with separate lid(k)		133mm		150.00
Empire loving cup bearing 18 arms of United Kingdom and Colonies		133mm		175.00

NOTE: As a variation, some of the above may have square handles for which add £5.00

A loving cup descriptive leaflet can be found and is worth £ 25.00 (see page 59)

Mugs - Two Handled			£	p
	(a)	38mm		9.00
	(b)	51mm		11.00
	(c)	57mm		16.00
	(d)	70mm		17.00
	(e)	76mm		19.00
	(f)	82mm		21.50
	(g)	110mm		30.00
	(h)	121mm		50.00

NOTE: As a variation, some of the above may have square handles for which add £5.00

Mugs - One handled			£	p
	(a)	38mm		7.50
	(b)	51mm		8.00
	(c)	57mm		10.00
	(d)	68mm		12.00
	(e)	76mm		14.00
	(f)	82mm		17.50
	(g)	121mm		35.00

NOTE: As a variation, some of the above may have square handles for which add £5.00

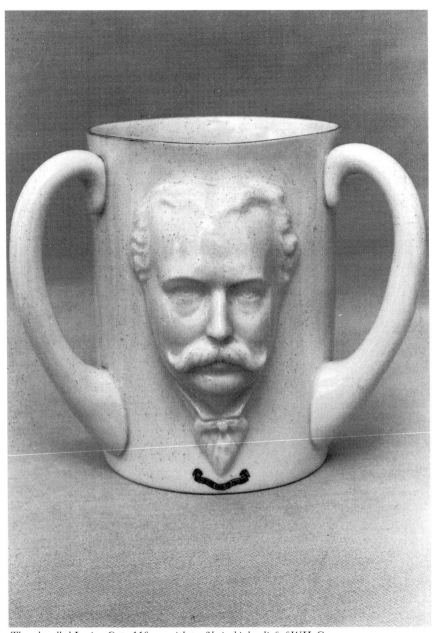

Three handled Loving Cup, 110mm with profile in high relief of W.H. Goss.
Inscribed in the banner ribbon W.H. GOSS F.G.S. F.R.MET.SOC

		£ p
Barrel-shaped mug, one square handle.[1]	75mm	25.00

With blue handle: add £ 15.00

Tankard Mug, taper, with everted rim and angular handle	73mm	17.00

Tankard Mug,taper,no rim	(a) angular handle	75mm	17.00
	(b) square handle	85mm	17.00

N.B. See note on Minor Variations in Size. (Chapter 3
Notes for the Collector) The items in this section vary
considerably in size and the nearest height should
be taken.

21 MARGARET GOSS DECORATIONS

Normally identifiable by the monogrammed letters
M.G. and the date 1922, 1923, 1924 or 1925. Margaret
Goss was a grand-daughter of William Henry Goss and
daughter of William Huntley Goss. Margaret (known
as Peggy) designed a number of coloured scenes,
usually depicting humourous animal and nursery
rhyme themes for childrens' mugs and plates. See *The
Price Guide to Arms and Decorations on Goss China*, Section
N. l. for the detailed list and additional values.

22 DECORATIONS IN RELIEF

The following may be found on two or three-handled loving cups:
Profile in high relief of **W.H. Goss**

with the arms of W.H. Goss and Stoke Upon Trent	110mm	165.00

(Produced after his death in 1906)
Inscribed in the banner ribbon: *W.H. GOSS F. G.S. F.R.MET.SOC.*
In bas-relief Profiles of:

King Edward VII	two handled	90mm	140.00
King Edward VII	three handled	90mm	155.00
King Edward VII	three handled	120mm	165.00
King George V	two handled	90mm	140.00
King George V	three handled	120mm	165.00

These are usually found with corresponding
commemorative devices.

The following decorations in relief may also be found and
details are given in the relevant chapters:

Durham Abbey Knocker	10E
Mary Queen of Scots	10E
Stratford Sanctuary Knocker	10E
Shakespeare	10K.6
Lincoln Imp Beaker	10L.11

A pair of Hat-pins with arms of St. Helena. Wire spike Length 255m

Pompeian Centre piece on trefoil plinth decorated with Forget-me-Nots, William Henry Goss's favourite flower, in the distinctive turquoise blue which he developed and used widely on his wares 340mm

Silver Pin Box, hinged lid, height 45mm, porcelain insert with arms of Calcutta

Goss Plated Spoon 120mm

Brass Holder 190mm with wall pocket style Porcelain Posy Vase

Copper and Porcelain dish Dia. 110mm overall

Brass Pipe Rack, length 220mm, with Commemorative Porcelain insert

M Metalware

TEASPOONS

A metal teaspoon was produced with the permission of W.H. Goss, bearing the name Goss in the bowl, and having a handle in the shape of the Portland Vase. On the handle was an enamelled coat of arms, usually that of London, but several others are known.

One example has the word SILVER clearly impressed into the shaft but the base metal is obviously nickel-silver, which takes on a dull yellowish hue unless kept regularly polished. Presumably these spoons were originally silver plated, but time and wear have resulted in many losing the plating.

Production of the spoons is estimated to have taken place from about 1905 until the mid-1920s, and they were made in Birmingham by the firm of Arbuckle (no longer in existence). Arbuckles were large producers of such seaside souvenirs, and the Goss spoons would have represented only a very small portion of the firm's total output. They were retailed by many Goss agents at 1/- each with various coats of arms enamelled in correct colours. Retailers obtained their supplies from the sole wholesale agent, Henry Jones & Co. Ltd., St. Paul's Churchyard, London.

Length of Spoon 120mm £55.00

See also 10L. I 1 DOMESTIC AND UTILITY WARES for porcelain spoon.

BRASS ORNAMENTS

These, as listed hereunder, can be found with Goss porcelain inserts, usually bearing arms commemorating Queen Victoria's Diamond Jubilee, not of a design found elsewhere on Goss china. The combination of porcelain and brass was the idea of William Henry Goss himself. The brass manufacturer was Harcourt, and a registered number of 128998 is quoted, which indicates a date of 1889. Possibly Harcourts were anticipating the Golden Jubilee, but there are probably other examples with normal coats of arms. (Note: it is necessary to dismantle these items to find the Goshawk/ W.H. Goss mark. Sometimes the corners of the plaques have been trimmed to fit the brass holder by the manufacturer).

£ p

Ink stand, ornate, with hinged lid, and glass inkwell insert
160mm sq. Height 135mm 300.00

Mantel Clock 135.00

Matchbox holder 125.00

Match holder and striker 175mm 135.00

Pipe rack Length 220mm Height 150mm 135.00

Posy vase holder Height 190mm 125.00

For porcelain 78mm insert Add £25.00 per Metalwork item

In addition to the above brass ornaments, other metal surrounds are found fitted to Goss porcelain items with flat, circular bases, converting them to a variety of ashtrays, pin trays, or tea strainers, examples of which are as follows :

£ p

(a) Copper dish, raised rim, Flags of the Allies
decoration. Porcelain fitting   Dia.   70mm
                                        Overall Dia.   110mm   35.00
(b) Silver, raised rim. Porcelain fitting decorated
with coats of arms   42.50
(c) Silver pin box, hinged lid. Porcelain insert
with arms of CALCUTTA on lid   Height   45mm   75.00
(d) Tea Strainer inside EPNS three-legged ring
supporting EPNS strainer, produced for the
Canadian market   Dia.   80mm   35.00
(e) Tea Strainer, metal, on surround as the top of
a shallow porcelain dish   Dia.   75mm   30.00

for **Hatpin**
see 10L DOMESTIC AND UTILITY WARES 19, MISCELLANEOUS

for **Sugar Castor with EPNS top**
see 10L DOMESTIC AND UTILITY WARES 11, OTHER ITEMS OF TABLEWARE

N Dolls

During the First World War, Huntley Goss manufactured dolls in an attempt to save his ailing factory. He thought that the Goss Factory could become the chief source of supply for porcelain dolls' heads, arms and legs because the German firms could no longer export their ware to Great Britain as trade with the enemy had been cut of since 1914.

It took much time and expense to buy the correct equipment and make themoulds, as well as organise the sales. Goss dolls, with their mohair and beautiful hand painted faces, had only just begun to capture the toy market, despite their high price, when the war ended in November 1918. In no time at all the German factories resumed their highly competitive exports and the English trade tailed off. Noel Goss, eldest son of Huntley, said that the firm did not manage to break even with this line and the extra losses only added to thefirm's financial troubles. Manufacture had commenced in 1916 and no more were made after 1918.

Goss dolls can be identified by the word GOSS impressed into the base of the neck at the back, quite unlike any other Goss mark. Under this was a mould number, sometimes prefixed with the letter G. Each doll has an oval purple stamp on the back on the stuffed body incorporating the words TRADEMARK REGISTRATION APPLIED FOR or BRITISH TOY COMPANY around the word WARDOL.

Dolls were made for the British Toy Co., Wardol Works, Stoke-on-Trent, whose doll manufacturing was organised by Mrs. Ritner, wife of the local M.P. The heads were made by W.H. Goss, and the dolls themselves at the Wardol Works where W. Huntley Goss was also a director.

From head to toe, lengths varied from 160mm to 700mm, depending on whether they were baby, child or girl dolls. All left the Goss factory dressed in Edwardian style clothing with frilly petticoats and lacy outer garments.

Value is dependent on condition, a wig being preferable to moulded hair, and glass eyes more interesting then painted ones. If a doll has its original clothing, it is of higher value than one without.

The following dolls have been recorded to date. The publishers will be pleased to learn of any further varieties for inclusion in future editions of this guide.

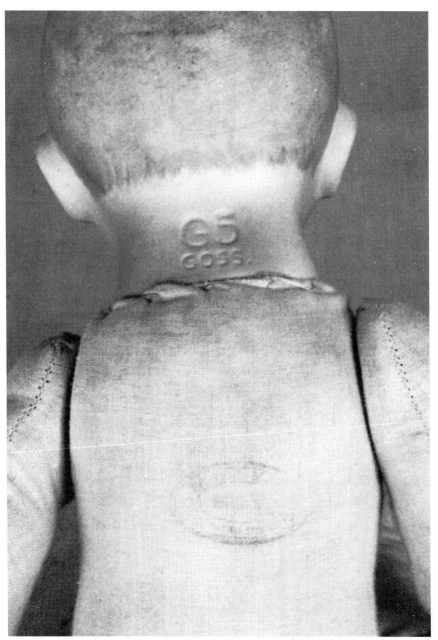

This photograph of the back of doll model G5 shows clearly the model number and factory name impressed into the nape of the neck. Note the oval purple trade mark which will be found on the back of every doll.

Model Number

Model Number	Type	Length	Hair	Eyes	Arms	Legs
8	Child	700mm	mohair	painted	china	china
8	Child	700mm	mohair	painted	stuffed	stuffed
14	Child	340mm	mohair	painted	china	stuffed
15	Girl	400mm	real	glass	china	china
16	Child	400mm	mohair	glass	china	china
17	Girl	420mm	mohair	glass	china	china
18	Child	440mm	mohair	glass	china	china
19	Child	650mm	real	glass	china	china
21	Girl	560mm	real	glass	china hands	stuffed
23	Baby	160mm	mohair	glass	china	china
25	Child	440mm	mohair	glass	china	china
30	Child	400mm	mohair	glass	china	stuffed
31	Child	340mm	real	glass	china	china
32	Girl	620mm	real	glass	china	china
33	Girl		real	glass	stuffed	stuffed
35	Child	340mm	real	glass	china	stuffed
36	Child	340mm	real	glass	china	stuffed
G4	Baby	350mm	painted	painted	china	stuffed
G5	Baby	330mm	painted	painted	china	stuffed
G7	Boy	325mm	real or painted	painted	china	stuffed
G9	Child	400mm	mohair	painted	china	stuffed
G10	Child	500mm	mohair	painted	china	stuffed
G11	Girl		real	glass	china	china
G12	Child	400mm	mohair wig	painted	china hands	stuffed
G13	Young Boy	230mm	painted	painted	china	stuffed
G13	Baby	265mm	painted	painted	china	stuffed
G11	Girl	495mm	real	glass	china	china
G20	Girl		real	glass	china	china

N. B . The following G4 version does not carry the usual purple stamp, and is inscribed: *Copyright As Act Directs. W.H. Goss. Stoke on Trent Dec. 1. 15.* Another doll. G8. has the date *Jan 30th 1916* inscribed.

G4	Child	425mm	painted	painted	china	china
G8		290mm	red		china	stuffed

Values range between £500 and £750

Doll Model 23

Doll Model 15

Doll Model 30

Doll Model 35

Doll Model 31

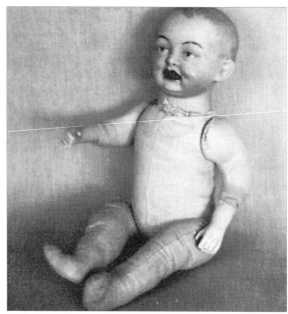

Doll Model 31

Doll Model G5, unclothed

11 The Third Period 1929-1939

Period Symbols

Where a shape was known to have been made during more than one period, the number in brackets after its entry denotes the other period(s) during which it was manufactured .

The First Period   [1]   1858-1887

The Second Period   [2]   1881-1934

The Third Period   [2]   1929-1939

Introduction

Heraldic ware continued in production until 1934, and this has been listed as Second Period as the majority of pieces were produced between 1881 and 1929 during the family ownership of the pottery. After 1930, the new owner, Harold Taylor Robinson, renamed the firm The Goss China Co Ltd, and had control over many other crested china firms, including Arcadian, Coronet Ware, Swan, Robinson and Leadbeater, etc. (See *The Price Guide to Crested China* by Nicholas Pine for the full story). Moulds from these other potteries were used at the Goss Works, as well as original Goss moulds. Pieces made during this period include porcelain (glazed parian) and pottery. The latter were glazed on the base, making the Goshawk blacker and darker. This situation continued until 1934, although Robinson was made bankrupt in 1932. After May 1934 when he took over Willow Art, the Goshawk appeared on china from Willow Art moulds. The word ENGLAND appeared on most, but not all, of the factory marks, mainly after 1935. The pattern books of The Goss China Co Ltd were registered in the name of Messrs Allied English Potteries Ltd., and included the Royal Buff designs used on the beige earthenware tea services.

The sales of heraldic ware alone were not enough to keep the firm viable and production began to change to the brightly coloured toby jugs, comical figures and animals, Cottage Pottery tea sets, Royal Buff Ware, and earthenware Commemorative mugs and ashtrays, in an attempt to keep up with changing trends and fashions in the roaring twenties. During the thirties, trade was grinding to a halt and one former works manager said at that time, that the predominant products were the famous Goss flower girls, bowls of china flowers and the like, mostly for the American market. In 1939 the factory was closed.

The Goshawk was used during Robinson's ownership in preference to other factory names because Goss had always been the market leader and stood for quality and perfection. The cataloguing of the other factories' wares for the *Price Guide to Crested China* has shown which of the Third Period Goss, or Goss England as it was popularly known, originated from Arcadian, Willow Art etc., the most common ranges being white glazed buildings and black cats.

A large amount of domestic ware, difficult to describe and list, of the late period, is constantly coming to light. All of this is of relatively little value and the reader is advised to refer to the DOMESTIC AND ORNAMENTALWARE Chapters in both Second and Third Periods and to take the value of a similar item for the piece in question .

It should be remembered that all prices in this book are for the *items* of Goss only and not for any decorations which may appear on them, details of which can be found in *The Price Guide to Arms and Decorations on Goss China* by Nicholas Pine (Milestone Publications).

O Buildings and Monuments   £   p

Except where noted, all these models were white-glazed, and usually carried the appropriate coat of arms. Many of them can alternatively be found bearing the manufacturer's mark of an associated company, usually Willow Art or Arcadian.

An Clachan Cottage - in full colour, produced solely as a souvenir of the 1938 Scottish Empire Exhibition, Glasgow, at which had been built a full size replica of this cottage.   Length   106mm   1450.00
Inscribed on back: *An Clachan Cottage* and the Red Lion motif captioned *Empire Exhibition Scotland 1938* on the base, with the WH GOSS ENGLAND mark.

A second version of the **An Clachan Cottage** can also be found but it is, in fact, the small version of **Robert Burns' Cottage** merely re-named and, on the example seen, displaying the motif of the 1938 Exhibition and a W H GOSS ENGLAND mark
                                              Length   62mm   925.00

		£	p
Banbury Cross	(a)Whitewitharms	127mm	100.00
	(b) Brown or Blue/Brown	127mm	235.00

Inscribed front plinth or above: *Banbury Cross*.
Inscribed left front plinth: *Ride a Cock Horse to Banbury Cross*.
Inscribed right front plinth: *To see a Fine Lady ride on a White Horse*.

Burns Statue
Seated with dog at feet   170mm   80.00

Bury St. Edmunds Abbey Gateway
(Same as Willow model, but inscribed: *W. H. Goss England*)   80mm   80.00

Big Ben usually with Big Ben inscribed on front of base		103mm	55.00
With some colouring		103mm	60.00
		134mm	60.00
		152mm	65.00
		170mm	65.00

Canterbury Cathedral   64mm   65.00

Cenotaph, Whitehall   90mm   50.00
Inscribed on plinth:*Model of Cenotaph*   145mm   60.00
Matching arms: *CITY OF WESTMINSTER* for which add £20.00

Chesterfield Church   76mm   85.00

Chesterfield Church

Banbury Cross

Big Ben

Norwich Cathedral

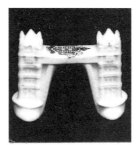

Tower Bridge

St. Paul's Cathedral

The Cenotaph, Whitehall

Westminster Abbey,
West Front

Temple Bar

Norwich Edith Cavell
Memorial

The Old Curiosity Shop

Windsor Round Tower

Clachan Empire Exhibition Tower and Stadium   £   p
Glazed, grey colour, green trimmed dished tray bearing late
colour transfer of the *EMPIRE EXHIBITION THE CLACHAN*
Inscribed on base in red: *EMPIRE EXHIBITION SCOTLAND 1938* and motif.
Also usual Goshawk mark. This model may have been intended
for use as an ashtray.   Length 115mm   Height   135mm   300.00

Clifton Suspension Bridge Length 170mm   Height   64mm   135.00

Dover Patrol Monument   130mm   80.00

Edith Cavell Monument, Norwich   100mm   55.00
Inscribed left side: *Humanity*.   180mm   80.00
Inscribed right side: *Sacrifice*
Inscribed reverse: *Edith Cavell Nurse Patriot and Martyr*.

(Ann) Hathaway's Cottage, fully coloured   Length   50mm   60.00
Inscribed: *Model of Ann Hathaway's Cottage*   63mm   60.00
Shottery near Stratford-on-Avon Rd. No. 208047.   78mm   60.00
                                                                110mm   70.00
                                                                133mm   80.00
                                                    Length   65mm   50.00
Royal Buff or Cottage Pottery Version   Length 75mm Height   55mm   125.00

Hindhead Sailor's Stone   95mm   85.00
Inscribed on front: *The Sailors Stone, Hindhead.*
Inscribed on reverse: *'Erected. In detestation of a barbarous*
murder committed here on an unknown sailor, on Sept. 24th. 1786.
by Edward Lonegon, Michael Casey and Jas. Marshall, who
were all taken the same day and hung in chains near this place.
"Who so sheddeth man's blood by man shall
his blood be shed." Gen., Chap. 9 ver.6.'

Houses of Parliament   64mm   85.00

King Alfred's Statue, Winchester   170mm   90.00

John Knox's House in full colour   102mm   340.00
Inscribed: *Model of the house in Edinburgh where John Knox*
the Scottish Reformer died 24th Nov. 1572.

Lighthouse on Rocks   95mm   40.00

Marble Arch, London (found with top glazed and unglazed)   40mm   55.00
                                                                 57mm   55.00
                                                                 62mm   55.00

Nelson's Column   100mm   100.00

Norwich Cathedral   Length   105mm   100.00

The Clachan Cottage

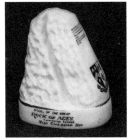

Rock of Ages

Shakespeares's Birthplace

John Knox's House Edinburgh

Clifton Suspension Bridge, Bristol

King Alfreds Statue

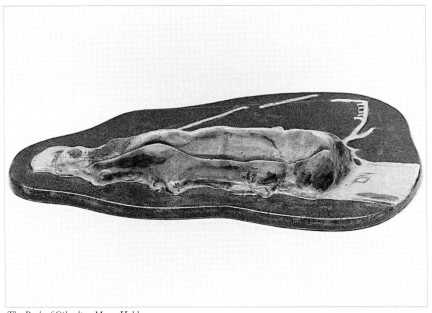

The Rock of Gibraltar Menu Holder

			£ p
Old Curiosity Shop		46mm	65.00

Rock of Ages with verses of hymn of the same name on the front.   79mm   40.00
Inscribed on side of base: *Model of The Great ROCK OF AGES,*
Burrington Coombe, Near Cheddar Som.

Rock of Gibraltar, menu holder, coloured   Length   160mm   275.00

Rufus Stone   100mm   15.00
For inscription see SECOND PERIOD 10 E HISTORIC
MODELS AND SPECIAL SHAPES

St. Paul's Cathedral   75mm   65.00
Inscribed on front step: *St. Paul's Cathedral*   90mm   65.00
                                                                  120mm   75.00

Shakespeare's Birthplace in full colour   Length   40mm   45.00
Inscribed: *Model of Shakespeare's House.*   50mm   50.00
Rd. No. 225833.   60mm   60.00
                                                                  67mm   65.00
                                                                  78mm   70.00
                                                                  102mm   75.00
                                                                  115mm   80.00
                                                                  130mm   95.00
                                                                  158mm   95.00

Temple Bar   65mm   85.00

Tower Bridge   58mm   75.00

Westminster Abbey, West Front   52mm   55.00
                                                                  73mm   55.00
                                                                  125mm   60.00
                                                                  133mm   60.00

Westminster Abbey (West Front)
Standing on rear of rectangular ashtray. Gilding to edge of tray,
and tips of tower pinnacles .
Inscribed on rear: *Westminster Abbey*   85mm   65.00

Windsor Castle   Length 65mm   53mm   65.00

Windsor Round Tower   55mm   50.00
inscribed: *Round Tower Winsor*   76mm   60.00

York Minster   56mm   85.00

Clachan Empire Exhibition Tower and Stadium [3]

P Flower Girls

The brightly coloured porcelain flower girls, as they were called by the factory, were the last successful series made by the Goss factory and spanned the 1930s. Several of these were made in two sizes and ranged between the tiny 68mm, often a cruet, and the more elegant 170mm.

All but one of the larger sizes of these ladies are named, the exception being the Bell lady. Small sizes were often unnamed, probably because of lack of room on the base to do so. They were all hand painted by paintresses who signed their initials in enamel on the base . No two flower girls are decorated the same and the range of colours includes purple, blue, pink, yellow, green and crimson, with great variation in colours used. The word ENGLAND appears on most, but not all, of the factory stamp marks.

Lady Beth and Lady Freda, listed in previous editions of this work are not now thought to exist.

		£	p
Annette	135mm	250.00	
"Annette" pink dress, black bonnet (not always named)	160mm	300.00	
Balloon Seller	90mm	150.00	
	137mm	225.00	
Barbara seated on settee	110mm	325.00	
Bell Lady	92mm	135.00	
Bridesmaid (see also The Wedding (a)	90mm	125.00	
Group, this section) (b)	140mm	235.00	
With variations to usual model (c)	135mm	225.00	
Bunty		375.00	
Cruet two ladies in full colour, one salt, one pepper,			
(a) Bridesmaid and Granny Each	68mm	170.00	
(b) Lorna and Peggy Each	85mm	150.00	
(c) Bridesmaid and Granny			
(both painted brown base) Each	87mm	135.00	
(d) Flower Girl pepper pot	90mm	110.00	
(e) Balloon Seller salt pot	90mm	110.00	
(f) Dutch Girl pepper pot	90mm	150.00	
Daisy	120mm	275.00	
Daisy Flower Girls mounted on wooden bookends	Pair	550.00	
Doris	120mm	300.00	
Dutch Girl	87mm	225.00	
Edyth	140mm	200.00	

for Flapper reclining on cigarette box
see THIRD PERIOD 11R FIGURES AND ANIMALS

| **Granny** | 90mm | 150.00 | |

Annette 135mm

Annette, Pink Dress, Black Bonnet 160mm

The Baloon Seller 137mm

Bell Lady

Bridesmaid 140mm

Dutch Girl

Cruet Salt Granny

Cruet Salt Bridesmaid

Edyth

One of a pair of Daisy Bookends

Daisy

Granny 90mm

		£ p
Gwenda	130mm	250.00
Joan	130mm	275.00
"June"	115mm	400.00
Lady Betty	160mm	250.00
Lady Marie	145mm	275.00
Lady Rose	170mm	300.00

for Lady on cigarette box
see THIRD PERIOD 11R FIGURES AND ANIMALS

Lorna	90mm	250.00
Miss Julia	170mm	275.00
Miss Prudence	135mm	250.00
Mistress Ford	100mm	375.00
Mistress Page	105mm	375.00
Peggy	90mm	175.00
	125mm	250.00
Phyllis	95mm	325.00

**A series of 6 figures entitled 'The Wedding Group'
modelled from the original designs of the American artist
C.H. Twelvetrees, were produced as follows:**

The Bride
Inscribed: *God Bless Her*   95mm   250.00

The Bridegroom
Inscribed: *God Help Him*   100mm   250.00

The Best Man
Inscribed: *No Wedding Bells for Him*   95mm   340.00

The Mother-in-Law
Inscribed: *But a Very Nice One*   105mm   240.00

The Parson
Inscribed: *Solemn and Businesslike*   100mm   240.00

The Bridesmaid
(two moulds with variations)   99mm   225.00
Inscribed: *"The Bridesmaid Sweet as a Rose " Rd . No. 804763*
The registered number is probably an error as Registration
numbers ceased being required for Goss China in 1914,
the last number bing 630174.
for Child kneeling on a cushion, at prayer 165mm,
fully coloured, see FIRST PERIOD 9B FIGURES

Gwenda

Lady Betty

Joan

Lady Marie

Lady Rose

Lorna

Miss Julia

Miss Prudence

Mistress Page

Peggy 125mm

Phyllis

Barbara

A pair of Daisy Flower Girls mounted on wooden bookends.

The Bride

The Bridegroom

The Best Man

The Mother-in-Law

The Parson

The Bridesmaid

Q Toby Jugs

Apart from the Stratford Toby Jug and basin and the Churchill Toby Jug, all Goss Toby
Jugs are Third Period products and a wide selection of other crested china manufacturers'
moulds were used. Sizes range from miniatures, little more than 40mm high, to larger
sizes in the region of 160mm high. Female Toby Jugs were also made. The same jug is
often found in a variety of colours. All handles are at the back unless otherwise stated.

Churchill Toby Jug with blue or green coat.
Inscribed on base: *COPYRIGHT 1927* and on top hat:
Any Odds - Bar one That's me who Kissed the Blarney Stone [2]   164mm   175.00
This model was produced after the then Chancellor
of the Exchequer, Winston S Churchill introduced
the country's first betting tax in 1927. The serious
nature of the piece indicates that the subject hoped
the tax would be well received by the nation.

Toby Jug British Sailor blue colouring   60mm   85.00

Toby Jug white glazed and crested   67mm   47.50
          80mm   60.00

Toby Jug miniature, circular base   (a)Male   44mm   100.00
          (b) Female   44mm   125.00

Toby Jug sitting on chair with mug and pipe, wearing red coat   65mm   140.00

Toby Jug Standing with pint mug and pipe, tricorn hat
high at front, multi-coloured, circular black or brown base.   90mm   85.00

Toby Jug Lady in green or pink bonnet with white ruff, yellow
or blue dress and green or orange spotted white apron, carrying
yellow or brown basket and holding black gamp. The largest
size has blue or green dress and blue or white spotted
white apron and carries a brown basket and black gamp.

          (a) Red dress, blue spotted apron,
             black hat and basket   40mm   145.00
          (b) White   70mm   50.00
          (c) Multi-coloured   70mm   140.00
          (d) Multi-coloured, with removable
             hat as cover, only found on circular base   80mm   160.00
          (e) Multi-coloured   95mm   165.00

Toby Jug sitting cross-legged, one arm forming the handle   85mm   115.00
Green jacket with black edging, orange knickerbockers,   110mm   125.00
black/yellow hat, brown circular base   170mm   150.00

Toby Jug Male standing on brown base, yellow coat
and pale blue trousers   100mm   155.00

Toby Jug Male in black tricorn hat, multi-coloured wearing
green red or blue coat with pint pot and pipe, seated with crossed
legs on brown circular base   100mm   125.00

                          £   p

Toby Jug Male in black tricorn hat, red, blue, green or dark green jacket, red on blue knickerbockers, yellow hose, black boots, with pint pot and pipe, sitting on a plain white stool, or with the four corner legs in black or brown   65mm   125.00

Toby Jug Male in black tricorn hat, red, green, blue or dark green jacket, blue knickerbockers, yellow hose, black boots, with pint pot and pipe, sitting with feet on plinth   127mm   135.00
Inscribed on plinth front: *No tongue can tell*   160mm   150.00
                               No heart can think
                               O how I love
                               A drop of drink

Welsh Lady with removable hat as cover, coloured   85mm   220.00
(Found in blue or orange) (Rare)

for Stratford Toby Jug and Stratford Toby Basin see 10 E HISTORIC MODELS

for Royal Buff Toby Jug see 11T COTTAGE POTTERY, ROYAL BUFF AND BASKET WEAVE

Toby Jug 100mm cross legged on brown circular base   *Toby Jug 65mm seated on stool*   *Toby Jug 85mm, one arm as handle, brown circular base*

Toby Jug 90mm standing on black circular base   *Toby Jug 160mm feet on plinth with verse*   *Toby Jug, Female 68mm standing*

Tennis Players and Umbrella (from right)

Tennis Players and Umbrella (from left)

Ann Hathaways Cottage Cottage Pottery

Judy, Toby and Punch Cruet

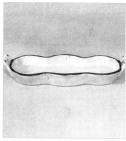

Tray for Punch, Judy and Toby Cruet

Golfer with golf ball match holder, green.

Churchill Toby Jug [2]

Black Mammy in Bath as ashtray

Two babies on tray

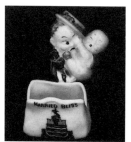

Father and child beside Open Bag, Married Bliss

Gin and "it" Two Ladies seated on dish

Two Coloured Children on Log

R   Figures and Animals

Many figures were incorporated into ashtrays, cruets, posy-holders, and other domestic wares - while some appear to be purely ornamental. Ware in this section almost without exception originated from the Arcadian and Willow Art factories. For pieces not listed here, consult *The Price Guide to Crested China* where the model should be found. The prices will be similar.

		£ p
Babies (two) seated on Ashtray	70mm	100.00

One in a yellow romper suit, the other in blue
Inscribed: *That's the one Daddy told Nurse!*

Ballerina, Bust of	150mm	125.00

Holding fan as knop of lidded fluted pin box.
Made for *EMPIRE EXHIBITION SCOTLAND 1938.*
Yellow with green trim.

Black Baby as Pin Tray, red bow, green scarf

	Length 90mm Width 68mm	Height	68mm	170.00

Black Boy red and yellow hat, yellow trousers, holding
a white box as a match holder.

Inscribed: *Matches or Cigarettes*	100mm	150.00
also found in white, crested and with no inscription	100mm	75.00

Black Boy sitting on soapbox eating slice of melon, yellow trousers.	83mm	170.00
Black Boy and Girl seated on log	80mm	150.00
Black Boys, two seated on log	80mm	150.00
Black Cat in Boot	58mm	80.00
Black Cat on Dish	115mm x	70mm	75.00
Black Cat (seated) on Horse shoe-shaped Pin Box	70mm	75.00
Black Cat Playing Golf standing on Golf Ball	60mm	100.00
Black Cat on Pouffe blue handles	93mm	65.00

Inscribed: *Good Luck*

Black Cat Seated at Head of Horse shoe	Approx.	42mm	65.00

as Ashtray

Black Cheshire Cat identical to white variety	90mm	105.00
Black Mammy in Bath as Ashtray, multi coloured	40mm	165.00

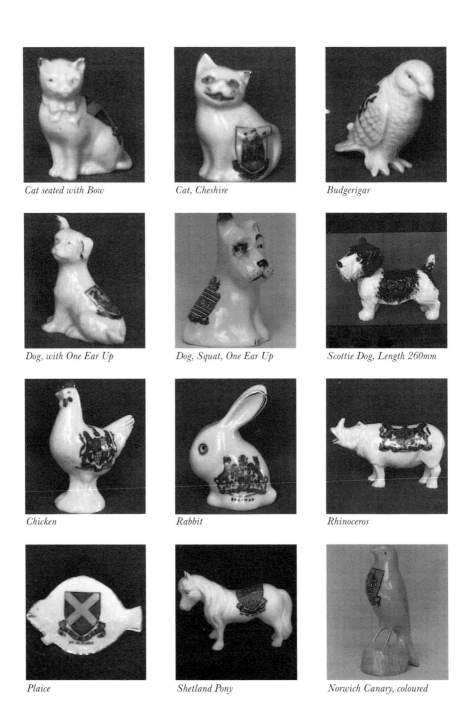

Cat seated with Bow

Cat, Cheshire

Budgerigar

Dog, with One Ear Up

Dog, Squat, One Ear Up

Scottie Dog, Length 260mm

Chicken

Rabbit

Rhinoceros

Plaice

Shetland Pony

Norwich Canary, coloured

£ p

Black Moma as Ashtray holding skirts; found fully coloured
or partly coloured, with colour variations from version
to version Length 90mm Height 68mm
(a) Fully coloured 190.00
(b) Partly coloured 165.00

Budgerigar 42.50

Burns, Robert, Bust on square base 136mm 55.00

Burns, Robert, Bust on socle plinth 136mm 55.00
145mm 55.00

Cheshire Cat (No base) (a) coloured 65mm 80.00
(b) white 98mm 65.00
All cheshire cats have colouring to the face.
Some appear in all blue for which add £20.00

Cat, grotesque smiling, with bow 69mm 42.50

Cat, Seated, with White or Coloured Bow at Neck 60mm 42.50

Chicken (a) Coloured 50mm 80.00
(b) White 50mm 50.00

for Cigarette Box
see Flapper Reclining on lid of cigarette box

Comic Figure - a portly, bald, bespectacled dipsomaniac 80mm 85.00
clinging to the neck of a bottle 95mm 95.00

Crest Faced Man With coat of arms on fat face 80mm 55.00

Cruet. Punch (Salt), Judy (Pepper) and Toby (Mustard)
in full colour - all on tray. (a) Punch 75mm (b) Others 65mm 260.00
NOTE: Items from the above set may be found
white glazed or in varying shades of lustre Price Each 70.00
with black trim to tray. Tray length 160mm

Dog and Whiskey Bottle on Ashtray
Inscribed: *His Master's Breath* Some colouring Length 82mm 75.00

Dog, Scottie with blue Tam O'Shanter 60mm 47.50

Dog, Scottie, Black and White with glass eyes Length 260mm 135.00

Dog, squat, one ear up, some colouring 90mm 65.00
Inscribed: *Daddy wouldn't buy me a bow*

Dog, comical with one ear up. (a) Coloured 70mm 75.00
(b) White 70mm 55.00

Black Cat in Boot

Black Cat in Horse Shoe Ashtray

Dog and Whiskey Bottle on Ashtray

Falstaff

English Folksong Bride

Pixie on a Toadstool

White Boy Holding open Matchbox

Scottish Lion on Ashtray

Punch and Judy Pepper and Salt

Shakespeare Bust

Gnome, carrying shells of produce under each arm

Golfer, standing on golf ball holding clubs

416

			£	p
English Folksong Bride		93mm	85.00	
Standing beside ancient chest				

Falstaff	(a) Coloured	105mm	175.00
	(b) Coloured	150mm	175.00
	(c) White	150mm	85.00

Fish, Plaice, two sizes	Length	78mm	35.00
		125mm	45.00

Flapper in Bath Tub
The top lifts off as a pin tray, coloured, both ends blue washed
with criss-cross pattern   Length 130mm Height   60mm   325.00

Flapper in Bath Tub
Fully coloured, with pale aqua blue   Length 130mm Height   60mm   325.00
water and brown tub.

Flapper Reclining on Lid of Cigarette Box
decorated in art deco style   Length 110mm Height   82mm   500.00

Frog   60mm   65.00

Gin and It Two seated ladies at side of dish, coloured   100mm x 65mm   75.00
Inscribed: *GIN AND "IT"*

Golf Caddy standing on golf ball, holding clubs   76mm   160.00

Golfer standing on golf ball, holding clubs-   40mm x 75mm   85.00
In centre of hexagonal dish

Golfer and club with golf ball match holder
on glazed ashtray base.
All coloured green. No arms.   Length 120mm Height 110mm†   170.00

Gnome standing, carrying a shell filled with
produce under each arm, fully coloured   128mm   550.00

Goose, comical, long neck   145mm   85.00

(Ann) Hathaway Bust,	(a) Coloured, unglazed	80mm	45.00
Inscribed, black printed,	(b) Coloured, unglazed	135mm	55.00
on plinth: *Ann Hathaway*	(c) White glazed	80mm	40.00
	(d) White glazed	140mm	45.00

Hippopotamus   Length   88mm   95.00

Jester On heart-shaped Ashtray, holding hearts	Coloured	65mm	100.00
for trumps, with heart-shaped handle	White	65mm	47.50

for Judy see Cruet

Frog

Owl

Royston Crow, coloured

Penguin on Ashtray

Scots Boy on thistle dish, holding heather, coloured

Flapper reclining on Cigarette Box Lid

Man in the Moon

Jester on Ashtray Hearts are Trumps

Three Welsh Ladies at Tea Table

Leaking Boot at Cleethorpes

Sergeant Major Pepper Pot

Toucan on Ashtray shaped as Bird's Foot

418

		£	p
Lady in Bathing Costume and Cap on Ashtray base		125.00	
Lady Godiva on Horseback. Small, glazed	80mm	75.00	
Leaking boot at Cleethorpes standing figure of boy holding boot aloft	155mm	150.00	
Lifeboat Man	140mm	65.00	
Man in the Moon A face in a crescent-shaped moon	56mm	50.00	
Married Bliss Posy Vase, coloured Schoolgirl, holding baby, with open bag in front Inscribed: *Married Bliss*	82mm	130.00	
for Monkeys see Three Wise Monkeys			
for Mr Punch see Cruet			
New Forest Pony	65mm	80.00	
Norwich Canary coloured	102mm	110.00	
Mermaid Seated on rock. Coloured with holes in base. (For flower arrangement)	190mm	200.00	
Owl one eye shut with verse: *an aged owl sat in an oak*	100mm	80.00	
Penguin	90mm	150.00	
Penguin on Ashtray base	92mm	200.00	
Pig Inscribed: *Won't be Druv*	80mm	80.00	
Pixie seated on toadstool, coloured	54mm	100.00	
Policeman with raised hand. Inscribed: *'Stop'*	94mm	100.00	
for Mr. Punch see Cruet			
Rabbit and Duck combined Inscribed: *Isn't This Rabbit A Duck?*	75mm	65.00	
Rabbit styled, with giant ears, blue, yellow, green, brown, or Royal Buff	40mm	60.00	
	50mm	65.00	
	60mm	65.00	
	80mm	65.00	
	85mm	65.00	
	100mm	68.00	

£ p

Rabbit white   60mm   45.00

Racehorse and Jockey oval base, with differing
coloured jerseys and silks.   108mm   250.00
The agent for Goss England Porcelain in Newmarket
was P J Hobbs. He ordered models of the racehorse
and jockey on oval base. The oval base was glazed
and bears the arms of Newmarket whereas the
horse and jockey were unglazed. The colours were
painted to order by girls in the back room of the agency.
On race days, the result of the race would be rushed
back to the shop by a boy on a bicycle and the girls
would paint quickly in the colours of the winner so
that the pieces would be immediately ready for sale.
This explains why the jockeys in this model are unglazed
and appear to have been repainted when in reality, they are not.
Similar examples sold by the Ascot agent can
also be found bearing the arms of Ascot.
Matching arms: *NEWMARKET* OR *ASCOT*

Rhinoceros   Length   90mm   100.00

Royston Crow almost always unmarked.   (a) Black   66mm   150.00
Inscribed: *Royston Crow* and additionally   (b) Coloured   66mm   250.00
Corvus Cornix on the plinth of the black model.
Rd. No. 64718
The Royston Crow was the name of the local
newspaper in Royston, Herts. The Goss study of this
bird was possibly given away as a gift by the
newspaper or used in promotions.

Sailor standing, vase, white   100mm   45.00

for Sir Walter Scott, bust on socle base.
Identical to First Period example see FIRST PERIOD 9A BUSTS   135mm   50.00

Scots Boy coloured, holding a bunch of heather on a thistle
shaped dish
The dish (a) White (crested) (b) grey lustre, or (c) coloured   90mm   95.00
All the same price.

Scottish Lion styled, standing on square ashtray base.
Empire Exhibition Scotland 1938. Coloured, green trim   103mm   125.00

Sergeant Major Pepper Pot coloured   83mm   65.00

Shakespeare Bust   £   p
Inscribed black printed on plinth: *Shakespeare*
Impressed on back: *H & L.*
(Note: The exception is the
bust on two books which

			£ p
has no inscription)	(a) Coloured, unglazed	75mm	25.00
	(b) White, unglazed on two books	75mm	21.50
	(c) White, unglazed	80mm	25.00
	(d) White, unglazed	110mm	35.00
	(e) White, unglazed	118mm	35.00
	(f) White, unglazed	135mm	35.00
	(g) Bronzed	135mm	55.00
	(h) White, unglazed	142mm	55.00
	(i) Bronzed	165mm	65.00
	(j) White, unglazed	165mm	55.00
	(k) Bronzed	175mm	75.00

Shetland Pony (No base)   76mm   80.00

Swan   50mm   45.00

Tennis players, a couple, sheltering under a
coloured umbrella, one side blue.   Length 85mm Height   65mm   300.00

Three Wise Monkeys on a wall
Inscribed: *'I Speak No Evil '*
       'I See No Evil '
       'I Hear No Evil '
Selfridge & Co. on base   Length 50mm Height   70mm   45.00

Toff in Top Hat and Evening Dress on a Brown Bed
with scattered playing cards on the multi-coloured bedspread
covering the drunk, with cigarette in one hand.
Matchbox holder. Can also be found unmarked.
     Length 83mm Width   55mm   225.00

Toucan Match holder on Ashtray shaped as a bird's foot
(Art Deco style) coloured. Colours can vary, for example:
     (a) Blue/orange/yellow
     (b) Brown/orange/green   Length 90mm Height   61mm   120.00

Tortoise   66mm   55.00

Tortoise, being ridden by a jockey holding reins
held in tortoise's mouth. Fully coloured
with brown carapace to tortoise.   Length 100mm Height   53mm   300.00

Trusty Servant coloured.   132mm   400.00
(Not to be confused with the First Period version)

Welsh Lady Bust, with some colouring   62mm   45.00

Welsh Ladies three at tea table on oval base   52mm   65.00

Basket containing six milk bottles

Bass Bottle and Glass on Tray

Bottle with cork, One Special Irish

Bowl, 85mm Dia., Matt Black or Lustre

Chess Pawn

Eygptian Canopic Jar with fixed Anubis Head

Coloured Lantern

Shoe, John Waterson's Clog

Square Vase 60mm

Weston-Super-Mare Floral Clock Surround

Whiskey Bottle, Soda Syphon and Glass on Ashtray

Whiskey Bottle, Two-piece, Hip-Flask

S.1 Ornamental Articles and Domestic and Utility Ware

1   ORNAMENTAL ARTICLES

			£	p
Basket biscuit colour, with tiny flowers at base of handle	90mm x	75mm	60.00	
Basket containing six milk bottles		50mm	50.00	
Bass Bottle and Glass on Dish	60mm x	35mm	50.00	
Bass Bottle and Silvered Tankard on Horse Shoe Dish	115mm x	70mm	50.00	
Boater straw-cream with multi-coloured ribbon	Length	90mm	50.00	
Boot	70mm x	40mm	35.00	
Bottle with Cork		70mm	35.00	
Bottle with Cork Inscribed: *One Special Irish* OR *One Special Scotch*		95mm	40.00	
Bucket		55mm	25.00	
Chamber Pot	(a) 52mm x 35mm		25.00	
	(b) 55mm x 40mm		25.00	
Cheese dish and cover, one piece or two pieces.	Length 60mm		30.00	
Chess Pawn		50mm	65.00	
Chess Rook		50mm	47.50	
Egg with Flapper's Head projecting out thereof can be found inscribed: *A little bird from...*		60mm	50.00	
Egyptian Canopic Jar with Anubis Head One-piece, fixed head		75mm	60.00	

See also SECOND PERIOD 10E NAMED MODELS AND SPECIAL SHAPES and THIRD PERIOD 11S DOMESTIC AND UTILITY WARE for other versions

			£	p
Egyptian Mocha Cup bowl shaped (unnamed)		40mm	7.50	
Ewer		55mm	10.00	
Fireplace with Kettle and Black Cat Inscribed: *There's No Place Like Home* OR *Home, Sweet Home* 90mm x 90mm			50.00	

Ashtray, Edward VIII
Dia. 132mm

Box Ashtray, Burns and
S.E.E. 1938 length 120mm

Circular Ashtray with Three
Rests Dia. 110mm

Ashtray, Rectangular
135mm long

Hexagonal Cruet 65mm

Taper Cream Jug curved
handle 60mm

Cigarette Box rectangular,
domed lid

Cream Jug, Double lip,
No Handle 40mm

Bulbous Milk Jug 100mm

Tea Pot and Lid
Length 180mm Height 90mm

Taper Milk Jug rope handle
97mm

Bulbous Milk Jug 100mm

		£ p
Glastonbury Salt Cellar	80mm	19.00
Grandfather clock	115mm	35.00
Jardiniere	90mm	24.50
Lantern coloured, hexagonal, with handle inscribed *EMPIRE EXHIBITION SCOTLAND 1938*	200mm	250.00
Lavatory Pan brown seat. Inscribed: *Ashes*	60mm	30.00
Norwegian wooden shoe not named	Length 103mm	30.00
Prime Cheddar Cheese, white glazed [2]	62mm	40.00
Puzzle Jug	70mm	35.00

Rose Bowl. Pink, with green foliage, with rose lid

(a) rose knop	80mm x50mm	47.50
(b) butterfly knop	60mm x40mm	55.00

This piece is something of an anomaly in that it appears to be early
yet bears a late mark.

Scallop Shell on three short legs See also SECOND PERIOD 10K5 ORNAMENTAL (same model)	Length	76mm	12.50
Shell, Cannon		70mm	22.50
Shoe - Named as John Waterson's Clog in Arcadian Inscribed on side of heel: *Hawkshead The Early Home of* *Wordsworth the Poet*	Length	102mm	70.00
Slipper		38mm	35.00
Tankard, foaming over, with verse		55mm	35.00
Thimble		38mm	47.50
Thistle Vase		44mm	15.00
Thistle Vase coloured, no arms, with *EMPIRE EXHIBITION SCOTLAND 1938*		65mm	40.00
Thistle Vase unglazed parian, green base, purple top, with *EMPIRE EXHIBITION SCOTLAND 1938* motif inside rim		67mm	45.00
Umbrella open	50mm x	35mm	35.00

£   p

Vases. Various shapes and sizes under 70mm.   Each around   7.50
including the following specific examples:

(a)	Ostend Vase Shape [2]	50mm	7.50
(b)	Hexagonal	55mm	7.50
(c)	Pedestal,taper octagonal	58mm	7.50
(d)	Letchworth Carinated Roman Vase shape, with styled sunflowers decoration, black trim, numbered 27 [2]	60mm	80.00
(e)	Shaped with two scrolls to neck	50mm	7.50
(f)	Conical with crinkle top and rounded base	67mm	7.50
(g)	Ball vase, crinkle top	45mm	7.50

Vase Art Deco (Clarice Cliff style), ribbed, brightly coloured   188mm   80.00

Vase, shaped, grey lustre   200mm   165.00

Welsh Hat plain crown, longest place-name (*Llanfair PG*)
inscribed around brim. Inscribed underneath:
Made for Souvenir Shop Llangollen.   Dia. 72mm Height   52mm   55.00

Welsh Hat, double rim   40.00

Welsh Leek   (a)White   92mm   15.00
           (b) Light green leaves   92mm   17.50
For inscription see SECOND PERIOD 10E HISTORIC MODELS
AND SPECIAL SHAPES

Weston-super-Mare Coloured Floral Clock Surround
Can be found with original fitted clock, for which add £35.00
           Length   230mm   125.00
Whiskey Bottle, Soda Syphon and Glass on
          (a) Horse Shoe Ashtray   87mm   45.00
          (b) Thistle Ashtray   87mm   45.00

Whiskey Bottle. Hip-flask type, two-piece   120mm   85.00

COLOURED AND LUSTRE ITEMS
Items such as coffee and tea cups and saucers, sugar basins,
milk jugs, tea plates, pin trays, candle holders etc. appear in a
variety of colours and lustres . Details of these are given in *The
Price Guide to Arms and Decorations on Goss China*. Historic models
appearing in lustre have thickly gilded handles and look most
attractive.

2   DOMESTIC AND UTILITY WARE

				£	p
Ashtray. Circular with three or four rests	(a) Dia	70mm		15.00	
	(b) Dia	110mm		15.00	
	(c) Dia	118mm		17.50	

Ashtray. Oval, with rests at each end   Length   100mm   15.00

Ashtray. Rectangular with rests in each corner.
Length 135mm Width   103mm   17.50

Ashtray. Square, red and black card suit symbols in each
corner   60mm sq.   40.00

Ashtray. Box-shaped. Thistle, spray of heather, Bust of
Burns transfer, Burns' cottage transfer and the
EMPIRE EXHIBITION SCOTLAND 1938 motif appear
on this and similar very late pieces   Length   120mm   45.00

Ashtray. Shamrock shaped   Length   95mm   27.50

Ashtray. Coronation, Crown, Flags, ER and
Edward Vlll, Crowned May 12 1937 outpressed in bas-relief   Dia.   132mm   40.00
(Various colours; pale blue, dark blue, green, pink, purple,
and yellow)

Bowl, miniature, crinkle top   Dia.   45mm   8.00

Bowl oval, deep fluted sides, green trim   Length   190mm   15.00

Bowl shallow, turquoise blue exterior,
matt black interior, rubber stamp printed mark.
Dia. 265mm Height   55mm   70.00

Bowl with three floral sprays in relief around inside
rim and two coats of arms in centre   Dia.   128mm   15.00
(Found numbered 27 with an 8 above)

Bowl miniature, frilled edge
similar to Second Period miniature   Dia.   47mm   13.00

Bowl. (a) Matt black inside and out.	Dia.	76mm	14.00
(b) Black lustre inside and out	Dia.	85mm	17.00
(c) Pearl lustre inside and out	Dia.	85mm	25.00

Butter Dish in Wooden Surround with *BUTTER* carved
around rim   Dish Dia. 105mm. Overall Dia.   155mm   18.00
These dishes can also be found with a variety of place
names carved around the rim of the wooden surround

Butter dish and lid plain knob, circular   80mm   18.00

Cup and Saucer curved, loop handle

Cup and Saucer curved, drip free rim

Cup and Saucer curved, loop handle

Cup and Saucer curved, loop handle

Cup and Saucer taper, loop handle

Cup and Saucer curved, loop handle

Cup and Saucer, straight, everted rim, shaped handle

Cup and Saucer taper, shaped handle

Cup and Saucer curved, loop handle

Cup and Saucer, taper everted rim

Cup and Saucer, Scalloped edge, ornate handle

Cup and Saucer, straight, curved handle

£   p

Cake Plate, circular, with two moulded bow handles
	(a) Width	220mm	20.00
	(b) Width	240mm	20.00
	(c) Width	248mm	20.00

Cheese Dish   Width 160mm Length   200mm   17.00

Cigarette Box rectangular, domed lid, floral decoration   40.00

Comport   Top Dia.190mm Height   100mm   40.00

Coronation Mug *1937 GEORGE VI & ELIZABETH*   80mm   50.00
This and any other item bearing this design would be worth
approximately the same.

Cream Jugs
	(a) Double lip, no handle	60mm	7.50
	(b) Taper, one lip, curved handle	60mm	8.50
	(c) Melon, black trim, styled	85mm	50.00
	sunflowers decoration		
	(d) Shaped	65mm	8.50

Cruet (various) Salt and Pepper pairs:
	(a) Bulbous	Each	54mm	20.00
	(b) Hexagonal	Each	65mm	16.00
	(c) Octagonal	Each	85mm	16.00

Cruet. Trefoil dish, with combined salt tray, separate pepper,
and two-piece mustard   35.00

(See also Egyptian Canopic Jar with Anubis Head adapted as cruet)

Cups and Saucers, various	Saucer Dia.	Cup Height	
(a) Scalloped edged, plain	118mm	43mm	8.00
(b) Curved, loop handle	134mm	60mm	8.00
(c) Curved, plain, shaped handle	139mm	60mm	8.00
(d) Straight-sided, plain, slightly curved saucer, loop handle	135mm	68mm	8.00
(e) Curved, plain, loop handle	136mm	68mm	8.00
(f) Taper, everted rim, loop handle, double indentation rim to base of cup and inside saucer	135mm	70mm	8.00
(g) Curved, tall, cup on drip-free rim, loop handle	138mm	72mm	8.00
(h) Fluted, whorl pattern		70mm	10.00

N.B. With late cups and saucers, the saucers are usually plain,
with the arms/decorations on the cup, but sometimes on both.

Cylindrical Pot and lid with shaped knob
                        Overall Dia. 115mm Height   55mm   20.00

*Cake Plate square with two
shaped ends 248mm*

*Cake Plate circular two
moulded bow handles 240mm*

*Cake Plate coupe shaped
240mm*

*Cake Plate square with two
shaped ends 248mm side view*

*Cake Plate circular two bow
handles 240mm side view*

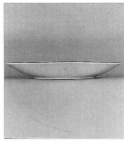

*Cake Plate coupe shaped
240mm side view*

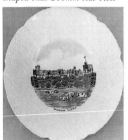

*Dish basket weave in relief
pattern Dia. 145mm*

*Cake Plate circular two
moulded bow handles 220mm*

*Cake Plate, Burns and S.E.E.
1938, 250mm*

Soup Bowl, octagonal

*Butter Dish in Wooden
Surround*

Tea Plate, Dia. 150mm

			£ p
Dish quadriform	Length	143mm	12.50
Dish twelve-pointed oval	Length	145mm	17.50
Dish oval, with tapered sides, green trim and rose decoration inside	Length	190mm	40.00
Dish oval, fluted crinkle edge.	Length	105mm	12.00
Dish circular, shallow taper edges	Dia.	80mm	10.00
Dish circular	Dia.	105mm	10.00
Dish circular, with two round handles	Length	160mm	17.50
Dish oblong, fluted edges *CORONATION GEORGE VI & ELIZABETH 1937*	130mm x	100mm	50.00
Dish circular, with pink roses transfer	Dia.	140mm	40.00
Dish circular, rim deep-patterned with three panels of basket weave and three wider panels of flower sprays, all in relief, with colour transfer in bowl	Dia.	145mm	40.00
Dish shaped, oval	Length	142mm	15.00
Dish (for sweets or nuts) with bow tabs, maroon trim. *EMPIRE EXHIBITION SCOTLAND 1938*	Length	145mm	35.00
Dish oval, tapered (scalloped sides) green trim, floral centre	Length 190mm Width	165mm	20.00
Dish Scallop edge rim and six floral patterns in relief	Dia.	190mm	20.00
Egg cup beaker-shaped		40mm	20.00
Egg cup goblet-shaped		58mm	21.50

Egyptian Canopic Jar with Anubis Head

(a) **Pepper pot** in the form of the Anubis Head (Egyptian Canopic Jar No. 1) with filling hole secured with metal-topped cork plug in the bottom, and pouring holes on the Jackal's snout; Blackpool arms; inscribed on the base: *Made in England.*   75mm   45.00

(b) **Salt Pot** in the form of the Anubis Head, as described for the above pepper version, but with the pouring hole in the end of the Jackal's snout.   75mm   45.00

(N.B. Both have fixed heads, unlike the named [2] model, but with the same gilding line) .

£   p

Honey section dish and cover square
    (a) White with Bee knop [2]   50.00
    (b) Coloured, Bees and Clovers   70.00
    (c) Black trim, styled poppies   80.00
                 Cover 115mm x 115mm
                 Dish 145mm x 145mm

Lip Salve Pot and lid, cylindrical Grey lustre		
Dia. 43mm Height	35mm	20.00
Match Holder octagonal	45mm	20.00
Outpressed: *Matches* on base edge.		
Menu Holder upright, plain front bearing		
arms of St. Helena, with back leg.	165mm	130.00

Milk Jug,   (a) Bulbous   90mm   8.00
                (b) Bulbous   100mm   8.00
                (c) Plain, rope handle   97mm   16.00

Mug with floral decoration, two handled	118mm	26.00
	133mm	26.00
Mug one handled	80mm	15.00
	100mm	17.00
Mug, Little Red Riding Hood Scene, in relief	100mm	125.00
(Also with *EMPIRE EXHIBITION SCOTLAND 1938*)		

Pin Tray   Dia.   70mm   7.50
                                  Dia. 100mm 14.50

Pin Tray Spade-shaped   85mm x   85mm   25.00
Inscribed on rim: *Pin Tray*

Pin Tray Heart-shaped   80mm x   87mm   25.00

Pin Tray Heart-shaped   105mm x 112mm   30.00
with *CORONATION GEORGE VI & ELIZABETH 1937*

Plate, cake geometric border.   Dia. 250mm   45.00
Scottish Empire Exhibition motif and colour
transfer of *BURNS COTTAGE, ALLOWAY, AYR.*

Plate, cake, coupe shape   Dia. 240mm   15.00

Plate, cake octagonal - with late colour transfer   Dia. 215mm   35.00

			£ p
Plate, cake primrose-shaped - with late transfer	Width	265mm	55.00
Plate, cake square, with two ends shaped	Width	248mm	20.00

Plate, cake, Burns, Cottage Alloway, Ayr, thistles, heather
EMPIRE EXHIBITION SCOTLAND 1938   Width   250mm   45.00

Plate Tea, ribbed edge, dark red trim
EMPIRE EXHIBITION SCOTLAND 1938   140mm   25.00

Plate Tea, black trim, styled sunflowers decoration   160mm   45.00

Plate Tea, various	125mm	7.00
	150mm	7.00
	160mm	7.00
	165mm	7.00
	175mm	7.00
	180mm	9.00

Posy Rings and Holders blue, brown, or green				
(a) Circular	Dia.	90mm	15.00
(b) Circular	Dia.	155mm	15.00
(c) Elliptical	Length	190mm	15.00
(d) Horse Shoe 110mm x	115mm	15.00
(d) Horse Shoe 160mm x	230mm	15.00

Preserve Jars and Lids
(a)	Shaped	60mm	35.00
(b)	Orange shaped with peel pattern in bas-relief, orange colour	90mm	80.00
(c)	Straight-sided, plain knop	100mm	20.00
(d)	Straight-sided, blackberry knop	100mm	25.00
(e)	With knop, and spoon cut-out	115mm	20.00
(f)	Decorated scallop pattern in relief, white glazed, gilded with knop and spoon cut out Dia. 60mm Height	95mm	80.00
(g)	Quilted pattern in relief	90mm	25.00

Powder Bowl and lid rose knop, yellow lustre   Dia.   130mm   80.00

Shaving Mug	(a)	100mm	60.00
Ride a Cock Horse Rhyme	(b)	100mm	75.00

Soup Bowl	(a) Two handles	Dia.	157mm	20.00
	(b) Octagonal	Dia.	150mm	20.00

EMPIRE EXHIBITION SCOTLAND 1938

Orange Preserve Jar and lid

Sugar Basin circular 60mm

Taper Water Jug Potters Coil Pattern 235mm

*Bowl, with 1938 Scottish
Empire Exhibition motif*

Coronation Mug 80mm

Green Posy Ring

Quadriform Dish

Octagonal Sugar Bowl

Welsh Lady Teapot

£ p

Sugar Basins and Bowls

				£ p
(a) Octagonal		Dia.	70mm	10.00
			85mm	12.00
	Height 35mm Dia.		95mm	12.00
			100mm	14.00
(b) Shaped	Height 45mm Dia.		80mm	6.50
(c) Circular	Height 60mm Dia.		95mm	6.50
	Height 65mm Dia.		120mm	6.50
(d) Taper, pedestal base	Height 60mm Dia.		110mm	6.50
(e) Taper, flat base	Height 60mm Dia.		110mm	6.50
(f) Vertical flutes.	Height 60mm Dia.		80mm	35.00

CORONATION GEORGE VI & ELIZABETH 1937

Sweetmeat Dish green	Length	120mm	18.00
		165mm	20.00

Tankard shaped with curved handle. Huntsman with hounds and
fox in bas-relief. Coloured   95mm   150.00

Tea Pot and Lid in form of Welsh Lady, coloured, her arms
forming handle and spout.
Inscribed on the front: *Cymmerwch Gwpaned O De*   152mm   125.00

Tea Pot and lid

	(a) Length 180mm	Height	90mm	40.00
With sunken lid	(b) Length 205mm	Height	100mm	35.00
Georgian style	(c) Length 210mm	Height	120mm	40.00

for Tea Strainer,
see M METALWORK chapter

Toast Rack green   Length   100mm   25.00

Tray shaped and multi-crested   Width 320mm Length 440mm   40.00

Water Jugs
(a) Pedestal base, angular handle, coloured bandings around
    base, floral decoration on body   195mm   60.00
(b) Potters Coil pattern, coloured   235mm   60.00
(c) Taper angular handle, decorated as in (a)   235mm   60.00

COLOURED AND LUSTRE ITEMS

Items such as coffee and tea cups and saucers, sugar basins,
milk jugs, tea plates, pin trays, candle holders etc, appear in a
variety of colours and lustres . Details of these are given in *The
Price Guide to Arms and Decorations on Goss China* by the same author.
Historic models appearing in lustre have thickly gilded handles
and look most attractive.

Menu Holder 165mm

*Taper mug 85mm
Cottage Pottery*

Cream Jug, shaped 65mm

*Cheese dish and Cover
Two-piece*

*Preserve Jar and lid Quilted
Pattern*

*Powder bowl with brooch as knop
in Orange lustre Dia 130mm*

Vase, Ostend shape 50mm

*Shaped Vase with two scrolls
to neck 50mm*

Hexagonal Vase 55mm

T W.H. Goss Cottage Pottery, Royal Buff and Basket Weave

There is a deal of inconsistency in the factory marks appearing on Cottage Pottery and Royal Buff wares.

Cottage Pottery is pale yellow and usually, or should, carry the marks: W H Goss Cottage Pottery, in copperplate script sometimes with the addition of ENGLAND under the Goshawk.

Royal Buff is a darker, brown colour and tends to be thicker and usually, or should, carry the mark: Royal Buff W H Goss ENGLAND again in copperplate script with the exception of the word ENGLAND. However, pieces of apparently Cottage Pottery or Royal Buff can appear with either mark, probably due to lack of care during manufacture.

The pieces have been listed in four groups in this section.

1. Cottage Shapes, which are pieces in the shape of a typical English thatched country cottage.

2. Cottage scene, where the items are decorated with an English country garden scene around a cottage.

3. Royal Buff, which is normally found decorated with crocuses, poppies or similar.

4. Basket weave, which is modelled in the shape of a woven basket, and variations thereof to suit the shape, sometimes with coloured fruit designs in bas-relief.

The reader should, therefore, look for the shape first under the above headings and not be too concerned if the factory mark is apparently incorrect.

COTTAGE POTTERY - DOMESTIC WARE

1. PIECES IN THE SHAPE OF A COLOURED COTTAGE			£ p
Biscuit Barrel and lid		150mm	75.00
Butter Dish and lid	Length 107mm Height	90mm	45.00
Butter Dish and lid, square		120mm	45.00
Cheese Dish and cover	Length 170mm Height	120mm	65.00
Coffee Pot and lid	Length 125mm Height	140mm	120.00
Dish rectangular, with two twig handles containing a two piece toast rack, square marmalade pot and lid and open square preserve dish	Length	245mm	75.00
Egg Cup		35mm	25.00
Egg Cups, four		Set	110.00
Add for circular tray Dia.		130mm	35.00

Elongated octagonal dish

Dish, octagonal rim with inset circular bowl and two twig handles

Cottage Pottery Plate
Shakespearian Cottages

Rectangular dish, two twig handles containing two-piece toast rack, square marmalade pot, and open square preserve dish

			£	p
Milk Jug, square		56mm	47.50	
		65mm	47.50	
		75mm	47.50	
		98mm	55.00	
		125mm	65.00	

Mustard Pot and lid   50mm 35.00

Pepper Shaker   50mm 35.00

Salt Shaker   50mm 35.00
The above three items can be found on a rectangular tray,
for which Add £35.00

Serviette holder   72mm 35.00

Sugar Basin and lid   70mm 55.00

Sugar Bowl   Length 110mm Height 56mm 45.00

Tea Pot and lid   Length 150mm Height 115mm 100.00
        Length 190mm Height 115mm 120.00

Toast Rack (a) To hold two slices Length 70mm 45.00
     (b) To hold two slices Length 105mm 55.00
     (c) To hold four slices Length 105mm 55.00

COTTAGE POTTERY - DOMESTIC WARE

2. PIECES DECORATED WITH A COTTAGE SCENE

for Advertising Stand
see 8. ADVERTISING WARE AND LEAFLETS Chapter

Cake Plate, circular   Dia. 240mm 35.00

Cake Plate, square, with handles   240mm 35.00

Coffee can and saucer Dia. 110mm Length 56mm 40.00

Cups and Saucers
 (a) Curved, dark yellow brown trim
      Saucer Dia. 134mm Cup Height 66mm 20.00
 (b) Taper, angular handle   70mm 20.00
 (c) Taper, curved handle with thumb rest 75mm 20.00

Dish, two handles, cottage scene in relief 57mm 40.00

Dish, round, two twig handles   Dia. 157mm 45.00

Cottage shaped Tea Pot

Cottage shaped Cheese Dish

Cottage shaped 4-slice Toast Rack

Cottage shaped Pepper Pot

Cottage shaped Milk Jug

Cottage Scene on oval dish

Cottage Pottery Cup and Saucer curved

Royal Buff Pottery beaker, 114mm

Cottage Pottery Cup and Saucer, taper

Egg Cup Stand for 4 egg cups Basket Weave

Royal Buff Honey Section Dish and Cover Bee Knop

Royal Buff Beehive Honey Pot and lid

           £   p

Dish, octagonal rim with inset circular bowl

cottage scene in relief					£ p
(a)	Dish	Dia	150mm	30.00
(b)	Dish with two twig handles	Dia	170mm	45.00
(c)	Dish with two twig handles	Dia	235mm	55.00
(d)	Dish with two twig handles	Dia	245mm	55.00
(e)	Plate	Dia	150mm	30.00

Dish, oval   Length   125mm   30.00

Dish, elongated octagonal   Length   210mm   50.00
two twig handles

Shakespearian Cottages Plate
Decorated with three coloured cottages, flower tubs, and trees.
Inscribed: *Famous Old English Cottages by W.H. Goss.*
Made in England   Dia.   230mm   50.00

Sugar Basin and lid   43mm   30.00

Tankard, Cottage decoration in relief   100mm   50.00

Tea Plate   Dia.   150mm   25.00

3. ROYAL BUFF

Much late ware only appears with transfer printed pictorial views, or hand printed flowers and/or mottoes for which Add £15.00-£25.00

for Advertising Ashtray
see 8. ADVERTISING WARE AND LEAFLETS Chapter

Beaker, Taper, without handle	85mm	15.00
	105mm	20.00
	114mm	20.00

Beaker, *KING COLE AND HIS FIDDLES THREE*
on reverse, in relief, coloured   100mm   90.00

Bowl and lid, with fish shaped knop handle, decorated   35.00
with red poppies. No details of size.

Butter Dish decorated with tulips or similar, in wooden surround
carved with: *TAKE A LITTLE BUTTER*   Dia.   115mm   25.00

Cheese dish and cover, Banbury cross
decoration,: *Ride a cock horse to Banbury*
Cross to see a fine lady on a white horse   Length   167mm   40.00

Royal Buff Jug, taper

Royal Buff Jug, bulbous

Royal Buff Sugar Bowl, curved

The Little Brown Jug

Royal Buff Taper Milk Jug

Royal Buff Two-handled Cider Mug 100mm

Royal Buff Preserve Pot and lid, with Proverb

Bulbous Jug, Widdecombe Fair Decoration

Royal Buff Tankard with Hunting Scene

Tankard, Cottage Decoration in relief

Cottage Pottery Teaplate

Tankard with Little Red Riding Hood Scene

£   p

Cheese dish with carved wooden surround
with *CHEESE* carved around rim.   Dia.   115mm   25.00

Coffee Pot and lid octagonal   200mm   75.00

Coffee Pot and lid in the style of an upright
Victorian Silver coffee pot, green trim.   160mm   75.00

Coffee Cup and Saucer octagonal   65mm   25.00
                                                                90mm   25.00

Cup and Saucer   (a) Curved sided   65mm   15.00
                            (b) Straight sided with everted rim 75mm   15.00

Egg cup pale yellow with brown trim.
Ride a Cock Horse verse & transfer.   53mm   20.00

Fern Pot scallop edge   92mm   25.00

Ann Hathaways Cottage
Inscribed: *Ann Hathaways Cottage, Shottery,*
near Stratford-on-Avon. Rd. No. 208047   Length 75mm   Height   55mm   125.00
Can also be found with the Cottage Pottery mark

Honey Section Dish with Bee as knop [2]   Square 145mm x   145mm   50.00

Honey Pot and lid. Beehive shaped with Bee as knop
on lid and coloured bees moulded on side
and spoon. Cut out from lid.
                            (a) White   100mm   45.00
                            (b) Coloured   100mm   85.00

Horse Shoe Posy ring   120mm   18.00

Jam Dish fluted   Dia. 150mm   17.50

Jugs
              (a)   Cream size   55mm   13.00
              (b)   Taper Tankard, diamond handle
                    yellow, with transfer   75mm   17.00
              (c)   Bulbous, yellow, green trim   84mm   21.50
              (d)   Cylindrical   100mm   21.50
              (e)   Bulbous,Widdecombe Fair decoration   100mm   85.00
              (f)   Taper, green rim, sprays of pink roses: 160mm   37.50
                    EMPIRE EXHIBITION SCOTLAND 1938
              (g)   Bulbous, striped horizontal decoration   300mm   35.00
              (h)   With oak leaf handle   100mm   30.00

Little Brown Jug upright, with title, or verse, and sometimes also
a Black Cat decoration, or From. . with resort name
                            Sizes (various) 60mm to   110mm   40.00

443

		£ p
Mug, taper	85mm	15.00

Mug, twig handle, decoration in relief: *Ride a cock horse*
and on a milestone: *To Banbury Cross*   75mm   75.00
On reverse, a girl on a toy horse on wheels   90mm   75.00

Mug, decorated in low relief with Old King Cole and his Fiddlers
Inscribed: *Old King Cole was a Merry Old Soul*   100mm   90.00

Mug, Cider, two-handled, decorated with apples
Inscribed: *Yaa 's tis thursty wurk 'ave a drop a ' Zomerzet Zider*   100mm   60.00

Mug, peg handle, WIDDECOMBE FAIR scene in relief,   100mm   80.00
with the song words on reverse

Mug, one handle, MARY AND LITTLE LAMB scene in relief,   100mm   85.00
with rhyme and cottage scene in relief on reverse

Pepper and Salt Pots, egg-shaped   Each   55mm   12.50

Pepper and Salt Castors, shaped   Each   90mm   12.50

Pepper Pot, Pixie, coloured   145mm   60.00

Pin Tray circular   Dia.   70mm   10.00

Plate   265mm x   230mm   40.00
Inscribed: *Education is Better than Wealth*

Preserve Pot and lid poppies decoration
Inscribed on pot: *East West Home's Best* or other proverb, or verse. 110mm   35.00
Also found with Pixie Finial

Preserve Pot and lid, taper   95mm   27.00

for Rabbit see 11R FIGURES AND ANIMALS

Sugar Basin	(a)	Octagonal		80mm	17.50
	(b)	Taper, everted rim	Dia. 85mm Height	50mm	17.50
	(c)	Taper, everted rim	Dia. 95mm Height	65mm	17.50

Sugar Bowl curved, green trim   Dia. 117mm Height   62mm   17.50

Tankard, Hunting scene in relief, coloured   75mm   75.00
Huntsman, hounds and fox   95mm   75.00

Tankard, shaped, one handle   95mm   17.50

		£ p
Tankard, shaped, everted rim, LITTLE RED RIDING HOOD	100mm	110.00

Coloured scene in relief.
Also found with: *EMPIRE EXHIBITION SCOTLAND 1938*

Tea Plate green trim	Dia.	166mm	17.50

Tea Pot and lid taper	115mm	55.00

Tea Pot Stand	(a) Dia.	103mm	20.00
	(b) Dia.	145mm	25.00

Toast Rack with coloured Pixie seated at each end	80mm	55.00

Toast Rack, two slice	Length 97mm Dia.	83mm	45.00

Toby Jug	68mm	50.00

Vase with green and black horizontal bands
(similar to Shelley Harmony Ware)   155mm   65.00

4. BASKET WEAVE POTTERY

Basket (see Cruet)

Beaker beige	100mm	20.00

Cheese dish and cover	Length 168mm Height	87mm	50.00

Cruet

(a) Salt Castor, apple shaped, coloured		30mm	50.00
(b) Pepper Castor, orange shaped, coloured		30mm	50.00
(c) Basket, beige, holding (a) and (b)	Length	80mm	50.00
(d) The above three items as a set			175.00

Egg Cup taper, coloured,	40mm	17.50

Egg Cup taper, fruit in relief	40mm	17.50

Egg Cups and Stands (a) Four egg cups (as above) inset
into stand, with four circular
indents. Two handles one
decorated with orange and
green leaves, the other with
grapes   Length 138mm   45mm   105.00
(b) Six egg cups (as above)   45mm   140.00

Royal Buff Mug, with proverb

Royal Buff Beaker, taper, with handle

Royal Buff Horse Shoe Posy Ring

Royal Buff Mug, Mary and Lamb, in relief

Royal Buff Mug (reverse) Rhyme and Cottage, in relief

Basket Weave 2-slice Toast Rack and Preserve Dish

Basket weave Cruet, Apple and Orange

Basket Weave 2-slice Toast Rack

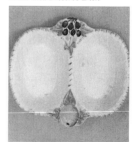

Basket Weave 2-section Jam Dish

Basket Weave Boat-shape Jam Dish

Basket Weave Jam Dish, Blue

Basket Weave taper Jam Dish and Lid

£ p

Jam Dishes
   (a) Taper, and lid, with striped handle, fruit decoration on lid
       Inscribed: *From....* (e.g. *LULWORTH*) Height 75mm Dia. 110mm   25.00
   (b) Circular, with a single fruit on one side, and a bunch of small
       fruits on the other side, both inside the rim   Dia. 123mm   20.00
   (c) Oval, or Boat-shaped, beige, coloured orange at one end, and
       coloured bunch of grapes at the other end
       Inscribed: *From....* (e.g. *DYMCHURCH*)   Length 160mm   25.00
   (d) Two-section, beige, joined by a coloured orange and leaves
       on one side, and coloured grapes and leaves on the other side
                                    Length 160mm   30.00
   (e) As (d) in all one colour, e.g., pale green   Length 160mm   21.50

Nut Tray (see Jam Dish (c) version above)

Preserve Pot and lid cream, orange knop; pot decorated with
blue, mauve and yellow grapes   115mm   100.00

Tea Plate floral, and lady in period dress in relief:
Ride a Cock Horse to Banbury Cross To see a Fine Lady Upon a
White Horse   Dia. 150mm   25.00

Toast Racks
   (a) Two-slice; decorated with fruit at each end, and with
       stripes matching the taper jam dish (a) above   Length 110mm   25.00
   (b) Two-slice; the sections striped as above, and with two
       dishes for marmalade or preserve, one at each end of
       the rack. Decorated with coloured fruit at each end.
                                      Length 175mm   40.00
   (c) Two-slice, coloured blue   Length 110mm   25.00

U Hand Painted Ware

As well as the normal W.H. GOSS ENGLAND trade mark, there is also a W.H. Goss Hand Painted mark, usually found on domestic ware Royal Buff and Cottage pottery (as opposed to porcelain). The hand painted ware covers a large range of items, varying from a cottage-shaped tea set to the Little Brown Jug versions, beakers, cups and saucers, and various other items of domestic ware. These will be found in the preceding chapter T.

Obviously the original Goss moulds were still available during the Third Period, and a number of shapes were used to carry a range of floral patterns extending from delicate pastel shades to rather garish hand painted examples.

It is difficult to accurately list all Third Period ware as there are so many variations. If a similar piece to one shown is found, then a price in the same region will apply.

The reader should also consult DOMESTIC AND UTILITY WARES, ORNAMENTAL ARTICLES and the First Period after checking all possibilities in Third Period Goss.

For full details and values of all decorations on Goss China, see *The Price Guide to Arms and Decorations on Goss China* by Nicholas Pine (Milestone Publications) .

12 American Wares
V   GODFREY WILLIAM GOSS

William Henry Goss's second son, Godfrey William, emigrated to America in 1882 and lived at Trenton, New Jersey. In the City Directory in the State Library, Godfrey is listed between 1885 and 1889 successively as decorator, kiln firer or potter. Little is known of his products while at Trenton, but a pierced cake basket made by him there is in the possession of the family in America. In 1886 he was joined by his betrothed, Alice Buckley, a paintress from his father's factory at Stoke-on-Trent. They married immediately upon her arrival in America, and moved straight to Godfrey's farm. By 1891 Godfrey's ambition to further pursue his pottery skills caused him to seek work at Peru, Indiana, where he set up his own factory and fired his first kiln. Alice then sold the farming stock and joined her husband, eventually moving on to Kokomo in Indiana, and employing at their factory two emigrants from the Staffordshire potteries, one a skilled kiln firer, the other a clay presser. For his enamelling, Godfrey used recipes received from his father at Stoke.

This brief foreword is intended to draw attention to some of Godfrey's pottery produced in America. Although his main line at the Kokomo factory was the production of electrical insulators, his pottery was never a viable proposition. Godfrey did, however, produce other pieces, decorated by Alice, of interest to Goss enthusiasts. They were not generally for sale commercially, apart from those listed hereunder, copies of which have appeared with increasing regularity in America, and which were definitely retailed there. In addition to the pieces listed, which have all appeared in Britain, it is said that Godfrey also made floral crosses but none have as yet come to light. His pottery activities had ceased by 1907 when he moved to Eldorado, Oklahoma, to farm, and where he helped to found the First State Bank of Eldorado before moving on to Raymondville, Texas, where he died in 1939, Alice having previously died there in 1936.

The full story of their lives in England and their adventures in America is told in the biography: **WILLIAM HENRY GOSS The story of the Staffordshire Family of Potters who invented Heraldic Porcelain** by Lynda and Nicholas Pine (Milestone Publications).

The heading of a special circular issued by the Goss China Company Ltd. to all the former agents stocking Goss China in 1934, announcing the creation of the new firm by Harold Taylor Robinson

£   p

Comport moulded and mottled in relief,
plate top decorated with birds   Dia. 220mm Height   110mm   250.00

Cake Basket pierced, white   Dia.   220mm   200.00

Plate multi-coloured, floral rim, tree, grasses and birds in centre.
Inscription hand written on base: *Alice Buckley paintress*   Dia.   225mm   250.00

Electrical Conductor, Invented and manufactured
by Godfrey in Kokomo, Indiana.   Dia. & Height   40mm   25.00

Tea pot and lid and Sucrier and cover made by
Goefrey William Goss at Trenton, New Jersey, U.S.A.
in brown earthenware   Sucrier   100mm   200.00
                                          Tea Pot   150mm   200.00

Multi-coloured floral plate decorated by Alice (Buckley) Goss

Comport modelled by Godfrey, height 110mm, width 220mm with bird decoration in bas-relief

Teapot and lid brown earthenware

Reverse showing Alice's signature

Pierced cake basket, 220mm dia., made by Godfrey in Trenton, New Jersey

Sucrier and cover, brown earthenware

W   LATE WARES

A range of wares was made for sale in the U.S. apparently after the sale of the original company. These were marked "Goss China". The mark was hand written in an apparent paint smear or, in earlier versions, was rubber stamped "Hand Painted Underglaze by Goss" in script similar to that used for the Royal Buff and Cottage Pottery. At this time the pottery was owned by Harold Taylor Robinson and renamed GOSS CHINA CO. LTD (see copy of advertisement on page 449) It must be assumed that any new Goss products manufactured during this period would be labelled accordingly. This was a time of great confusion and contraction in the crested/souvenier china manufacture resulting from the collapse, and the resultant merging of large parts of the industry, due to the world wide recession. The range of Third Period coloured flower girls and toby jugs was exported to the Southern States of America during the 1920s.

The new range of wares included duck and pheasant ashtrays and duck shaped open and closed dishes. Also modelled were a Derringer pistol and a powder horn to extend the hunting motif. These all bear the rubber stamped mark. From these items it would seem that the market was directed towards duck hunting much favoured in the Southern and Eastern states.

Later a series of tankard mugs and a black cat were produced with a simple one word "Goss" in script inscribed in a similar fashion on a leaf shaped paint smear. The Tankard Mugs have a horse racing theme and depict famous Kentucky thoroughbreds of the period:- The horses illustrated include Whirl Away, Gallant Fox, Seabiscuit and Man o' War - all famous during the 1930s and 1940s. The mug handle depicts a brown riding crop.

More information as to the period when these items were produced can be ascertained from the decorator of the pieces: The decorator's name, LYNN BOGUE HUNT, is prominently displayed on the decoration next to the horses. An exceptional illustrator of hunting themes Hunt's work features prominently in *Field & Stream* and can be seen in decorated calendars and gun ammunition advertisements in the 1940/50s. This would indicate that, from the dates involved, these pieces may be some of the last to come from the factory.

Other earlier pieces made for the American market are two plates each approximately 210mm in diameter. One is a scalloped dinner plate gilt edged with crab apples on a blue green background covering the entire plate marked "Goss '06" (hand written with the "G" and "ss" in pronounced serifs and marked "Limoges, FRANCE" underglazed on the underside). The other is a two handled fruit dish, marked "GDA/FRANCE" underglaze which has been hand decorated similar to the first with raspberries and leaves on a white background and a series of 8 large gilt Greek key motifs around the gilt edge. The underneath outer part of the dish which is visable has been coated with a white lustre similar to the coating on many Goss pieces.

It is likely that these were decorated by decorators outside the Limoges factory, maybe even by Goss paintresses (or by someone named Goss) during the early part of the century. The decoration is of a high standard and may have been on themes stipulated by the Limoges firm.

All of the above have been listed here.

Mark on base of Duck

Leaf mark on base of
Black Cat

Leaf mark on base of Tankard

Black Cat Length 225mm

Tankard Mug with brown crop
handle

Powder Horn brown

Pheasant as Ashtray

Tankard with brown crop
handle

Tankard, 120mm

A pair of Derringers showing
factory mark

Tankard with Racehorse
transfer in black

Tankard with Goss mark in
leaf shaped surround

£ p

Dinner Plate by American pottery Haviland and
also marked GDA. The decoration is of strawberries
and leaves fully covering the piece and signed Goss,
with pronounced serifs on all letters.   Dia. 200mm   100.00

Tankard with brown handle in the form of a riding
crop decorated with black transfer of one of the
following horse portraits by Lynn Bogue Hunt:-
Gallant Fox, Whirlaway, Seabiscuit, Man o' War OR
an unnamed racehorse standing by a fence
GOSS CHINA on black leaf mark   Length 120mm   100.00

Cat, black, laying down, legs forward, white paws,
yellow eyes and some white marks. Marked
underglaze with a leaf in black with *Goss China*
scratched out therefrom.   Length 225mm Height 112mm   150.00

All the following items are inscribed in manuscript on the base:
Hand Painted Underglaze Porcelain by Goss.

Derringer, multi-coloured *hand painted*
reproduction of Derringer circa 1840.   Length 205mm   150.00

Tufted Duck Posy Holder with black & green head,
brown chest, black wings and
tail and yellow underbody   Length 100mm   100.00

Mallard Male Posy Holder and ashtray with white
cigarette rest decorated in natural colours with
dark grey, pale grey or white underbody
(either Pintail or Redhead)   Length 140mm   150.00

Mallard Trinket Box & Lid natural colouring   Length 165mm   200.00

Mallard Duck, Male, Posy Holder, with beige
brown, blue and green feathers and yellow beak.
This example has two openings in its beak to
hold flowers   Length 225mm   225.00

Pochard Duck, Duck, Male Posy Holder or Ashtray,
with pink head, black beak, chest and tail ,
grey wings, white underbody.   Length 90mm   100.00

Teal Duck Posy Holder, 100mm long with speckled
front and brown and green head   Length 100mm   100.00

Pheasant as ashtray ,with rest, naturally coloured   Length 220mm   150.00

Pheasant Posy Holder, decorated in
natural woodland colours.   Length 220mm   150.00

Powder Horn for wall hanging brown and white   Length 150mm   125.00

Mallard Posy holder or Ashtray
Length 140mm

Tufted Duck Posy holder
Length 100mm

Mallard Trinket box and lid
Length 165mm

Mallard male Posy holder and ashtray
Length 140mm

Glossary of Terms

To aid the reader who may not be familiar with the meaning of some of some of the terms used in this encyclopaedia, a glossary has been provided. Many definitions given here are not the same as those given in dictionaries. In this work, they refer to Goss China and explain terms used by either the Goss factory or the author.

Acanthus	An artists representation of the leaf of the acanthus, a prickly leaved plant.
Amphora	Jar or vase, normally two-handled but often not in the case of Goss china, used by Greeks and Romans for holding liquids.
Angular	Sharply tapering, or tapering in different directions.
Anubis	The ancient Egyptian Jackal-headed god of the dead.
Bagware	In the form of a paper bag tied with a coloured cord around the neck.
Ball	Circular, in the shape of a ball
Bas-relief	Low relief. A sculpture in which the figures only stand out from the ground on which they are formed by a small amount.
Bulbous	Bulging out at the bottom.
Canopic	An Egyptian vase with a mummy's head.
Carinated	Boat shaped or having a keel.
Cartouche	A scroll like ornamentation.
Caryatid	A female figure used instead of a column to support a tazza.
Castor	Tall container for dispensing sugar at the table.
Centre Piece	A striking piece suitable for the centre of a table. Alternatively, the centre of a group of vases.
Cinerary	Used to hold the ashes of the dead.
Classical	Relating to Greek or Roman mythology.
Club	A circular vase tapering inwards towards the top but with concave sides.
Coloured Trim	Blue, green or red paint, usually around the top rim of a piece in the same manner as gilding.
Cone	A circular vase tapering inwards toward the top.
Coupe	Plate with very gentle curvature upward at the edges.
Crinkle	Small indentations around the rim of a piece.
Elongated Oval	Rectangular but with outwardly curving ends.

455

Embossed	Large lettering appearing on a piece as part of the mould.
Everted rim	Turned Outwards at top.
Everted Base	Turned outward at the base.
Fern	Capable of planting with an indoor fern.
Figure	Male human form.
Figurine	Female human form.
Flapper	1920s term for a flighty young girl.
Fluted	Vertical grooves, usually on the body of a piece.
Frilled	Large, wavy decorative edge.
Geometric	Decoration comprising shapes used in geometry brought together in a design.
Gilding	A ring of pure gold, usually around the top rim of a piece.
Globe	Ball shaped
Globular	Circular
Goblet	A single stemmed drinking vessel with globular top and circular foot. Similar to a traditional egg cup.
Hexagonal	Six sided.
High Relief	With the subject or decoration raised from the back ground by a substantial amount.
Honey section dish	A square dish into which a honeycomb fits.
Impressed	Lettering stamped into the wet parian ware with a hand stamp containing metal characters.
Incised	lettering written in manuscript with a knife in the wet clay.
Jewelling	The process of decorating with rich gilding and enaels,especially the application of spots of enamel in the form of a dot so to imitate gemstones.
Jewelling	The process of insetting jewels, coloured glass or stone in imitation of gemstones, into the porcelain body.
Jewels	See Turquoise jewels
Kohl	A fine powder of antimony used to blacken the eyes in ancient Egypt and the east.
Knop	Knob
Knurled	Having small knobs or excrescences or ridges,usually to a handle.
Loving cup	Having two or three opposite handles.
Lozenge	Upright diamond shaped or rectangular with four corners chamfered

Melon	With four slight vertical indentations on a circular body.
Miniature	Too small for use, very small, for decoration only.
Night- light	A model, either a cottage or ovoid shape used to contain a small long burning candle to provide light.
Octagonal	Eight sided
Oviform	Egg shaped
Ovoid	Oval with a broad base.
Pedestal	The support for a piece.
Plated	Silver or EPNS (Electro Plated Nickel Silver) plated.
Plinth	Base of a bust.
Posy	Suitable for either a single bloom or a small bunch of flowers.
Quadrifoliate	Having four lobes or sections.
Quadruple	Four
Relief	With the subject or decoration raised from the body.
Rounded Base	The lower part of the side is rounded as it meets the base.
Scallop	A series of semi-circles each shaped like a scallop shell to form a decorative effect.
Socle	A shaped foot of a plinth of a bust having the base larger than the top.
Specimen	To hold one bloom only.
Squat	Low and wide.
Shamrock	A four leafed clover shape.
Silks	The silk jerseys worn by racehorse jockeys.
Taper	Straight sided but tapering, usually out from the bottom in the case of domestic wares.
Tazza	Shallow bowl mounted on a foot.
Thistle	In the shape of the flower of the wild, prickly plant off the same name which is the national symbol of Scotland.
Trefoil	Having three lobes or sections.
Tricorn	Three cornered.
Trumpet	A very narrow base, splayed top and long thin body.
Turquoise Jewels	A form of decoration comprising small dots of enamel paint, in this case turquoise in colour.
Unique	Only one is definitely known to exist.
Whorl	A group of similar members arising from the same level around a circular body in an upward spiral

The Price Guide to Arms and Decorations on Goss China

Nicholas Pine

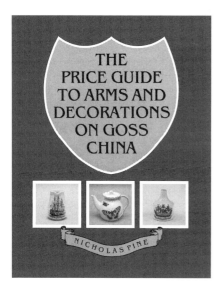

After ten years of research, Nicholas Pine and Editor Norman Pratten have produced a complete listing of all known Goss arms and decorations in a magnificent 320 page, large format Hardback book with full colour jacket.

The book provides a unique and comprehensive listing, with values, of the 10,000 plus coats of arms and decorations which adorned Goss China during its period of production spanning 80 years.

Also included are chapters on the Manufacture and Decoration of Goss China and a History of W H Goss and his factory.

The largest section, geographical place names, now contains 2,200 entries, only *one-third* of the number contained in the first (green cover) book of Arms and Decorations. The majority of those listed in this volume are now known *not* to be Goss First, Second or Third Period, but instead were introduced by Arkinstall & Son (Arcadian) when they took_ over the works in 1929. All these Arcadian place names, 4,400 in all, are listed in a special section of the new book so that collectors for the first time can ascertain the arms used only by the Goss factory.

The book comprises themes used by the factory including: Chapters on all Civic arms in the British Isles and overseas; Royal, Nobility and Personal; Educational, Medical and Ecclesiastical, Commemoratives and Exhibitions; Transfer Printed Pictorial Views and Enamelled Illustrations; Regimental Badges and Naval Crests; Flora and Fauna; Armour, Flags and Masonic, and late decorations known as Third Period.

The Guide contains over 2,000 illustrations, and every piece listed is priced or valued, subdivided into over 100 easy-to-use sections.

The book has been designed for use in conjunction with *The Concise Encyclopaedia and Price Guide to Goss China* by the same author. Collectors and dealers who possess a copy of the price guide are strongly advised to acquire this new book so that accurate up-to-date values may be obtained for each piece, for, as often as not, the decoration on a particular piece is worth much more than the piece itself.

Published 1992 260mm x 215mm. 320pages. 2000 illustrations. £19.95

William Henry Goss

*The story of the Staffordshire family of Potters
who invented Heraldic Porcelain.*

Lynda & Nicholas Pine

In this first ever biography of the man who is credited with inventing heraldic porcelain and his family who worked with him and at times against him, the authors tell the story of Goss china in fascinating detail.

From a promising start as a literary student, William Henry Goss used the important contacts he made in London to carve himself a career in the pottery industry in Stoke-on-Trent. At first he produced a limited, expensive range of Parian busts and figurines, but with the entry of his sons, Adolphus and later Victor and Huntley into the business, production switched to the small white models bearing colourful coats of arms for which the firm became famous.

The authors recount the stories of Godfrey, who ran away to New Jersey with a factory paintress, began a pottery there and founded the American branch of the family; the surprising Falkland Islands connection, still continuing today; why William refused to speak to his wife for the last twenty years of his life and how he came to have four homes all at the same time. The history of the three periods of production is complemented by fascinating chapters on how the porcelain was both manufactured and sold through virtually every town in the country.

The book is illustrated with over 350 photographs and maps, includes much material not previously published and comprehensive family trees.

As the story unfolds you can discover:

- About the three periods of Goss manufacture and how the trade developed leading eventually to mass popularity nationwide.
- The amazing Falkland Islands connection, how Port Stanley and the Upland Goose Hotel came to be so-named and the exciting story of how the Goss family came to emigrate to those barren islands - and the dreadful fate that befell them.
- Why youngest daughter Florence married a bewiskered Bostonian millionaire older than her father.
- The truth about the rumour that second son Godfrey got a factory girl 'into trouble' and was banished to America. Why did Godfrey emigrate to America? and did he start a US Goss factory?

- The beginnings of William's potting career. Why did he decide to become a potter?
- How the romantic young William became an obstinate and pedantic father and eventually a near recluse.
- Why William did not speak to his wife for the last 20 years of his life - and how he came to have four homes all at the same time.
- His amazing generosity towards his friends and workforce and his unbelievable meanness and cruelty towards his wife and children.
- How William viewed his two sons Adolphus and Victor as rivals.
- Who really invented heraldic porcelain and how it was manufactured and marketed.

260mm x 217mm 350 Illustrations 5 Family Trees 256 pages. Bibliography and Glossary.
Casebound. £19.95

The Price Guide to Crested China

Nicholas Pine

The book, now in its fourth edition, lists, describes and prices every known piece of Crested China. It incorporates the history of every factory, where known, now numbering over 300, and over 500 marks. The author has now incorporaed all information originally published in *Crested China* by Sandy Andrews, updated for 1992, resulting in a massive fount of information available in one book for the first time.

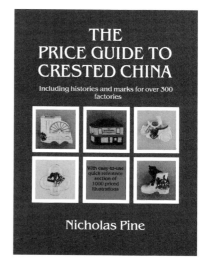

Particulars of over 10,000 pieces are given with their dimensions and relevant details where thought to be of interest. The Guide contains a complete listing of all the pieces made by every factory. The history of and all known information about over 300 factories is provided and a mass of other exciting facts answer all the questions that collectors ask such as 'Why does the same piece appear with a different factory mark?' 'Why do some pieces have no crest, factory mark or name?' 'Why are some pieces numbered?'; etc, etc.

In addition to all this information, over 500 line drawings of factory marks are shown to aid identification, the majority of which are not shown in any of the usual books on marks.

The story of Crested China, how the trade expanded and some of the colourful characters involved is also told.

Every item is priced at the current retail price charged by Goss and Crested China Ltd.

The Guide contains a special easy-to-use section of nearly 1000 illustrations, each described and priced, providing a quick reference for the expert, novice and dealer who want a quick visual guide to identification and price.

Published 1992 215mm x 155mm 500 pages. 1000+ illustrations. Casebound. £19.95

Goss & Crested China Ltd. are the leading dealers in Heraldic China.

We have been buying and selling for over 25 years and our experienced staff led by Lynda and Nicholas Pine will be able to answer your questions and assist you whether you are a novice or an experienced collector.

A constantly changing attractively priced stock of some 5,000 pieces may be viewed at the Goss & Crested China Centre and Museum in Horndean, including Goss cottages, fonts, crosses, shoes, lighthouses, models etc. and the full range of crested ware including military, animals, buildings etc. covering all the other manufacturers.

Visitors are welcome to call during business hours of 9.00 - 5.00 any day except Sundays and Bank Holidays. Those travelling long distances are advised to telephone in advance so that they may be sure of receiving personal attention upon arrival, but this is not essential.

Most of our business is by mail order and we publish *Goss & Crested China*, a monthly 32 page illustrated catalogue containing hundreds of pieces for sale from every theme and in every price range. The catalogue is available by annual subscription; please refer to the following page for details of this and the Goss and Crested China Club.

In addition, if you specialise, we will be pleased to offer your particular pieces or crests from time to time as suitable items become available. Please let us know your wants as with our ever-changing stock we will probably have something to suit.

Our service is personal and friendly and all orders and correspondence are dealt with by return. You will find us fair and straightforward to deal with, as we really care about crested china and this is reflected in our service.

Finally, we are just as keen to buy as to sell and offers of individual items or whole collections are always welcome. These will be dealt with by return and the very highest offers will be made.

Goss & Crested China Ltd,
62 Murray Road,
Horndean,
Waterlooville
Hampshire
PO8 9JL
Telephone: Horndean 01705 597440
Facsimile: 01705 591975
e-mail: info@gosschinaclub.demon.co.uk

Visit our website on:
www.gosschinaclub.demon.co.uk

Would you like to join

The
Goss &
Crested China
Club?

Exclusively for collectors and customers of Goss & Crested China Ltd.
Membership will provide answers to question such as:

How do I find the pieces I am looking for?

What is a fair price?

Where can I obtain information on Goss China and Goss collecting?

Where can I exchange or sell pieces I no longer require?

Join the Goss & Crested China Club without delay and receive the following
benefits:

FREE Specially designed enamel membership badge.

FREE Membership card and number.

FREE Telephone and postal advice service.

FREE Information on books about heraldic china collecting.

FREE Especially favourable Club members part-exchange rates for
pieces surplus to requirements.

FREE Without obligation search-and-offer service for any items and
decorations that you seek.

FREE Invitations to Club open days.

EXCLUSIVE Valuation service for your collection

EXCLUSIVE Club Members only special offers announced regularly in
Club members monthly catalogue *Goss & Crested China.*

Membership is free and is available to subscribers to Goss & Crested China the club's
monthly catalogue of pieces for sale.

To join, just send £18.00 or US$30 annual subscription* to The Goss &
Crested China Club, 62 Murray Road, Horndean, Waterlooville, Hampshire
PO8 9JL, and you will receive a membership application form with your first
copy of the catalogue. Upon receipt of the completed form, you will be sent
your enamel badge, membership card and full details of the club's special
offers and services.

*For Airmail outside Europe add £12.00 or US$20

462

The Goss & Crested China Museum

For some 30 years, Nicholas and Lynda Pine have been collecting Goss family memorabilia and this is now on display at the Goss & Crested China Centre and Museum at Horndean, Hampshire.

In the museum, the story of heraldic porcelain is told on a series of illustrated wallboards around the rooms.

Elsewhere, William Henry's personal photograph album is on display. Contained within its pages are the photographs of Royalty, the Nobility, poets and writers which Goss used to model his range of portrait busts.

Elsewhere can be found much ephemera of the Goss factory and family including many of William Henry's original recipe books and dozens of his eldest son Adolphus' original transfer printed views used to pictorially decorate the wares.

The museum also boasts family paintings, William's original seal, Adolphus' chair from Alsager District Council where he was chairman and a magnificent turquoise jewelled plaque made by William for his daughter Georgiana.

All books written by William Henry are on view - his own copies - and a number of important related books from Goss' own library as well as many letters from William and from Adolphus, the firm's commercial traveller writing back to the factory with orders.

Also on permanent show are displays of Goss China and ever changing temporary displays of particular collections or themes.

Entry to the museum is free of charge between 9.00am - 5.00pm six days a week. Why not visit The Goss & Crested China Centre to see both the showroom containing over 5000 pieces for sale and the museum?

The Goss & Crested China Museum
62 Murray Road, Horndean, Waterlooville, Hampshire, PO8 9JL

Other titles available from

Milestone Publications

Please send for a full catalogue of these and other books about antique heraldic porcelain

William Henry Goss. The Story of the Staffordshire Family of Potters who invented Heraldic Porcelain
Lynda and Nicholas Pine

The Price Guide to Arms and Decorations on Goss China
Nicholas Pine

The Concise Encyclopaedia and Price Guide to Goss China
Nicholas Pine

The Price Guide to Crested China
Nicholas Pine

The Goss Record 8th and War Editions
J. J. Jarvis A facsimile reprint.

Goss & Crested China. Illustrated monthly catalogues listing items for sale. Available by Annual Subscription. Details on page 462
62 Murray Road, Horndean, Waterlooville, Hants PO8 9JL